Reef Fish

To Jean and Faith

Reef Fish

Behaviour and Ecology
on the Reef and in the Aquarium

Ronald E. Thresher

John Bartholomew & Son Limited
Edinburgh

First published in the United States of America 1980 by
The Palmetto Publishing Company
4747 Twenty-eighth Street N.
St Petersburg
Florida 33714

First Published in the United Kingdom 1980 by
John Bartholomew & Son Limited
12 Duncan Street, Edinburgh EH9 1TA

U.S.A. edn ISBN 0-915096-09-9
U.K. edn ISBN 0-7028-8270-4

Library of Congress Catalog Card No. 79-28234

Typeset by Computacomp (UK) Limited, Fort William, Scotland.
Printed and bound in the United Kingdom by
Hazell Watson & Viney Limited, Aylesbury, Bucks.

CONTENTS

This book is for two kinds of people. First, it is for the marine aquarist who desires to do more than simply keep fish alive for a while. In order to provide those things that a fish requires to thrive, one must know both how and where that fish lives in the sea and what elements of its natural environment are critical to it. Unfortunately for aquarists, the books that are now available on the market provide little or none of this information. A few contain cryptic notes such as 'Found on the deep reef' or 'Eats invertebrates', but most lack even these, relying instead on old, and often inaccurate, information about a few fish, and perpetuating old myths. In this book however, field biology is emphasized. Information on a wide variety of fish has been drawn from many sources, and this information is then discussed with regard to the suitability of each species for captivity. With the information provided, an aquarist can make an intelligent and informed decision about whether or not to obtain a fish, can anticipate any problems likely to be encountered, and can then proceed to construct an aquarium setting contoured to its needs.

This book is also for the fish-watchers – professional and amateur – that skin or scuba dive on Caribbean reefs. For such people, a variety of fish identification guides are available, ranging from paperback books filled with more-or-less accurate paintings of the commonly seen species to professionally-orientated texts such as *Fishes of the Bahamas* by J. Böhlke and C. G. Chaplin, which provide detailed information on the basis of which even obscure species can be keyed out. This book is intended to supplement such guides. While it describes many species, gives diagnostic features for most, and contains pictures of many, its chief aim is to discuss the biology of the various fish, not their taxonomy. Food habits, habitat preferences, general behaviour, social organization, and reproductive biology are covered for each species, whenever such information is known. This information is drawn in part from scientific literature, and also from discussions with ichthyologists from Bermuda to Panama, but the greater proportion has been gleaned from studies and observations made by the author.

Scope of the book

There are, at present, just over 700 recognized species of fish found on or around western Atlantic reefs. About a third of them are covered in this book. Many species are excluded because they are either rare, very deep-dwelling, or small and cryptic. Because the emphasis of the book is on those species likely to be of interest to aquarists, most of the larger fish, such as sharks, rays, snappers, and groupers, are covered only briefly, or not at all. Instead, the author has concentrated on the small- to medium-sized, often colourful fish that are closely associated with the reef, ranging from inch-long gobies to two-foot angelfish. Most of the fish covered are common on the reef, though several of the less common and even some rare species are discussed because they are particularly attractive or interesting.

Most of the species covered are also widely distributed in the tropical western Atlantic. As a general rule, Caribbean reef fish can be found regularly off Florida, throughout the Bahamas and the Antilles, and at scattered locations along the coasts of Mexico and Central America. Many are also found off the coast of Brazil, an area somewhat isolated from the main Caribbean reefs and therefore lacking some species and having several others endemic to it. Reef fish are also found, though usually on a scattered and irregular basis, in the Gulf of Mexico, along parts of the northern coast of South America, and along the south-eastern coast of the United States.

Organization of the book

The book is divided into 22 chapters, each of which deals with a group of systematically or ecologically allied species. In most cases, the species covered are either members of the same genus or belong to the same family. A few chapters on miscellaneous fish deal with ecological groups such as predators or herbivores.

Each chapter is divided into five sections. The first of these (after a brief general introduction to the group) is *Species Account*, a listing of the members of the group likely to be encountered, with diagnostic features provided for each. These features involve primarily colour cues, obvious morphological differences, differences in distribution, and ecological cues, that is, features that can be readily used by a non-specialist. In some cases, differences in fine detail, such as scale counts and number of fin rays, are mentioned, but not emphasized; these are included only when they are necessary in order to differentiate species that are otherwise identical.

The second and third sections deal with the behaviour and ecology of the fish on the reef. *Field Biology* covers in detail foods and feeding, habitat preferences, general behaviour, and ecological separation between closely related fish. *Reproductive Biology* discusses what is known about reproductive behaviour, including information on spawning sites, care of spawn, if any, and duration and characteristics of the planktonic larval stage.

Aquarium Biology, the fourth section, discusses the suitability of each species to captivity. Food preferences, general behaviour (especially as related to the community aquarium), special problems, and, where available, details of spawning in captivity are provided. The final section is a listing of *Relevant Literature*, sources to which interested readers can go for further and more detailed information about the fish covered. Unfortunately, many species have not yet been studied in detail and little information beyond that presented may be available. In a few cases, there are only a few references available for entire families.

Descriptive terms

Where possible, technical terms and scientific jargon have been avoided. Unfortunately, some such terms are necessary to describe a fish effectively and concisely. Most of these terms refer to the parts of a fish's anatomy and are illustrated in the accompanying line drawings. Those terms not so identified and used in the text are self-explanatory.

Additional Literature

Several scientific papers and books have been published within the last several years that are of particular use in studying the behaviour and ecology of Caribbean reef fish. In addition, several popular and scientific periodicals regularly publish new information about them. Interested readers may wish to follow these regularly in order to keep abreast of the rapidly expanding body of knowledge about the fish.

Books and Major Papers

Böhlke, J. E. & Chaplin, C. C. G. 1968. *Fishes of the Bahamas and adjacent tropical waters*, Livingston Public. Comp., Wynnewood, Pa

Longley, W. H. & Hildebrand, S. F. 1941. 'Systematic catalogue of the fishes of Tortugas, Florida, with observations on color, habits, and local distribution', *Papers Tortugas Lab.*, **34** (Carnegie Inst. Wash. Publ. 535): 1–331

Randall, J. E. 1967. 'Food habits of reef fishes of the West Indies', *Stud. Trop. Oceanog.* (5): 665–847

Randall, J. E. 1968. *Caribbean Reef Fishes*, Trop. Fish. Hobbyist Publ., Neptune City, New Jersey

Results of the Tektite Program: 'Ecology of coral reef fishes', 1972, Collette, B. & Earle, S. A. (eds.). *Science Bull.* **14,** Natural Hist. Mus. Los Angeles County

Scientific Journals

(Usually available in university libraries.)
Bulletin of Marine Science, Copeia, Zeitschrift für Tierpsychologie.

Popular Journals

(Usually available from public libraries and by subscription.)

Sea Frontiers (International Oceanographic Foundation, 3979 Rickenbacker Causeway, Miami, Florida 33149, U.S.A.)

Tropical Fish Hobbyist (Tropical Fish Hobbyist Publ., Neptune City, New Jersey 07753, U.S.A.)

Acknowledgements
Many people have assisted in the preparation of this book. Chief among them is Dr Patrick L. Colin, at present on the staff of the Department of Marine Sciences of the University of Puerto Rico. Dr Colin is most gratefully thanked for all his help, which ranged from acting as a dive partner to providing pre-prints of his scientific publications. I also wish to give special thanks to Ann M. Gronell, who has helped in 921 different ways. Numerous scientists have contributed their thoughts about a wide variety of fish, and their help is gratefully acknowledged. Worthy of special mention are C. and D. Arneson, I. Clavijo, B. Chalker, J. C. David, C. Dowd, A. Emery, E. Fischer, C. Gilbert, M. Gomon, E. Houde, A. P. Klimley, R. Livingston, G. Loisel, A. A. Myrberg Jr, D. R. Robertson, C. R. Robins, R. Rosenblatt, R. Scheckter, M. Schmale, W. Smith-Vaniz, J. Staiger, and not least of all, R. Stevenson. Finally, I thank C. G. Messing for drawing the figures.

Terms Used in Describing Fish

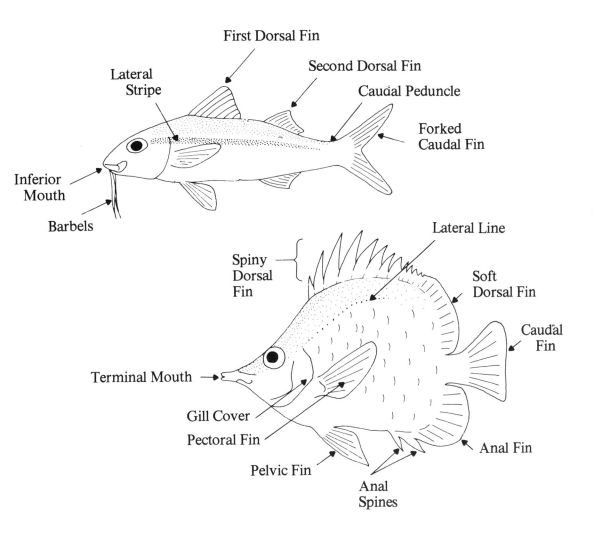

Distribution of Western Atlantic Reef Fish

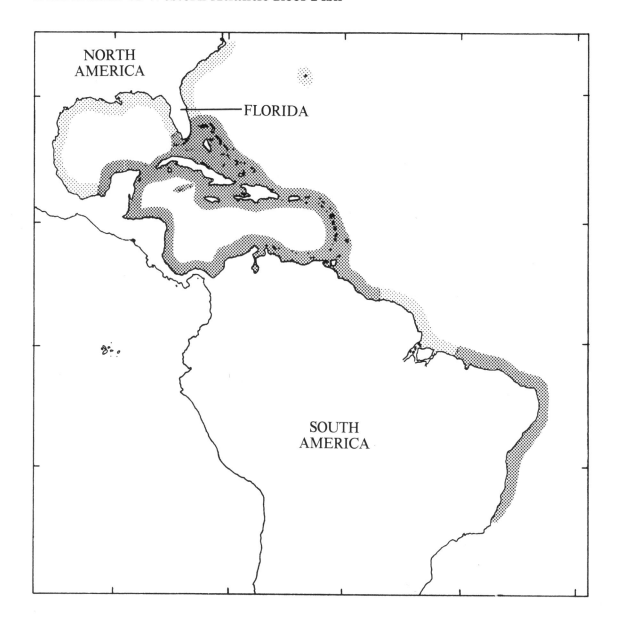

Chapter 1

Serranus

The *Serranus* are sea basses. Not the 40lb striped basses caught by fishermen (to which *Serranus* is only distantly related), or the giant groupers which provide interesting, if largely untrue, stories in adventure magazines (and to which *Serranus* is much more closely allied), but rather the generally small, often colourful predatory fish that are found on and around reefs throughout the world. They are extremely diverse, so much so that the serranids in general constitute one of the largest and most important components of the reef community. As such, they well deserve a place in the balanced aquarium, providing an attractive counterpoint to the largely herbivorous damselfish, angelfish, and butterflyfish that usually make up the aquarium community.

The *Serranus* species belong to the family Serranidae, as do the groupers and a variety of other smaller bass-like fish (see the chapters on Hamlets and Basslets). They are also closely related to the soapfish (family Grammistidae) and, possibly, the basslets (family Grammidae) so that on some occasions all three groups have been placed in one huge family, Serranidae. All of these are predatory fish, usually closely associated with the bottom, and share a number of 'advanced' characteristics. 'Advanced' implies that these fish are on the forefront of the main stream of fish evolution and, indeed, a listing of 'advanced' fish characteristics reads like a description of the Serranidae: spiny dorsal fins, pelvic fins relatively far forward on the body, and ctenoid, as opposed to cycloid, scales.

The characteristics that separate *Serranus* itself from the other serranids are much less obvious and often require anatomical study to pinpoint. In general, *Serranus* are small fish, rarely exceeding 8 or 9 inches (many are much smaller), and are obviously bass-like. Most have large mouths and are full-bodied; all are predators.

Members of *Serranus* (or something very similar to it) are found worldwide in the tropics. From the western North Atlantic 14 species have so far been described. Slightly more than half are common and sufficiently attractive in terms of colour, size, and disposition, to be interesting to the marine aquarist. Most of these are commercially available, though on a scattered basis, and so the aquarist is likely to come in contact with them at some time or another.

Species Account
While not strictly true from an evolutionary standpoint, the western Atlantic species of *Serranus* largely fall into two natural groups: those that hover somewhat off the bottom and feed mostly on plankton, and the more active hunters which stay near the bottom. The former group is a small one, only two species, and since they are similar in many respects, they will be discussed together. As adaptations to their off-the-bottom lifestyle, both are slender-bodied, streamlined fish with rather blunted heads and, for a *Serranus*, small mouths. Typically, they are seen hovering anywhere from 6 inches to a foot or two off the bottom, usually facing into the current and moving with short, fast darting movements to seize their prey. Prey consists mainly of small crustaceans, though on occasion (i.e., when they can catch them) small fish are also eaten.

The more shallow-dwelling of the two fish is the Tabaccofish, *Serranus tabacarius*, which reaches a maximum length of about 7 inches. This is a largely red-brown and yellow-or-white fish. Adults typically have a basal brown colour, becoming pale ventrally. The brown on the top half of the body is overlaid by a series of yellow or white markings, each an incomplete vertical bar, that stretches in a row from the snout to the base of the caudal fin. Juveniles are bright white above and below a broad, reddish band that runs horizontally down the centre of the body. The white above is broken up by dark brown or black markings which, with maturation, will merge with the brown centreline to form the adult colours. *Serranus tabacarius* is a common fish near the reef, though not on it. It frequents the sand spits and basins between and around coral outcrops, usually not too far from a small rock or mound of coral to which it flees when threatened. Tabaccofish are found throughout the tropical western Atlantic, and while recorded from a depth of as little as 15 feet and as much as 225 feet, they are most common between 75 and 150 feet.

The deeper-dwelling member of the pair looks and acts remarkably like the Tabaccofish, though it is only distantly related to it. *Serranus tortugarum*, the chalk bass, differs in appearance largely by the substitution of pale blue for the yellow and white of the former species. Over this bluish cast is laid a series of incomplete vertical red-brown bars running across the dorsal half of the fish. In the aquarium, the species often develops a salmon cast ventrally. The adults (the species reaches a maximum length of about 4 inches) and juveniles are coloured identically and are found in the same areas, often in mixed schools. The favoured habits of these fish are the rubble mounds, rocks, and small coral outcrops which dot the sand plain at the base of the reef. This sand plain, starting at approximately 90 feet and extending as deep as several hundred feet (off the coast of Florida), is swept by reasonably constant currents. Chalk basses, a dozen or so clustered around each outcrop, face into this current and forage for their planktonic food. At the shallow end of their depth-range these schools often contain juvenile Tabaccofish, the combination of the two species so different in colour and yet so similar otherwise, creating a striking sight.

A third, very tiny species of plankton-feeding *Serranus* has recently been described from the Caribbean. Found typically on deep-reef areas (90 feet or more), *Serranus incisus* reaches a maximum length of only an inch or two. It is pale grey with a conspicuous brown spot on the leading edge of the dorsal fin and a pair of faint, brown horizontal lines on the body. *S. incisus* is apparently common in mixed schools of feeding juvenile grunts and other small serranids, where the similar coloration of the various small fish make it difficult to distinguish between them. This similarity explains why this apparently common species has remained undiscovered and undescribed for so long.

The remaining species of *Serranus* are not so sociable. Most are solitary predators, forming pairs only during the spawning season. Each fish (or pair) has a large territory which it defends from other members of its own species and, in most cases, other serranids. Typically, members of this second group of *Serranus* are disruptively coloured, that is, their colours are so arranged as to break up their outlines and thereby render them less conspicuous to potential prey. Such prey consists largely of the abundant small shrimps and crabs on the reef, along with an occasional small fish.

The most widespread member of the group, and the one most commonly seen in aquaria, is the Harlequin Bass, *Serranus tigrinus*. This 4 to 5in fish is both typical of and common on the shallow reef and is largely black on white: dark black spots, stripes, and lines peppered over a chalk-white body and pale fins. Fully mature fish have a yellow wash on the ventral surface and through their eyes, with yellow highlights on the caudal fin. Their black markings also tend to be darker than those on younger fish (though this depends in part on the background; like most fish, their colour lightens when they are over a bright bottom). The Harlequin Bass frequents a wide range of reef and rubble environments at depths from near shore to well over a hundred feet. Typically, one sees the fish swimming slowly over the bottom, around corals and through small caves, stopping periodically to inspect closely any potential prey.

Serranus baldwini, the Lantern Bass, is similar in its ecology to the Harlequin Bass, though tending to shy away from the coral reef proper and remaining in low relief areas. It is common on the broad rocky flats around turtle grass beds and slightly offshore of them. Somewhat smaller than the Harlequin Bass, it reaches maturity at approximately 3 inches. Also, unlike the Harlequin, its colours change with depth. In the shallow end of its range (less than 50 feet), the Lantern Bass is olive green dorsally, grey ventrally, and occasionally has a series of red-brown to yellow-orange blocks of colour along its venter. The eye is distinctly orange and there is a faint yellow line running down the centre of the body. At greater depths, the generally dull colours of this attractive, but subdued, fish really glow. It turns generally red, its spots are orange to orange-yellow, and its mid-lateral stripe becomes golden yellow and very conspicuous.

The third harlequin bass-like species is *Serranus annularis*, the Orangeback Bass(let). Unlike its two near-relatives, the Orangeback is rarely seen in the shallows. It is typical of water at least 90 feet deep and often does not become abundant until 120 feet or more. At these depths, it can be found near almost every protruding object, from rubble mounds to rocky outcrops. It is therefore frequently found close to the Chalk Bass and the two species often share the same habitats, the Orangeback patrolling around the mound and a number of Chalk Bass hovering over it. As the common name implies, the Orangeback Bass has an orange back, actually a series of small, pale orange blocks on its head. It also has several intersecting orange lines and blocks on its underside and a large, elongated chocolate-brown stripe above the mid-line just behind the head. All of these blocks, lines, and squares are set on a snow-white background.

Also found in the same general area, though far less frequently, is another colourful small *Serranus*, the Snow Bass, *Serranus chionaria*, which has only been described recently. That it was overlooked for so long was due to its tendency to live in deep water (some have been taken, via trawlnets, at almost a thousand feet) and also to its small size; the fish apparently reaches sexual maturity at less than 2 inches. The most striking feature of the fish is a large snow-white patch on the venter (the feature from which the common name is derived). Above and around this patch is a shaggy brown area, flecked with bronze highlights, which extends in a broad curve from the head, along the back, and down to the anal fin. Above this area on the back, and broadening towards the posterior to include the base of the caudal fin, is a creamy tan coloured stripe. To my knowledge, the Snow Bass has yet to be collected at much less than 150 feet, though it is apparently common below this depth throughout the Bahamas, Florida, and the northern Caribbean.

Seven other species of *Serranus*, apparently belonging to the harlequin bass group, are found in the tropical west Atlantic. Some, such as the Two Spot Bass, *Serranus flaviventris*, are fairly common, but almost without exception they are brown fish, usually with a few darker stripes or spots on the body, whose drab colours largely preclude them from any broad interest. They are generally similar to the Harlequin in terms of their habits and requirements.

Adult Tabaccofish, *Serranus tabacarius*, are more clearly barred and less brightly coloured than the juvenile shown.

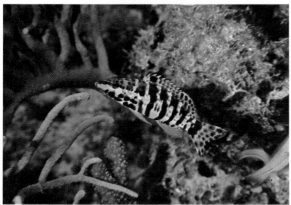

The Harlequin Bass, *Serranus tigrinus*, is a bold and active predator, feeding on small fish and crustaceans.

Field Biology

Most aspects of the field biology of the various species of *Serranus* have been covered above in discussing the various species, species groups, and where each can be found. Little of that material will be repeated here, except where it relates to niche partitioning by the members of this genus. Upon reviewing the biology of the *Serranus* species, one is struck by the nearly complete ecological separation of the many species, the spacing pattern or feeding behaviour of each neatly fitting in with the spacing behaviour and feeding types of the others. The two species of planktivores are an ideal example; though their general behaviour, appearance, and food preferences are nearly identical, one is consistently found deeper on the reef than is the other. Similarly, the predatory species can each be separated ecologically: the Harlequin Bass frequents the shallow reef proper, the Lantern Bass avoids the shallow reef and prefers instead the rock flats, and the Orangeback Bass prefers the deep-water sand flats and small rocky outcrops. The ecological separation between the Orangeback Bass and the Snow Bass is less clear, probably because so little is known about the biology of the latter species, but may be related to the size difference between the two species (the Snow Bass grows to only half the maximum length of the Orangeback).

Such ecological separation of closely related species is not unique to *Serranus*, or even to reef fish, but rather is a characteristic of all living groups. Referred to in the ecological literature as the principle of competitive exclusion, it states that no two species can indefinitely continue to occupy identical ecological niches; eventually, one will out-compete the other and eliminate it from that niche, perhaps forcing it to occupy a less preferable area. The typical result of the operation of this principle is the ecological separation of each species in clear areas of dominance over other similar species, as in *Serranus*. Similar ecological patterns can be worked out for angelfish and butterflyfish and the like, but for these species, the resources being divided among the various species are less clear than they are for the small sea basses.

Reproductive Biology

Serranus subligarius, the Belted Sandfish, is a small brown species, distinguished by a large black spot midway down the dorsal fin and by black pelvic fins. It is found all along the coast from North Carolina to Texas, except for the very southern tip of Florida. In 1959 this species was spawned successfully in the aquarium.

Typically, one fish, apparently heavy with roe, begins to s-curve and quiver just off the bottom. It is approached eventually and joined in its activities by another, slimmer and usually darker fish. The pair mutually court one another and finally s-curve close together, releasing the eggs and sperm. While this sounds normal so far as fish spawnings go, the quirk in the spawning is that both fishes are fully functional hermaphrodites. Each individual, not only of this species, but of all the *Serranus* so far examined, simultaneously have completely functional ovaries and testes. During spawning, one fish apparently assumes the female role, the other that of the male, but during the hour-long courtship and spawning, the roles can apparently be reversed, not just once, but several times. While on the reef, cross-fertilization is apparently the rule (that is, two individuals are always present in a successful spawning), in the aquarium, solitary sandfish have been seen to s-quiver and apparently release gametes, suggesting self-fertilization. Whether the eggs of such a spawning are viable and whether or not such behaviour ever occurs in the field is not known.

The spawning behaviour of most of the Caribbean *Serranus* is similar in most details to that of *Serranus subligarius*. Spawning invariably occurs at dusk, usually starting roughly an hour before dark and continuing until it is too dark for the fish to maintain effective visual contact. Some species, such as *Serranus tigrinus*, form what appear to be long-term stable pairs which jointly defend a common territory and which remain close to one another during the day. Triads are occasionally seen, but usually one fish is clearly subordinate to the other two and probably spawns relatively infrequently.

The spawning behaviour of the Chalk Bass, *Serranus tortugarum*, differs radically from that of the Harlequin bass-type species and the Tabaccofish (which forms pairs and spawns in a tight clasp, tumbling slowly towards the bottom). An aggregating species, at dusk the large cluster of chalk bass spread out into individual pairs of fish, each pair a foot or two off the bottom and several feet from other pairs. Both members of a pair hover close to one another, nervously watching the surrounding pairs. Spawning is a lightning fast rush up into the water column and quick s-curve by the pair; the whole sequence lasts no longer than a second. A given pair will spawn repeatedly each evening, at intervals of as little as 5 minutes.

The reason for the nervousness of the fish and their rapid spawning run is 'cheating' on the part of other chalk bass. When a pair begins its upward run, the 'males' from nearby pairs will dash at the pair and often split them just as they come together into the spawning clasp. It has been speculated that this cheating is adaptive to the cheater because by splitting the spawning fish, it can shed its own sperm and so fertilize some eggs that it would not otherwise get a chance to fertilize. Thus, throughout the spawning period, all of the fish carefully watch each other, looking for a chance both to cheat in the spawning of nearby pairs and to time their own spawning rush so that they, in turn, will not be cheated on. Some pairs actually 'counter-cheat', beginning a spawning run and then aborting it partway, that is, without releasing gametes, so that nearby fish will waste their sperm in trying to split them apart.

After spawning, the planktonic eggs hatch within a day and develop into tiny, relatively non-specialized larvae. Their appearance is essentially like a small fish; the larva has a large head, well-developed teeth, and relatively small fins. The length of time it remains in the plankton before settling out is not known.

Like many reef fish, the *Serranus* spawn year round in the warmer parts of the Caribbean and spawn from late spring to early autumn in the northern regions.

Aquarium Biology

Serranus are excellent aquarium fish, feeding avidly on almost anything. They retain their colours undiminished for long periods, and generally keep the peace. They are active fish, and so show up well in the community tank. Species such as the Chalk Bass and the Tabaccofish tend to hover above and around coral heads, near the top of the tank, while the Harlequin bass-like species remain close to the bottom. *Serranus*, therefore, can be used effectively to balance an aquarium that contains a preponderance of fish that prefer one or the other areas.

The only disadvantage these fish seem to have is that they are active predators, and will readily consume any small fish or shrimp in the aquarium (even cleaner species such as Neon Gobies); therefore they should not be kept with fish much smaller than themselves. They are also intraspecifically territorial, with the exception of the Chalk Bass, and so only one of a kind should be kept in any but the largest aquaria. Chalk Bass, in contrast, seem happiest when in small groups of three or more individuals.

The fact that the *Serranus subligarius* has already been spawned in an aquarium strongly suggests that the other species could also be spawned with relatively little effort. Indeed, even the problem of obtaining a male and a female is eliminated, as each fish can function as either. Conditioning the fish to spawn should require no more than warm water, 75 to 80 °F (24–27 °C), enough room for the fish to be comfortable (say a 29-gallon, long tank, at least), and heavy feeding with live food. If it occurs, spawning will take place in the evening.

Relevant Literature

Colin, P. L. 1978. 'Serranus incisus, new species from the Caribbean Sea (Pisces: Serranidae)', *Proc. Biol. Soc. Wash.* **91**(1): 191–196

Clark, E. 1959. 'Functional hermaphroditism and self-fertilization in a Serranid fish', *Science* **129**: 215–216

Robins, C. R. & Starck, W. A. 1961. 'Materials for a revision of *Serranus* and related fish genera', *Proc. Acad. Nat. Sci. Phila.* **113**(11): 259–314

Smith, C. L. 1965. 'Patterns of sexuality and the classification of Serranid fishes', *Amer. Mus. Novitates* (2207): 1–20

Chapter 2

Hamlets

The sea basses, family Serranidae, include a wide variety of fish, ranging from a few that are only an inch or so long and feed on plankton, to those that forage the reef front and can swallow lobsters whole. This amazing diversity is due mainly to the generalized nature of the basic sea bass. Being broad-scale predators with an unspecialized anatomy, the species within this family can rapidly evolve to fill specific, and often unique, niches. One of the most unique of these is filled by a group of closely related fish known as hamlets, genus *Hypoplectrus*.

Hamlets do not much differ morphologically or behaviourally from the other small serranids found on Caribbean reefs. Each hamlet has a large mouth, well-developed eyes, and a generally fish-shaped body and finnage. They reach a maximum length of 7 to 8 inches and they are, perhaps a little deeper bodied and less bullet-shaped than most other serranids. Like other such serranids, they are unspecialized predators, feeding on a wide variety of crustaceans, small fish, and soft-bodied invertebrates, all of which are captured within a territory vigorously defended against other hamlets and a few other small sea basses. Hamlets can be commonly seen swimming a foot or two off the bottom, around coral heads and rocky outcrops, while stalking the smaller animals they encounter. These are approached slowly and carefully, and engulfed (sometimes) with a single quick strike.

Unlike other sea basses, however, the hamlets have for many years been an enigma to systematically orientated ichthyologists, and at times have stimulated considerable, though always polite, argument about their validity as separate species. The difficulty with this group, and a large part of their fascination, lies in their colour patterns. Unlike most sea basses, which tend to be cryptically coloured (as befits predators), hamlets are often spectacularly coloured and stand out on the reef; also unlike other sea basses, which usually have but a single colour pattern (or at most a few similar ones), the hamlets are wildly variable in colour patterns, so much so that after a while one begins to suspect that every hamlet one sees is a uniquely coloured individual. To understand why the hamlets are so diverse and, at the same time, why they are a systematic oddity requires knowledge of both their hunting behaviour and their reproductive biology.

Species Account

Hamlets are found only in the tropical western Atlantic, with at least 12 recognizably distinct colour-forms known. Nine of these have been formally described in the scientific literature as valid species, and so have been given formal names; the other three have only recently been discovered and their descriptions are being held up until the status of the group is settled. Each of the 12 hamlets can be readily identified on the basis of colour pattern, except in the few 'odd' cases discussed below.

The most widely distributed and frequently most abundant member of the genus is the Barred Hamlet, *Hypoplectrus puella*. In its most widespread form, the fish is pale brown, with a few electric blue lines crossing the head and a series of broad, somewhat irregularly pigmented dark-brown bars on its body, the first running vertically through its eye and the last crossing the caudal peduncle. On close inspection, these bars turn out to consist of bunches of 'fuzzy' vertical bands that end about two-thirds of the way down the side of the body. Setting the pattern for many of the other hamlets, however, the Barred Hamlet varies a great deal in the intensity and length of its barring. The pattern described above is referred to as the 'striped-bar' variant of *Hypoplectrus puella* and is the most common and most widely distributed variant. In the northern Bahamas, however, the most common Barred Hamlet is the 'centre-spot' variant. On this fish, the vertical bars are very pale and just barely discernible from the background body colour. Their centres, however, are very dark, creating a series of dark spots that run horizontally down the centre of each side. A third Barred Hamlet is the 'solid-barred' variant, common off Florida and off Jamaica. This form has broad, very clearly delimited, and very dark vertical bars that completely cross each side of the body.

The solid-barred variant of *Hypoplectrus puella* is similar in its general colour pattern to another recognized species of hamlet, and in many instances the two seem to merge into one another. The Indigo Hamlet, *Hypoplectrus indigo*, is pale blue, rather than pale brown, and has solid, dark blue bars rather than brown ones, but the patterning, width, and length of those bars are identical to those on the solid barred *Hypoplectrus puella*. One commonly finds otherwise normal solid-barred variants with blue edges on the bars, or blue highlights in them, suggesting that in evolution these two species are not far distant from each other. Occasionally one even sees other variants of *Hypoplectrus puella*, such as the 'centre-spot' variant, which are blue rather than brown.

The Butter Hamlet, *Hypoplectrus unicolor*, is also a widely distributed member of the genus and is probably the most abundant hamlet in the northern Bahamas. It is pale yellow-white, usually with a slight blue tint, and has two distinctive marks on its body – a large black spot on its caudal peduncle and a smaller, blue-ringed black spot on its snout. This latter spot is usually accompanied by a series of irregularly shaped blue lines running vertically and diagonally across its head. This nasal spot and blue lining is a feature common to many, though not all, hamlets, and is better developed on some than on others. It is typically lacking on the barred hamlet, for example. Even within a species, its presence may be a variable feature. Butter Hamlets in the Bahamas, for example, typically have the spot, while those in Florida and the southern Caribbean typically lack it.

The Black Hamlet, *Hypoplectrus nigricans*, is also widely distributed and, with the Barred Hamlet, it is the species most tolerant of silty conditions and is therefore one of the most common species in the back-reef area and close to shore. Like the Barred Hamlet, the Black Hamlet has three distinct colour forms: a light brown variant found in the northern Bahamas, a dark black variant common off Florida and in the northern Caribbean and southern Bahamas, and a dark blue variant common in the southern Antilles. None of these forms has a nasal spot.

The Yellowtail Hamlet, *Hypoplectrus chlorurus*, is identical to the Black Hamlet except for having a bright yellow tail. Its variants even match those of the latter species – in the northern Bahamas, one finds light brown hamlets with yellow tails; in the southern Bahamas and off Jamaica, one finds black fishes with yellow tails; and in the southern Antilles, including the Virgin Islands, one finds dark blue hamlets with yellow tails.

Hypoplectrus aberrans, the Yellowbellied Hamlet, is horizontally bicolour – dorsally grey and ventrally yellow. Its caudal fin and the trailing edge of its dorsal fin also tend to be yellow. The amount of and the intensity of the grey on the body varies widely, however, such that one can find both fish that are almost entirely dark grey (sometimes blue-grey) with only a hint of yellow on the pelvic, pectoral, and caudal fins and a faint yellow wash along the venter, and also fish that are broadly yellow, with the pale grey area restricted to the top and forward halves of the fish. The Yellowbellied Hamlet usually has a small nasal spot, but lacks both the blue ring around it and the blue lines on the head. It is found throughout most of the tropical western Atlantic, but is not common in the northern Bahamas or off the coast of Florida.

The Blue Hamlet, *Hypoplectrus gemma*, is, not surprisingly, blue – a bright, shiny blue that covers the entire head and body. Its only distinctive markings are thick black lines along the top and bottom edges of the caudal fin and a fine black line along the top edge of the pectoral fins. The Blue Hamlet has thus far been reported only off the coast of Florida, where it is very common, and at sites along the coast of Central America.

Hypoplectrus guttavarius is one of the most colourful of the hamlets found commonly on well-developed reefs. The Shy Hamlet is black and yellow, usually, but not always, with a large and conspicuous blue-ringed nasal spot just ahead of its eye. Its body is black, while its head and its dorsal, anal, pelvic, and caudal fins are yellow. The extent of the black area on the body varies however, suggesting the presence of at least two variants. On most fish, the black area encompasses the entire rear half of the body proper; on others, the underside of the fish, that is, the region just above the anal fin, remains yellow; the resulting fish look like crosses between Shy Hamlets and Yellowbellied Hamlets.

Finally, the Golden Hamlet, *Hypoplectrus gummigutta*, is the most spectacular of the hamlets and the most widely sought after for aquaria. Its base colour varies from brilliant golden yellow to a dull grey-gold (often darkening dorsally) and it invariably has a very large and very conspicuous nasal spot, so large in fact that is often covers the entire snout in front of the eyes. The Golden Hamlet, while not really rare, is the least common of the widely distributed species and prefers deeper water than most. It is not commonly found at depths much less than 50 feet and may not become common until 70 or 80 feet.

The three, newly discovered hamlets, still lacking formal names, are all geographically restricted. The Tan Hamlet, an apparent off-shoot of the Black Hamlet, is found off Florida and off the coast of Central America. It has a dark black or brown centre to its body, surrounded by a golden tan head and fins. Off the coast of Panama, a variant of this form is horizontally bicolour (darker below than above), has blue pelvic fins, and a faint blue wash around the jaws. The Blue-back Hamlet, an apparent off-shoot of the Yellowbellied Hamlet, has thus far been found only off the coast of Jamaica. Horizontally bicolour, it is blue-and-yellow rather than grey-and-yellow and, unlike the Yellowbellied Hamlet, has a number of blue lines on its head. Finally, the Bicolour Hamlet, thus far reported only off the coast of Isla Providencia in the southern Caribbean, is similar to the Butter Hamlet, but has a black caudal fin (the black is occasionally restricted to the upper and lower edges of the fin), a half-black, half-clear pectoral fin, and a black tear-shaped mask covering the eyes.

The above listing and description of the various hamlets, long as it is, still does not completely catalogue the tremendous colour variation found in the group. One frequently encounters 'odd-ball' fish that have unique colour patterns (such as pale grey with a caudal peduncle spot, a nasal spot, and black edges on the caudal fin). Such oddities are apparently most common in the Barred Hamlet and the Black Hamlet. Finally, one occasionally finds apparent hybrids, like those discussed above, between the Barred Hamlet and the Indigo Hamlet, that cannot be readily assigned to either species.

Though the degree of colour variation shown by *Hypoplectrus* is extreme, there are cases of other vertebrates (especially fish) showing as much, if not more variation, and such colour differences would not alone pose much of a difficulty for systematists to handle. The difficulties arise when one looks at the variability of other characters on the hamlets, especially those characters normally used to separate species. Based on such features as scale counts, fin ray and spine counts, and body proportions, the hamlets are so broadly overlapping in all details that there is no logical reason to separate them into separate species – apart from colour differences. This extreme conservatism in the group has led many systematists to suggest that the hamlets are, in fact, only one, very polychromatic species. They argue that if any of the forms were good species, that is, reproductively isolated from the other forms, it would have evolved at least slightly different meristic and morphometric counts. If in fact the hamlets are freely interbreeding, then by the rules of scientific nomenclature, the entire polychromatic species must be called by the first scientific name ever validly applied to any hamlet. Ironically, this first name is 'unicolor', which means 'one colour'!

Field Biology

To understand the function of the extremely diverse colour patterns manifested by the hamlets, one must first appreciate their position on the reef. All hamlets are predators, with the largest single component of their diet being, by far, small shrimps and crabs. These crustaceans, however, are also preyed on by well over a hundred other Caribbean reef fish, so that the hamlets must compete for their food not only with other small sea basses, such as *Serranus*, but also with a variety of specialized predators such as scorpionfish and squirrelfish, not to mention other hamlets. Competition for the crustacean prey must be fierce and under such conditions any factor that increases the hunting proficiency of a fish without severely hindering it in some other fashion would be heavily selected. For the hamlets, this competitive edge is conferred by the use of mimicry.

Looking at the hamlets, one is struck by the familiarity of their colour patterns. In fact, most of them are remarkably similar, colourwise, to other Caribbean reef fish. The black-and-yellow combination on the Shy Hamlet, for example, duplicates closely the same colour combination on the Rock Beauty,

The Tan Hamlet has never been
formally described as a species, though
it is common off the coast of Florida
and, with a slightly different colour
pattern, off Central America.

An unusual 'centre-spot' variant of the
Indigo Hamlet, *Hypoplectrus indigo*.
Similar variants of the barred and butter
hamlets occur in the same area,
suggesting some interbreeding between
the three 'species'.

This Bahamian Butter Hamlet,
Hypoplectrus unicolor, has a prominent
nasal spot; those from the southern
Caribbean usually lack such a spot.

Yellow Bellied Hamlets, *Hypoplectrus
aberrans*, range in colour from the pale
form shown, to dark grey with only a
trace of yellow along the underside.

The Blue Hamlet, *Hypoplectrus gemma*,
is one of the mimetic species. Compare
its colour pattern with that of the Blue
Chromis.

The Shy Hamlet, *Hypoplectrus guttavarius*, belies its common name by being conspicuous and bold. It is a mimic of the adult Rock Beauty.

The Golden Hamlet, *Hypoplectrus gummigutta*, is the least often seen member of the genus. Though common, it prefers deep water.

Butter Hamlets in a spawning clasp. From this position, gametes are shed as the fish slowly tumble towards the bottom.

Holacanthus tricolor, a common Caribbean angelfish. Other hamlets are similar to a variety of bottom-orientated Damselfish and one is even similar to the Spanish Hogfish, *Bodianus rufus*. These mimicked fish all share two features: all are commonly found close to the reef's surface, where the hamlets are found, and none feed heavily on small crustaceans; most, in fact, are herbivores. These common features strongly suggest that hamlets are aggressive mimics.

An aggressive mimic is a predator that copies one or more features of a non-predator in order to be mistaken for the non-predator by the prey, thereby increasing its chances of successfully approaching and capturing that prey. Theoretically, a foraging shrimp would ignore a harmless Rock Beauty swimming near by, but would hurry for shelter at the approach of a hamlet. By simulating a Rock Beauty, then, the hamlet could approach the shrimp closely without scaring it into cover.

Evidence for this mimicry comes from the nature of the mimicry itself. To a diver, a Shy Hamlet and a Rock Beauty are clearly different, easy to tell apart. The differences between them, however, mainly involve shape, a feature which human eyes, and vertebrate eyes in general, are well capable of distinguishing. Crustaceans, however, have compound eyes, much like those of insects, which are very poor at shape discrimination, though still good at discerning colours. Thus, for a hamlet to mimic a Rock Beauty, at least well enough to fool a shrimp, it need only be coloured like a Rock Beauty – not shaped like one.

If this hypothesis is correct, then the diversity of hamlet colour patterns can be accounted for by a feature common to all such mimicry situations. Except in a few unusual cases, a mimic must always remain much less common than its model. If a mimic becomes too common, then it becomes adaptive for the prey to begin reacting to both model and mimic alike as if both were dangerous; in such cases, the mimicry fails and the population size of the mimics, dependent on the extra hunting success their mimicry has allowed, crashes. Each mimic hamlet species, then, is restricted to a population size determined by the abundance of the prey and the population size of its model. Because of this limit, no one species of hamlet can expand to out-compete other hamlets, so there is room on the reef for many different mimics, as well as a number of non-mimic species which can still compete effectively with other small, generalized sea basses. (The colour pattern of the Indigo Hamlet, for example, is the ideal one for a predator that wishes to be cryptic by breaking up its outline against the deep blue water over the reef). The eventual outcome of such a situation is a proliferation of mimics and a mix of many different mimics on the same reef – the situation in which one finds the hamlets.

The combination of the population limits imposed on it by being a mimic and the poor shape discrimination of the crustacean prey can also explain the systematic limbo of the hamlets. Once it has evolved to a certain point, the point where its prey mistakes it for the model species and it has reached the population size limit imposed on it, there is no longer any selective advantage for a hamlet to improve its mimicry. As long as it can maintain itself at a certain minimum effectiveness, there is no longer any need for either colour constancy or even total reproductive isolation. Lacking such selective pressure, the ultimate stable point reached for such a fish is partial isolation, in which most matings occur between members of the same colour form, but in which a few per cent still involve species of different colour forms. These occasional crossmatings not only increase the gene pool for each colour form, and thus increase the probability that it will be able to evolve into a second, entirely new mimic (as has apparently happened with the Yellowbellied Hamlet and the Blue-back Hamlet, for example) and so expand its population size, but also minimize morphometric and meristic differences between the various colour forms.

Reproductive Biology

As implied above, spawning between hamlets usually involves pairs consisting of two fish of the same colour pattern. A recent study, however, found that cross-pattern spawning occurs about 5 per cent of the time, confirming the almost, but-not-quite species status of the various hamlets. Several questions still remain unanswered however, chief among them being whether the observed cross-pattern spawnings are fertile (if not, the various forms may yet be reproductively isolated, and so good species) and whether or not same-species spawnings even breed true (does a spawning of two Butter Hamlets produce only more Butter Hamlets, or does it produce a mixture of many different hamlets?) Answers to both questions must await the laboratory spawning of hamlets and the successful rearing of the young.

Spawnings by hamlets occur mainly at dusk. At such times, a ready hamlet will leave its territory to seek a mate, often a mate it regularly spawns with. Finding a suitable partner, it courts by arching its back, spreading its fins, and vibrating its body while swimming in short dashes in front of its intended partner. Courtship may last an hour or more, but eventually culminates in a series of brief spawning clasps. The two fish simultaneously dash 2–3 feet off the reef and wrap their bodies tightly together crosswise. While vibrating rapidly, the pair slowly sink towards the bottom, then split apart before reaching the reef. The entire sequence takes less than 30 seconds. Following more courtship, clasping will occur again and again throughout the evening. It most cases, a pair will stay together for the entire spawning period, but in a few cases one fish may sequentially spawn with as many as three partners.

Though the courtship behaviour and the actual spawning clasp are similar to those of other fish, the hamlets differ from most by being simultaneous hermaphrodites. A spawning pair does not consist of a male and a female, but rather of two fish that simultaneously function as both male and female. During an evening spawning period, first one fish, and then the other, is the 'aggressive' partner and courts the other. During the series of spawning clasps, the fish apparently alternate releasing eggs and sperm and it is possible that the prolonged courtship serves to synchronize spawning efforts.

Larval hamlets are similar to larval *Serranus* and spend several weeks in the plankton feeding on a variety of tiny crustaceans and invertebrates before metamorphosing and settling on to the reef. Juveniles less than an inch-and-a-half long are extremely shy and are rarely seen, usually being found hiding well back in coral crevices and in thick algal clusters. Such young fish all apparently have the same colour pattern – a pale grey body (similar to that of an adult Butter Hamlet, only darker) with a triple spot (one white between two blacks) on the caudal peduncle. When frightened, such fish develop bars and resemble small Barred Hamlets. The beginnings of the adult colour patterns develop when the fish reach a length of approximately 2 inches. One juvenile about this size seen in the Bahamas was uniformly grey except for faintly yellow caudal, anal, and dorsal fins. Another fish, slightly larger, also had a yellowish head. Both of these appeared to be transforming Shy Hamlets. Other small fish observed seemed to be transforming into Golden and into Black Hamlets.

Aquarium Biology

Regardless of colour pattern, most hamlets can be kept healthy in the average home aquarium, provided they are well fed (they will take flake food, but clearly prefer brine shrimp and chopped shrimp and fish) and given suitable places to hide. Juveniles adapt themselves to captivity better than adults, and so should be preferred by aquarists. The adults, unfortunately, are prone to be sensitive to handling, and should be moved as little as possible. Most adult hamlets will quickly recover from the trauma of being captured and transferred to an aquarium. Many, but not all, will also recover from being moved once, or even twice. Beyond this point, however, the fish become increasingly prone to 'over-reacting' to a move, hiding constantly and refusing to feed. In most cases, a fish in this condition will never recover and will slowly starve to death. If possible, such fish should be released. If this is not possible, all that can be done is to offer the fish live food (such as small live fish) in the hope that it will be tempted into eating again.

Young fish are less prone to this behaviour than the adults, and of the various species, the Shy Hamlet, ironically, is the boldest. Regardless of the species however, it is foolish to buy a hamlet that is already hiding in a dealer's tank; such a fish may never adapt despite your best efforts.

Relevant Literature

Barlow, G. W. 1975. 'On the sociobiology of some hermaphroditic Serranid fishes, the Hamlets, in Puerto Rico', *Mar. Biol.* **33**: 295–300

Fischer, E. 1978. 'On the evolutionary stability of simultaneous hermaphroditism in fishes: reproductive behavioral ecology of *Hypoplectrus Nigricans* (Serranidae, Pisces)', unpublished Ph.D. dissertation, University of California, Berkeley, Calif.

Randall, J. E. & Randall, H. A. 1960. 'Examples of mimicry and protective resemblance in tropical marine fishes', *Bull. Mar. Sci.* **10**(4): 444–480

Thresher, R. E. 1978. 'Polymorphism, mimicry, and the evolution of the Hamlets', *Bull. Mar. Sci.* **28**(2): 345–353

Chapter 3

Basslets

The term 'basslet' means small bass. In the Caribbean it refers to any of a group of distantly related fish, most of which are, or should be, of considerable interest to both marine aquarists and divers. The term describes members of four genera in three families, all of which are small at maturity and most of which are colourful. The drabbest of the group, the Four-eye Basslet, *Pseudogramma bermudensis*, will not be discussed here, since it has been covered in a later section with the soapfish, to which it is closely related.

The remaining basslets have been considered historically to be members of two serranoid families – Serranidae and Grammidae. The serranoid fish in general are a complex cluster of similar but morphologically unspecialized fish, within which divisions at even the family level are still in question. Serranidae in the past has often been expanded to include not only the serranids, but also the grammids and the soapfish (grammistids), both of which are now treated as separate families. Separation is based mainly on anatomical differences, such as the nature of the lateral line, the number of anal fin rays, and the number of dorsal spines. As work on these fish continues, changes in the taxonomic status of various clusters are likely to occur. One such recent change is the status of the basslets in the genus *Liopropoma*.

Liopropoma

The basslets in *Liopropoma* are brilliantly beautiful and secretive fish about which relatively little is known, despite their abundance on the reef. In the past they have been considered a sub-group in the family Serranidae, along with the sea basses and groupers, but recent work suggests that their strongest affinities are with the grammistids, the soapfish. Such a re-alignment is suggested by two lines of evidence. First, the placement and shape of the bones of the anterior vertebral column and the dorsal fin of *Liopropoma* are very similar to those of the soapfish, and very different from the arrangement of these bones in the other two serranoid lines – *Serranus* itself and the groupers. Second, each of the three serranoid lines has a distinctive planktonic larval form. Again, larval *Lipropoma* are very similar to larval soapfish, and very different from larval *Serranus* and larval groupers.

Based on such evidence, it is likely that *Liopropoma* will in the future be reassigned from the family Serranidae to the Grammistidae. In retrospect, such a move is logical when based on both the field biology and general appearance of the fish. Soapfish in general are secretive animals which slink about the reef from crevice to crevice, and which are characterized by pointed snouts and long, straight foreheads. On all three accounts, *Liopropoma* are similar: they are secretive; they have pointed snouts; and they have long, straight foreheads. The basslets are also characterized by torpedo-shaped, robust bodies (little or no lateral compression) and clearly separated first and second dorsal fins, the first of which has only eight spines (as opposed to many serranids, which have ten or more). Members of the genus are found in tropic seas around the world, generally living in relatively deep water.

Species Account

Five species of *Liopropoma* are known from the western Atlantic, four of which can be found within the diveable depth range. All are common on the reef, but they are so secretive that special efforts are usually required to see them.

Though each of the five species can be readily keyed out on the basis of meristic and morphometric features, all can also be easily identified by their colour pattern alone. The five species fall into two groups depending on whether or not they possess horizontal stripes on the body. Those with such stripes are *Liopropoma rubre*, *Liopropoma carmabi*, and *Liopropoma eukrines*; those lacking such stripes are

Liopropoma mowbrayi and *Liopropoma aberrans*.

Liopropoma rubre, the Swissguard Basslet (so named because its striped pattern is similar to that worn by the Swiss guards at the Vatican), and *Liopropoma carmabi*, the Candystripe Basslet, are a pair of ecologically similar species of similar appearance. Both bear a series of thin horizontal stripes of alternating colours running from the tips of their snouts to the caudal fins. Though superficially identical, they can be readily told apart on the basis of slight differences in colour pattern. The horizontal stripes on *Liopropoma rubre* alternate yellow-orange and red, with black highlights in the red. The striping on *Liopropoma carmabi* is darker – more orange and maroon. The two species also differ in fin coloration. Both have prominent black spots on the rear edges of the dorsal and anal fins, and a pair of such spots on the caudal fin, but those on the Swissguard are ringed by pale blue haloes; those on the Candystripe Basslet are unadorned. Finally, the two can generally be separated by noting their preferred habitats. *Liopropoma rubre* is the shallowest-dwelling member of the genus and can often be found in as little as 15 to 20 feet of water. In contrast, *Liopropoma carmabi* prefers the deeper reef, generally not appearing until 50 feet or so, and not becoming common until 80 or 90 feet. The depth ranges of the two species overlap broadly, however, so that on fully developed reefs in the 50 to 60 foot range, it is not uncommon to find members of both species swimming in caves among the coral. *Liopropoma eukrines*, the Wrasse Bass(let), differs from its relatives both in terms of colour pattern and distribution. Unlike the two species above, *Liopropoma eukrines* has only a single broad stripe running down the centre of its body. This lateral stripe is black, tinged with red, and is sandwiched between two thinner bands of yellow. The rest of the body is rose-coloured, paling slightly ventrally. Unlike most members of the genus, which are distributed broadly throughout the tropical western Atlantic, the Wrasse Basslet has a restricted distribution, thus far having been found only off the coasts of the United States and Mexico. Off the U.S.A., it has been reported as far north as North Carolina and as far south as Texas. It is very common off Florida, where it is generally found under ledges in low relief rock and coral patches at depths in excess of 130 feet. It seems to occupy a similar niche in other areas.

Though very different from any of the other western Atlantic *Liopropoma*, the Wrasse Basslet is similar in shape (slightly more robust than the other members of the genus) and colour to an (as yet) undescribed *Liopropoma* in the eastern Pacific. Called the Rainbow Basslet, this new species has several broad black horizontal stripes, rather than only one, and grows larger than *Liopropoma eukrines* (to at least 10 inches, as opposed to only 6), but such differences are minor. It seems likely that these are 'geminate' species, that is, they are the descendants of one ancient species that lived in both the Atlantic and the Pacific when the oceans were still joined across what is now Central America. When the land bridge formed, the two populations were isolated, and have subsequently developed as separate, but still similar species. Similar geminate species pairs can be found in the angelfish, the damselfish, and the blennioids.

The Swissguard Basslet, *Liopropoma rubre*, is the only common shallow-water member of the genus. The similar appearing Candystripe Basslet is found on the deeper reef.

The remaining western Atlantic species in *Liopropoma* lack extensive horizontal stripes. The Ridgeback Basslet, *Liopropoma mowbrayi*, has a uniformly red-purple body with a short yellow line across the snout and between its eyes, and with haloed black spots on its unpaired fins similar to those described for *Liopropoma rubre*. The Ridgeback Basslet, so named for the slightly raised ridge of flesh along its back between the two dorsal fins, lives in caves on the 'wall', the near vertical drop-off into deep water that surrounds most Caribbean and Bahamian islands. Such drop-offs are riddled with caves and ledges, and in some places, the Ridgeback Basslet can be extremely common, though like other members of the genus it is often overlooked. The depth range of the basslet varies widely from place-to-place, and it is dependent on the depth at which the 'wall' starts. When it begins at a relatively shallow depth (30 to 40 feet), the basslet is found at such depths; where it starts deeper (in some places, 150 feet or more) the basslet is also found deeper.

The final western Atlantic member of the genus is an exotic-looking, deep-dwelling species never seen by divers and rarely collected. *Liopropoma aberrans* is red with bright yellow fins and flecks of yellow scattered on its back. The lower third of its body is pale salmon. This beautiful species is typically found at depths in excess of 300 feet and is commonly observed on submarine dives on the very deep 'wall'. To date, none of these basslets have been brought back to the surface alive.

Field Biology

All five *Liopropoma* are ecologically similar and behave in similar manners on the reef. They are secretive fish, almost invariably seen swimming in caves or under coral ridges, and rarely venturing out into open water. On well-developed reefs, they can sometimes be observed dashing from coral head to coral head, pausing only when in the confines of protective coral. Their knowledge of the maze of boreholes and coral crevices under the reef is phenomenal; even the most secure-looking cave into which one has been chased will certainly have a bolt-hole through which the fish can escape.

Within these caves, *Liopropoma* are always seen as solitary fish (except during spawning periods), suggesting territoriality, though actual fighting between them has not been observed. Repeated dives to the same coral crevice often result in repeated and long-term observations of what appears to be the same fish, indicating that they are strongly site-attached, with each fish rarely, if ever, straying from its preferred home range.

Within its area, a basslet is bold, active, and constantly on the move. All are predators, feeding on a wide variety of small crustaceans and fish which they probably capture around the mouths of their caves. Despite the pointed snouts, which give them delicate and almost dainty appearances, each fish has a surprisingly large set of jaws, quite capable of swallowing even large prey. Ecological distinction among the five species is based in part on differences in geographic distribution, and in part on depth and habitat preferences, as discussed above.

Reproductive Biology

Little is known about the spawning of *Liopropoma*. The only hard facts are strictly anatomical and even these were only gathered within the last few years. Unlike most serranids and their near relatives, *Liopropoma* are apparently not simultaneous hermaphrodites, but rather individuals are either male or female. Since this is an exception to the general serranid pattern, it has been suggested that such separation of the sexes is secondarily derived from hermaphroditic ancestors. There is no apparent sexual dimorphism.

Courtship and spawning have not been observed for any of the species, but based on field observations, such are likely to occur at dusk. On dives at this time of the day, one frequently sees pairs of basslets, one fish following the other through the caves and crevices. Based on the general spawning patterns of other reef fish with pelagic eggs actual spawning probably takes place near the mouths of the caves, the area best suited for launching the fertilized eggs into open water.

Features of the eggs and the duration of development have not been reported, but the planktonic larvae themselves have characteristic appearances. Each is long and cylindrical, has a terminal mouth, and has two extremely long and prominent spines leading the dorsal fin. As noted earlier, such spines are also present on larval soapfish. Very small basslets, apparently newly settled out of the plankton, can be found on the reef year-round, though they are most abundant in spring and early summer, suggesting that some spawning occurs throughout the year.

Aquarium Biology

Liopropoma are outstanding aquarium fish. They retain their brilliant colours well, are active, show no fear of open areas of the tank, and feed readily, accepting most common foods and doing well on thawed brine shrimp and flake foods. In general, they are peaceful fish, rarely chasing anyone and rarely being chased in return. The only exceptions are the occasional conflicts between basslets and other cave-dwelling species, especially when only a few crevices are available in the aquarium. They fight occasionally with Cardinalfish and Spanish Hogfish, for example, and while there is usually little damage done, it is probably best to separate such fish since conflict often drives the already shy basslets to the rear areas of the tank. In this regard, the basslets are also very sensitive to harassment by tank bullies, and generally flee rather than fight. Again, this often results in rarely seen basslets, and can result in their deaths.

Liopropoma do have one drawback, however. While generally hardy, they are extremely sensitive to fouled water or a drop in oxygen level. As an example, the air pump on a temporary collecting tank failed on a trip to the southern Caribbean and before it could be replaced (several hours later), the single *Liopropoma* in the tank had died; yet, the remaining fish (grammas, butterflyfish, and wrasses) were only breathing slightly faster than normal and all recovered easily. Thus, with these basslets it is wise to be critical concerning overcrowding and overfeeding. With this precaution in mind, aquarists will have no trouble keeping these fish alive for years.

Gramma and Lipogramma

The systematic affinities of the second major family of basslets, the Grammidae, has also been questioned recently. Generally, they have been considered a specialized off-shoot of the serranid line, based on osteology, but their exact relationship has been unclear. Recent examinations of their internal anatomy, however, have shown that the grammids and the jawfish, family Opistognathidae, share many common features, and indeed may be more closely related than previously suspected. The work has yet to be verified, but if true, could explain much about the grammids. First, they look like jawfish, much more than they look like other serranids. Both jawfish and grammids, for example, are blunt-headed, typically with large eyes and prominent, elongated pelvic fins set far forward on the body. Members of both families are also typically seen either sitting in holes or dashing in and out of them. Jawfish dig their own burrows in sand, while grammids occupy naturally occuring holes in rocks and coral or construct shelter holes from algae. A close relationship between the two could also account for some aspects of grammid reproductive biology.

The Grammidae contain nine known species in two genera in the western Atlantic, the best known of which is the Royal Gramma, a very popular aquarium fish. Of the two genera, *Gramma* contains the largest and most abundant members of the group, with the species in *Lipogramma* generally being rare in shallow water, small, and, to a large extent, unknown by most divers and aquarists.

The two genera are similar in many respects; fish in both are elongate, robust, and blunt-headed, with long pelvic fins, large eyes, and a slightly forked caudal fin. Aside from ecological and behavioural differences, however, members of the two genera can be readily separated based on the length of the lateral line. The lateral line system on *Gramma* extends the full length of the body; that on *Lipogramma* terminates partway down each side. Whether or not such a difference justifies separation of the two at the family level has not been determined.

Species Account

There are three known Caribbean members of the genus *Gramma*, all of which are similar in maximum size (about 4 inches) and shape. Each, however, is distinctively coloured. The Royal Gramma, *Gramma loreto*, and the Blackcap Basslet, *Gramma melacara*, are brilliantly coloured. The former is vertically bicolour, purple-orange in front and lemon yellow to the rear, with a prominent black spot near the leading edge of the dorsal fin. The Blackcap Basslet is purple, with a darker purple (almost black) forehead and black edges on the dorsal and anal fins and on the upper and lower lobes of its caudal fin. Each species also has one or more lines on the head. Those on the royal gramma are maroon and run through and below the eye. The single line on the Blackcap Basslet is yellow, thin, and extends from each eye to the dorsal fin.

The Ridgeback Basslet, *Liopropoma mowbrayi*, is found only on the 'wall', the near vertical drop-off that surrounds many western Atlantic islands.

The Wrasse Basslet, *Liopropoma eukrines*, is common in very deep water off the southern coast of the United States.

The Blackcap Basslet, *Gramma melacara*, is one of the most attractive Caribbean fish, and one of the most popular with aquarists. Though not often found in shallower waters, it is extremely abundant at depths below 100 feet.

The Dusky Gramma, *Gramma linki*, is normally found at depths in excess of 200 feet. This one was photographed at 110 feet off Puerto Rico, where the species occupies the 'shallower' areas vacated by the absent Blackcap Basslets.

The attractive Bicolour Basslet, *Lipogramma klayi*, is a creature of the very deep reef. This one was photographed at 210 feet.

The third species in the genus, *Gramma linki*, the Dusky Gramma, has just recently been described. A relatively deep-water species that is not commonly collected, it is uniformly blue-green with a bold yellow ring around each eye and several wavy yellow lines on each gill cover.

Lipogramma also contains at this time, three recognized species, although three more are in the process of being described. The largest, most colourful, and best-known member of the genus is the Bicolor Basslet, *Lipogramma klayi*, which, in colour pattern, is similar to the Royal Gramma – purple-red anteriorly and yellow posteriorly. It lacks the spot on the dorsal fin characteristic of the *Gramma* however, and the transition between the purple and yellow is more gradual. The two species are also ecologically distinct. *Gramma loreto* is a shallow-water species, rarely found much below 100 feet; in contrast, *Lipogramma klayi* prefers the deep reef and is rarely seen at less than 150 feet. It often does not become common until 225 feet or more.

Though less well-known, the Threeline Basslet, *Lipogramma trilineata*, is the only common shallow-water member of the genus and probably has the widest distribution. A small (one to two inch maximum) and delicately coloured species, it is dusky yellow anteriorly and blue-grey posteriorly, with three parallel electric blue lines which run from the snout to mid-back and from which the species derives its common name. The last, already recognized species in the genus is the Spotfin Basslet, *Lipogramma anabantoides*. This species has yet to be collected alive, all specimens of it having been taken in poison stations on the reef. Freshly preserved fish are brown with a reddish cast, black pelvic fins, and two dark blotches on the dorsal fin. Another small species, it grows to only about an inch.

Recently, three additional, deeper water species of *Lipogramma* have been collected and are now in the process of being formally named and described. All three are very small (maximum length no more than an inch) and are apparently very secretive. One, the Royal Basslet, is delicately and attractively coloured: pale grey with fine yellow vertical lines on the body, several horizontal yellow lines on its head and gill covers, a broad white vertical bar near the middle of the body, and a prominent blue-ringed black spot near the rear edge of the dorsal fin. Despite its attractive colours, however, its small size and its depth preference (the only known specimens were collected from caves at depths in excess of 200 feet) preclude it from ever becoming a popular aquarium fish (though it does well in captivity). The Banded Basslet, another small species, has alternating vertical bands of black and white and has thus far been collected only in nets dragged over rock and coral bottoms between 400 and 800 feet. Finally, the Rosy Basslet is known only from a single specimen collected at 100 feet of Isla Providencia, off the coast of Colombia. It is rose-coloured with a single white stripe running up the forehead, a yellow caudal fin, and several tiny spots on the dorsal fin.

Scientific names have been provided for all three of these species, but because of the rules of zoological nomenclature, cannot be used until they are formally published with full descriptions of the species. For these names, plus detailed descriptions of all three species (including a colour plate of the Royal Basslet), the paper by Robins and Colin listed in the 'Relevant Literature' at the end of the chapter should be consulted.

Field Biology

The three species in the genus *Gramma* are broadly similar in their ecology and behaviour on the reef. All are plankton feeders, each fish hovering a few inches off the bottom and dashing back and forth to pick out particulate matter as it passes. Each individual apparently remains within one small area on the reef, where it is familiar with all of the bolt-holes. There is, however, no apparent territoriality, even though one occasionally sees jaw displaying between fish. The functions of such displays is not known, but possibly relates to some loosely size-related dominance hierarchy.

As is often the case with ecologically similar fish in the same genus, resource partitioning on the reef takes the form of habitat preference combined with slight differences in geographic distribution. For *Gramma*, as in the *Liopropoma*, habitat partitioning is based on preferred depths. *Gramma loreto* is the shallow-water member of the genus, commonly found in as little as 10 feet of water and reaching its peak abundance between 40 and 80 feet. At the shallow end of its range, it lives mainly in caves, often hovering upside down along the roof, but in deeper water, it is found typically in the open, associated with both live coral and rock. The Blackcap Basslet generally replaces the Royal Gramma at a depth of approximately 100 feet, and it, in turn, is replaced by the Dusky Gramma at 250 to 350 feet. Both of these deeper dwelling species are found typically in the open, hovering a few inches off the coral surface. The zones of overlap between any two of these three species is generally very narrow, frequently no more than 10 feet of vertical change.

While the Royal Gramma and the Dusky Gramma are common throughout the Bahamas and the Caribbean (none of the Gramma are found off Florida, despite misguided attempts by some individuals to introduce the Royal Gramma), the Blackcap Basslet has an odd hole in its distribution, as yet unexplained. Though found in the Bahamas and in the southern Caribbean, it is missing from many of the eastern Caribbean islands, such as Puerto Rico and Haiti. In such areas, its niche, i.e. the depth range from 100 to 300 feet, is invaded and occupied by the Dusky Gramma, so that in some areas the latter can be collected in as little as 80 feet of water. This invasion where the Blackcap is absent suggests that the latter is competitively excluding the former from an area it would otherwise occupy. A similar competition between the Royal Gramma and the Blackcap may be preventing the latter from invading water shallower than 100 feet.

Lipogramma are more shy than *Gramma* and, like *Liopropoma*, are most often found in caves and crevices in the reef (where the two can often be collected together). The exception to this pattern is the Bicolor Basslet, *Lipogramma klayi*, which for a basslet is quite bold. It can usually be seen anywhere from a few inches to a foot or so off the bottom, foraging for the plankton that constitutes the bulk of its diet. Even so, they frighten easily and dash into small holes in the bottom as a diver approaches, often while the latter is still 5 or 6 feet away.

Other than their general shyness and preference for caves and holes, little solid information is available about the various species of *Lipogramma* as none have been studied in detail. As a group, they are clearly deep-water fish, with only one representative common in shallow water. The Threeline Basslet, *Lipogramma trilineata*, can be collected in as little as 25 feet, but even this species does not reach its peak abundance until 60 or 70 feet and has been collected several times at depths in excess of 200 feet.

Where it is known, there appear to be differences in the distributions of the various species in the genus. *Lipogramma trilineata* has the broadest geographic range of the group, being common throughout the Caribbean, the Bahamas, and off the coast of Florida. The Bicolor Basslet has now been collected in Jamaica, Puerto Rico, the Bahamas, British Honduras, and Curacao, such that it too appears to be broadly distributed. This Basslet clearly prefers sharply sloping (70 degrees plus) zones of mixed sand and rock and is usually seen swimming about the sandy ledges on such drop-offs. Where present, they are generally very common, though one must often go to 250 feet or more to find them. Finally, the Spotfin Basslet, *Lipogramma anabantoides*, is evidently rare and has thus far been reported only from the Bahamas. Specimens have been collected from patch reefs in as little as 60 feet of water, but the species seems to be most 'common' on steeply sloping coral and algae-covered walls at depths in excess of 70 feet.

Reproductive Biology

Despite its abundance and popularity, surprisingly little is known about the reproductive biology of even the Royal Gramma; even less is known about the rarer or deeper-dwelling members of either *Gramma* or *Lipogramma*. Observations of spawning in the field have never been reported. Based on anatomical studies, they are apparently hermaphroditic. There is no conspicuous sexual dimorphism.

Despite the lack of field observations, there is one, largely preliminary, report of spawning by the Royal Gramma in the aquarium. While many details are lacking, those available are very interesting, and reinforce the possible relationship between grammids and jawfish. The aquarist reared four gramma in a single aquarium, and had two 'pairs' develop, each composed of a large and a small individual (sexual dimorphism based on size ?) Several days prior to spawning, the larger fish was seen to line a hole in a rock with strands of algae and then, one morning, was found in the hole with a conspicuously distended mouth. The fish proved to be mouth-brooding apparently demersal eggs, again much like a jawfish. Further observations were not possible since the eggs proved infertile and were discarded by the brooding fish the next morning. If such mouth-brooding in holes is characteristic of the species, it could well explain why open-water spawning of pelagic eggs, as is the rule for serranids, has not been observed for the grammids.

Aquarium Biology

The three species of *Gramma* all do very well in captivity and the popularity of the two relatively shallow-water species in the aquarium world is well founded. All three are hardy, active, and, aside from a little squabbling among themselves, peaceful. They do, however, have one drawback. All three tend to fade in aquaria and, while still attractive, are only pale reflections of their true colours after a week or so in captivity. It is a sad truth that most aquarists do not really appreciate the beauty of the Royal Gramma, having never seen the fish on the reef and assuming that the colours of the fish in the aquarium are all that it develops. It is an indication of how well the species does in captivity and how colourful it is that, even when faded, it is one of the most popular of marine fish. Why these fish fade in captivity is not known.

All three species are also prone to digging burrows in aquaria (like jawfish!), typically excavating the area under a rock or piece of coral by carrying mouthfuls of sand out of the burrow and spitting it out near its rim.

Lipogramma also do well in captivity and, within a week or so, become fairly bold and actively forage in open water. They clearly prefer vertical surfaces and should also be provided with some small cave or crevice in which they can find shelter. *Lipogramma klayi* are somewhat aggressive among themselves, so that crowded conditions should be avoided. Otherwise the various species are colourfast, hardy, and feed well. Because of their small size at maturity, they will do best if kept in a relatively small aquarium with other similarly sized fish.

One species of *Lipogramma* in particular is highly recommended, the Threeline Basslet, *Lipogramma trilineata*. It is a delicately beautiful fish that has never received the attention its good looks and attractive personality deserve. This may be due in large part to its shyness on the reef. Like the *Liopropoma*, even where common these tiny basslets are easily overlooked and so are not often obtained by professional collectors. If the opportunity presents itself, however, aquarists who can collect their own fish would do well to search diligently for this common little fish.

As a final note, *Lipogramma trilineata* may be unique among reef fish in that it constructs a shelter hole out of algae. An adult Threeline Basslet in captivity was observed to build such a shelter shortly after being introduced into the tank, apparently because no suitable shelter holes were already available for it to occupy. On a broad, flat, vertical piece of algae-covered coral, the fish spent over a week pulling at strands of algae, blowing on, nuzzling, and pushing them into place until a shallow mound was created. The fish then cleared a double-ended tunnel through the mound, and thereafter dashed into this tunnel whenever frightened. It also slept there each night. Though normally peaceful, it vigorously defended its shelter, open jaw displaying at and harassing small fish and hermit crabs that approached too closely. At one point, a larger fish swam through the mound and destroyed the tunnel, after which the basslet promptly reconstructed it.

Whether or not such shelter construction occurs on the reef is, like most aspects of the behaviour and biology of the basslets, not known. Within a few weeks of its construction, the tunnel was so overgrown with algae that it blended perfectly into the surrounding area and was effectively camouflaged. Even the openings at either end were difficult to see except when the fish was entering or leaving its shelter. So effective is this camouflage, that it is very unlikely that such shelters on the reef would ever be observed by casual divers. The ecological and behavioural significance of such shelter construction, if any, will not be discovered until detailed studies are made in the field of this species and its relatives. The similarity between this and the lining of a shelter hole with algae by Royal Gramma, described above, suggest that such behaviour may be a common feature in the group.

Relevant Literature

Böhlke, J. E. & Randall, J. E. 1963. 'The fishes of the Western Atlantic Serranoid genus *Gramma*', *Proc. Acad. Nat. Sci. Phila.* **115**(2): 33–52

Kendall, A. W. Jr 1976. 'Pre-dorsal and associated bones in Serranid and Grammistid fishes', *Bull. Mar. Sci.* **26**(4): 585–592

Randall, J. E. 1963. 'Three new species and six new records of small serranoid fishes from Curacao and Puerto Rico', *Stud. Fauna Curacao and other Caribbean Islands* (80): 77–110

Robins, C. R. 1967. 'The status of the Serranid fish, *Liopropoma aberrans*, with the description of a new, apparently related genus', *Copeia* 1967 (3): 591–595

Robins, C. R. & Colin, P. L. 1979. 'Three new Grammid fishes from the Caribbean Sea', *Bull, Mar. Sci.* **29**(1): 41–52

Rosti, P. 1967. 'Breeding the royal gramma', *Salt water Aquarium* **2**(5): 106–108

Smith, C. L. 1971. 'Secondary Gonochorism in the Serranid genus Liopropoma', *Copeia* 1971: 316–319

Starck, W. A. & Colin P. L. 1978. '*Gramma linki* – a new species of Grammid fish from the tropical Western Atlantic', *Bull. Mar. Sci.* **28**(1): 146–152

Starck, W. A. & Courtenay, W. R. Jr 1962. '*Choristium eukrines*, a new Serranid fish from Florida, with notes on related species', *Proc. Biol. Soc. Wash.* **75**: 159–167

Chapter 4

Angelfish

If any single group of fish characterizes the marine aquarium, it is these, the species in the family Pomacanthidae. Angelfish are generally so beautifully coloured that a properly set-up display tank containing a single full-coloured fish can be considered a success. A tank containing several can be overwhelming. Fortunately, the Caribbean contains its share of pomacanthids, including one species, the Queen Angel, which is considered by many to be the most beautiful fish in the world.

The pomacanthids, in the past, have been considered one part of the family Chaetodontidae – an amalgam of two morphologically and behaviourally similar groups, the angelfish and the butterflyfish. The angelfish are round, laterally compressed fish, usually with bluntly rounded heads, smooth, even fins with no obvious break in their continuous dorsal fins, and very prominent spines on the rear edge of each gill cover. The butterflyfish are similarly shaped, but usually have a projecting set of jaws, a strongly spined dorsal fin, and lack the opercular spine. The exact relationship between these two groups has always been unclear and some ichthyologists treated them as a single family, others as two related families. Recently, the internal anatomy of the two has been examined in detail and a number of major differences between them was noted, especially with regard to the structure of the nervous system. As such internal anatomy is considered to be very conservative evolutionarily, recent opinion now has it that the two groups may have, in fact, evolved from two different lines and that their similarity is not so much due to close relationship as much as it is convergence by two groups of fish to fill a common niche on the reef.

Pomacanthids are found around the world in shallow tropic seas and, as a group, are closely related to the coral reef environment. While they are most speciose in the Indo-Pacific, there are seven species, in three genera, in the Caribbean.

Species Account

Most Caribbean angelfish belong to one of two morphologically similar genera: *Holacanthus*, with three species, and *Pomacanthus*, with two. All are large fish, some reaching as much as 2 feet and all reaching at least a foot. Colour patterns are the most diagnostic feature among the species, though for reasons discussed later, even these can be confusing.

The most distinctive, most common, and best known member of this group is the Rock Beauty, *Holacanthus tricolor*. Adults are black centrally, surrounded by brilliant orange-yellow on the head, the fore part of the body, and fins. The pointed dorsal and anal fins are usually edged with red and very large adults (more than 8 inches) commonly have a black mouth. Even the eyes are brightly coloured, blue and yellow around a black pupil, set in a yellow head. Small juveniles are coloured differently than the adults, though the same colours are involved. The black area is restricted to a blue-ringed spot located on the back just under the soft portion of the dorsal fin. The rest of the fish, except for the black-and-blue eyes, is bright yellow, less orange than the adults. As the fish matures, the black spot gradually expands, obliterating the blue ring and eventually covering the entire centre of the body. Up to a length of 3 inches, however, one can still detect a faint blue ring buried in this black region.

The remaining four species in these two genera fall into two closely related pairs of species. Natural hybrids between the members of one pair have been collected in fair numbers and have in the past even been given a now discredited scientific name. It has been suggested that the reason for this pairing of species is zoogeographic, that one member of each pair has evolved along the continental margins in often silty and turbulent areas, while the other of each, the more colourful member, developed around oceanic islands with clear water and full reef development. Why such a pattern should hold for these species and not for others has not yet been explained.

The first pair is in the genus *Holacanthus*: *Holacanthus bermudensis* and *Holacanthus ciliaris*, the Blue and the Queen angelfish respectively. Both are large, blue-and-yellow species as adults, and the two have virtually identical juvenile patterns (very different from the adult patterns). The adult Blue Angelfish is, not surprisingly, mostly blue − actually blue-grey − paling somewhat on the underside of the body. The long pointed tips of the dorsal and anal fins, as well as the rear portions of the caudal and pectoral fins, are yellow. The pelvic fins are entirely yellow. The general appearance is attractive, but subdued. In contrast, the Queen Angelfish is alive with shimmering iridescent colours; words, and even pictures, cannot adequately describe it. Crudely put, its basic body colour is yellow-green with shadings of light blue and a crescent of electric yellow edging each of its many large scales. The caudal, pectoral, and pelvic fins are also yellow and all unpaired fins are edged with a thin outlining stripe of electric blue. There is a blue wash on the throat and large blue spots on the gill covers, at the bases of the pectoral fins, and around the mouth. The eyes have black pupils, yellow irises, and each is outlined with blue. And finally, high on the forehead there sits the 'crown', a large black spot flecked with blue and outlined by a broad blue ring. Just above the crown, ahead of the dorsal fin, there is a tiny, brilliant spot of gold.

The juveniles of both species are dark blue fish with a pale yellow venter and yellow caudal fins. The dorsal and anal fins are outlined with pale electric blue. Five similarly coloured lines cross each fish vertically: one each before and after the eye, one behind the pectoral fin, one in the centre rear of the body, and the last, a short one, just ahead of the caudal peduncle. As juveniles, the two species can be most easily separated by the shape of the line that passes through the centre rear of the body. On the Queen Angelfish, the fourth line is curved (thus, four curved lines and a final straight one) and on the blue, the fourth line is straight (three curved lines and two straight ones).

The identification of the two species is made more confusing by natural hybrids, which run the full gamut from almost pure Queens to almost pure Blues. Thus, one finds juveniles with slightly curved fourth lines, adults with small or indistinct crowns, apparently good Queen Angelfish that lack a crown altogether, and so on. In the past, such fish have been called Townsend Angels, and given a non-valid scientific name, *Holacanthus townsendi*. In a study conducted at the University of Miami, the Angelfish collected formed a tri-modal population curve, based on Queen and Blue Angelfish characteristics. A large peak at one end represented the pure and near-pure Queen Angelfish, the peak at the other end represented the pure and near-pure Blue Angelfish, and then, halfway between the two and separated from them by a trough of relatively few fish, there was a minor peak of the hybrids.

In contrast, a natural hybrid between the members of a second, similar pair of angelfish species has never been reported. In the Caribbean, the genus *Pomacanthus* is represented by the continental *Pomacanthus arctuatus* and the insular *Pomacanthus paru*, the Grey and the French angelfish, respectively. As in the previous pair, the supposed continental form is the more mundane coloured of the two. A very broad fish which reaches a reported length of 2 feet, the Grey Angelfish is largely chocolate brown overlaid by an overlapping pattern of white ovals that outline and highlight the scales on the body, though not those on the head. The fins are brown, save a thin electric blue line on the rear edge of the squared-off caudal fin and a large, very conspicuous spot of yellow *inside* the pectoral fins. These spots are only exposed when the fish is sculling itself along by means of these fins. The significance of these normally hidden yellow signals is not clear, but it has been suggested that they help in pair formation.

The French Angelfish lack these yellow inner fins, but do have a spot of yellow at the *outer* base of the pectorals. Their bodies are also a much deeper black than those of the Grey Angel, with the rear edge of each scale outlined by a crescent of bright yellow. As on the grey, these markings do not extend onto the scales on the head. Each of the French Angel's eyes are bounded by fine, yellow, outlining rings (the eyes of the grey are entirely white around a black pupil). The French Angel also has a rounded caudal fin, as opposed to the squared fin of the Grey. As adults, both species also have a white area around the mouth.

As in the previous pair of species, the juveniles of the two *Pomacanthus* are very similar and very spectacular. Both are basically black and yellow with blue highlights on the pelvic and anal fins. The black body is crossed by five vertical bands of yellow: the first through the lips, the second behind the eye and ending just ahead of the pelvic fins, the third and longest running from the middle of the dorsal fin in an arc behind the pectorals to end just ahead of the anal fin, the fourth an arc that starts on the trailing edge of the dorsal fin and ends on the trailing edge of the anal fin, and the last a short arc across the caudal peduncle. The two species can be readily told apart by the shape of the black centre of the caudal fin itself. On the Grey Angel, the caudal spot is clearly hemispherical with a straight, clear, vertical trailing edge; on the French Angel the caudal spot is circular and is often completely ringed with yellow. There is also a difference in the yellow area around the mouths of the two species. Both have a vertical yellow line which runs off the forehead down to the top lip. On the Grey, this line continues through both lips; on the French, it stops at the base of the top lip, but also continues around the mouth to extend below it.

In both species, as in the *Holacanthus* pair, juvenile colours are retained until the fish reaches a length of 3 to 4 inches, at which size the vertical bars of youth gradually fade and are replaced by the speckled pattern of the adult. Size of transformation varies a great deal both between and within a species. As a general rule, Queens seem to reach a fully mature colour pattern at the smallest size (as small as 4 inches), while Grey Angelfish as large as 9 inches may still have a faint indication of barring (the head bars are usually the last to go).

The last genus Caribbean angelfish is *Centropyge*, the Pigmy Angels. It contains two similar species which are, in fact, so similar that separate status as species has only been resurrected within the last few years. The more widely distributed member of the genus, and the one aquarists invariably see in stores, is the Cherubfish, *Centropyge argi*. The body of this species is deep blue, outlined by electric blue on the unpaired fins, while the region around and below the eyes, across the lower part of the operculum, and down the base of the pelvic fins is yellow-orange with a few fine blue spots outlining the operculum. There is a great deal of intraspecific variation in the extent of the yellow area and the pattern of blue spots in it. On some fish, the entire eye is in the yellow area and is outlined by a complete ring of blue; on others, only the lower half of the eye is in the yellow and so only the lower half has a blue ring (here, a semicircle). Similarly, on some fish the rear opercular edge is clearly marked by flecks of blue; on others, the area has only a few blue highlights. The significance, if any, of such variation is not known.

The second species of *Centropyge*, *Centropyge aurantonotus*, looks like a super-yellow Cherubfish. Like the latter species, the body is mainly dark blue with a yellow 'face'; unlike it, the yellow on this *Centropyge* extends in a band along the back of the fish, to end near the rear edge of the soft dorsal fin. While the Cherubfish is found throughout the tropical western Atlantic, *Centropyge aurantonotus*, sometimes referred to as the Flameback Cherubfish, has so far been reported only from Curacao and Barbados (where it can be found with *Centropyge argi*) and off the coast of Brazil (where it completely replaces *Centropyge argi*).

Both species are small, rarely exceeding three inches in total length. Unlike the other Caribbean angelfish, the two pigmy angels lack any special juvenile coloration.

Field Biology

The Caribbean angelfish are all benthic fish, rarely straying more than a few feet off the bottom. The size of a fish's home range, that is, the area within which it roams on the reef and from which it rarely, if ever, strays, varies both with the size of the individual and with the species. Large adults of *Holacanthus* and *Pomacanthus* cover broad sections of the reef in a single day, usually roaming in pairs. They are inquisitive, generally peaceful fish neither bothering other fish nor being bothered in return. Of the various species, large Rock Beauties are the shyest of the group and the least nomadic. They frequently remain close to a single large coral outcrop and when approached, retreat into it, peering at you if you are diving, from a distance of a few feet and retreating even farther if you persist in following.

All of these species feed heavily upon sponges, the multi-coloured, vase-shaped, and encrusting animals that constitute a large part of the reef's sessile fauna. Vase sponges can often be found with v-shaped notches cut from their rims, these being the scars of past angelfish bites. The degree to which each of the species depends on sponges varies; at its extreme, sponges constitute more than 97 per cent of the diet of adult Rock Beauties.

The distribution of these angelfish clearly reflects, and probably suggested, the insular-versus-continental theory of their origin. Around inshore jetties, bridges, and rocky outcrops, Blue Angelfish and Grey Angelfish dominate the populations. On the reef itself, Queens and French dominate. Rock Beauties are strictly reef-associated and have apparently never developed a continental sibling species.

The Juvenile Angelfish

Lines Indicate Key Features

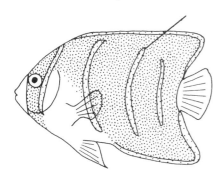

Holacanthus
ciliaris

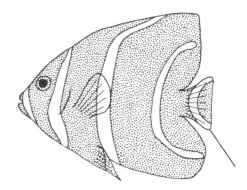

Pomacanthus
arcuatus

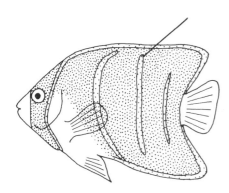

Holacanthus
bermudensis

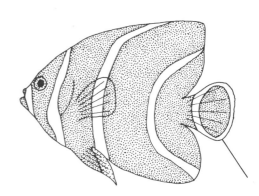

Pomacanthus
paru

◄ Small Rock Beauties, *Holacanthus tricolor*, are more brightly coloured than the large adults. Fish smaller than this one are yellow with only a blue-ringed black spot in the centre of the body.

Adult Blue Angelfish are more subdued in colour than the Queen Angelfish and are not often found around oceanic islands. ▼

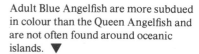

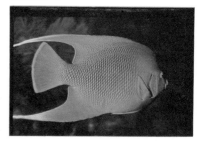

◄ Juvenile Queen Angelfish, *Holacanthus ciliaris*, are brilliantly colourful cleaners that are common around caves and ledges on the reef.

◄ Adult Rock Beauties feed almost entirely on sponges. Because of this, they do poorly in captivity.

Juvenile Blue Angelfish, *Holacanthus bermudensis*, are less brilliant than the similar juveniles of the Queen Angelfish. Note also the straight, light blue line that crosses the body below the dorsal fin.

Adult Grey Angelfish, *Pomacanthus arcuatus*, are less colourful than French Angelfish, and are more abundant in shallow water. ▼

◄ The adult Queen Angelfish is ranked by many aquarists as one of the most spectacularly coloured fish in the world. On the reef, they are often seen in pairs.

◄ Adult French Angelfish, *Pomacanthus paru*, are most readily distinguished from the similar Grey Angelfish by the conspicuous yellow spot at the base of the pectoral fin.

◄ Juvenile French Angelfish, *Pomacanthus paru*, are usually found in shallow water, while the adults prefer the deeper reef.

The same pattern of distribution holds for the juveniles; neglecting the differences in their colour patterns, one can usually figure out which member of a pair you have collected just on the basis of where it was found. Unlike the adults, juvenile *Holacanthus* and *Pomacanthus* are strongly site-attached and rarely stray more than a few feet from their shelter holes. Inshore, juvenile Blues and Greys are common around isolated coral and sponge heads, small rocky outcrops, or even around submerged shopping carts, old crates, and practically anything else that will both shelter them and provide a focus for their territories. The Blue Angelfish tends to be found in slightly deeper water than the Grey (more than 4 feet), is found more often around or on large rocky outcrops, and seems to require somewhat clearer water. Juvenile Grey Angelfish tolerate a wide range of bottom and water conditions and usually can be found wherever there is sufficient water-flow to prevent stagnant conditions. Isolated individuals are commonly found on grass flats, having set up a territory around a pile of rocks, a sponge, or some similar object. In such areas, they can be found in as little as 15 inches of water.

The juveniles of the Queen and French Angelfish and the Rock Beauty, in contrast, are found with the adults on the reef and all prefer large cavernous coral or rock outcrops. A favourite area for all three is the massive, usually hollow heads of *Montastrea* which dot the bottom in 40 to 50 feet of water around many Caribbean islands. On such heads, the Queens and French are often found around the base and underneath the head, while young Rock Beauties prefer the upper surfaces where they scoot from crevice to crevice. Other favourite areas for these juveniles are caves and overhanging ledges of coral and coral rock, where they are usually found on the underside. Of the three species, juvenile French Angels tend to prefer the shallowest water (most common between 10 and 30 feet), while juvenile Queen Angelfish and Rock Beauties can be found to at least 200 feet.

Juvenile *Holacanthus* and *Pomacanthus* are strongly territorial, each attacking most vigorously members of its own species, but also chasing others as well. In general, such territoriality is strongest in very small fish and mellows as the fish matures. (I once watched two tiny French Angelfish go at each other through a glass partition for two days, without ever letting up; it finally ended when one somehow worked its way around the partition across the tank and they ripped each other to shreds.) It is, therefore, not surprising that juvenile Angelfish are usually found as isolated individuals, widely separated from other members of their own species. To some extent, it was this uniform spacing of young Angelfish, combined with their brilliant colours, that led the noted ethologist, Konrad Lorenz, to hypothesize the relationship between territoriality and bright colours embodied in his concept of 'poster-coloration'.

In four of the five species (all but the Rock Beauty), these bright colours also serve to advertise their presence to prospective hosts. The juveniles of the Queen, Blue, Grey, and French Angelfish are all cleaners, that is, they will readily pick external parasites from the bodies of larger fish. The territory of each angel is, in essence, a cleaning station with which larger fish are familiar and to which they come regularly to be inspected by the angels. Often an angelfish will share such a cleaning station with either several neon gobies or with a young Spanish Hogfish, *Bodianus rufus*. Of the four species of angelfish that clean, the juvenile French Angelfish seems to be the most specialized as a cleaner, to the extent that it has developed a unique 'flutter-swim' which probably serves to attract potential hosts. While perfectly capable of swimming normally, and rapidly, a juvenile approached by a host begins exaggerated swimming motions, fluttering their vivid fins back and forth in a convoluted approach to the potential host. It usually keeps up this flutter-swim throughout a cleaning bout and will abandon it only when frightened.

Juvenile rock beauties have not yet been observed either to establish cleaning stations or to clean posing fish. As a general rule, the smaller the rock beauty, the less likely it is you will even see it. Very small fish, a half inch long or so, are found deep in narrow crevices in coral and coral rock and are seen very infrequently. What these juveniles feed on is not known, but is probably a combination of drifting plankton, small benthic invertebrates, and possibly the mucous produced by larger fish. Many nocturnal and crepuscular fish retreat deep into such crevices during the day and emerge only for their active periods. On one occasion, a small rock beauty was seen to pick, apparently randomly, at the sides of one such fish, a squirrelfish, *Holocentrus rufus*, suggesting that it was, in fact, eating the mucous secreted by this large-scaled species.

The Caribbean Pigmy Angelfish, *Centropyge argi* and *Centropyge aurantonotus*, differ in habits and life styles from the other Caribbean angelfish. These small species prefer low-relief, rubble-covered areas, usually in relatively deep water. They are rarely found on the reef itself, but rather are common around its base, with one or more pairs found on nearly every obstruction and possible refuge on the bottom. A favourite habitat for *Centropyge argi* is the pile of small rocks and shells created by the Sand Tilefish, *Malacanthus plumieri*, as the latter digs its *U*-shaped burrows. On such refuse piles, Cherubfish are often found in the company of small Bicolor Damselfish (*Eupomacentrus partitus*), *Chromis enchrysura*, the basses *Serranus tortugarum* and *Serranus annularis*, and deep in the rubble patches, the Four-eye Basslet, *Pseudogramma bermudensis*. The angelfish seem to subsist mainly on algae which they graze from the rocks, probably supplemented by some plankton.

As a general rule, Pigmy Angelfish are not common in the northern Caribbean at depths much less than 100 feet, though on rare occasions they can be found in as little as 40 feet of water. Around the southern islands, such as Curacao and Bonaire, however, they are common in as little as 15 feet of water, where they inhabit both rubble plains and low-profile reefs. Why this difference in depth preference along a north–south gradient should occur is not known, but it is also characteristic of several other species, including the Blackcap Basslet, *Gramma melacara*.

Regardless of the depth, Pigmy Angelfish, like their larger relatives, are normally found in pairs, typically one large fish and one small one. Both species are territorial and the area of large *Malacanthus* mounds may be divided up among several pairs, with very small juveniles sandwiched in between the territorial boundaries. On a shallow reef in the south, pairs will each maintain a territory of only a few square yards, such that a single outcrop may shelter as many as 12 pairs.

Reproductive Biology

Adults of all Caribbean angelfish are invariably found in pairs, suggesting that monogamous spawning may be a general rule for these fish. Such pairs occur year-round, even in the northern ends of the species ranges where spawning occurs only in the summer, and may represent life-long bonding of the sexes. Members of many such pairs are identical in terms of size, coloration, and behaviour, such that there is no conspicuous sexual dimorphism in the group. Pairs of Rock Beauties and Cherubfish however, often consist of a large and a small individual; this size difference may be sexually dimorphic, but detailed work on these species has not yet been done.

Courtship and spawning for most of the Caribbean species has not yet been observed in the field. French Angelfish, however, have been observed spawning on the deeper reef in the early evening. On calm, clear evenings, pairs of these large colourful fish are very conspicuous, cruising several feet off the reef. There is little interaction between such pairs, usually no more than a few short chases should two approach each other too closely, but solitary individuals are vigorously chased away from such a pair. Actual spawning is a stately affair, entirely befitting the appearance of the fish. A pair, swimming smoothly over the reef, slowly rises into the water column and, while continuing along, bring their venters close together. After a few seconds, the two fish separate and, as a pair, swim slowly back to the bottom. Eggs and sperm are released during these upward rises and such activity may be repeated several times each evening. Recent work in Puerto Rico suggests that *Holacanthus* may spawn in a similar manner, though apparently the rise up and down is much quicker.

Although the spawning behaviour of Caribbean *Centropyge* has not been described, that of a number of its close relatives in the Indo-Pacific has been studied, and all behaved so similarly that it is likely that the western Atlantic species follow the same pattern. The Indo-Pacific *Centropyge* spawn in the evening, usually within a very short period immediately before dark. One female and the usually larger male swim a few feet into the water column, with the male slightly behind and below the female. He presses with his snout against the abdomen of the female and, while in this position, eggs and sperm are shed into the water. The fish then sink to the bottom. The female apparently sheds all of her eggs at once, and does not spawn again that evening, but a single male may spawn repeatedly. Unlike the Caribbean species, which are invariably found in conspicuous pairs, several Indo-Pacific species form harems – a group of females dominated by a single male. Pairing by these species apparently occurs only in areas of low population density. Along with this harem formation, the species are also sequential hermaphrodites, starting life as functional females and, with achievement of large size and social dominance, becoming male. At the same time, the new male develops brighter colours than the females, apparently indicating his new status. The combination of a large fish and a smaller one in pairs of Caribbean *Centropyge* (and *Holacanthus tricolor*) suggests that a similar sex-change may be occurring in them as well, though neither seems to develop the sexual dichromatism of the Pacific species.

All angelfish produce transparent pelagic eggs, roughly 0.7–0.9mm in diameter, each containing a single drop of oil to provide buoyancy. A female releases anywhere from 25 to 75 thousand eggs each evening, the exact number depending upon her size and condition, and as many as 10 million eggs during each spawning cycle. The eggs hatch in 15 to 20 hours into minute pro-larvae attached to a large yolk sac, and lacking effective eyes, fins, and even a gut. The yolk is absorbed within 48 hours, during which time the normal characteristics of a free-swimming larval fish develop, and the larva begins to feed on small planktonic animals. Such larvae are not very active and each has a 'hairy' appearance, caused by thin and elongate teeth on each of its scales. Larger larvae are laterally compressed, round to oval in profile, and lack any conspicuous plating or armour on the body. Growth of the larva is rapid and settlement to the bottom as a juvenile angelfish occurs 3 to 4 weeks after hatching. These newly settled juveniles are approximately 15–20mm long and, as discussed above, are vigorously territorial.

Aquarium Biology

With one exception, the Caribbean angelfish do well in aquaria, though most have one or two quirks that need to be covered. First, let us consider the single species *not* recommended for a marine aquarium: the Rock Beauty. I have kept dozens of these fish, ranging from very small juveniles to full adults, and despite recommendations by popular literature and what your local dealer might tell you, Rock Beauties of all ages belong only in a sophisticated set-up with hobbyists who are willing to go to great lengths to maintain them. There are two reasons for this. The first is that Rock Beauties are often very aggressive, especially young ones in the 1–3 inch size range. They will chase persistently and pick at other aquarium inhabitants (perhaps picking at mucous), in some cases harassing them to the point of death and in all cases making their lives miserable. Large-scaled species, such as the Blue Chromis, *Chromis cyanea*, are particularly likely to be chosen as targets.

The second reason for avoiding Rock Beauties is an even more serious one. On the reef, Rock Beauties are selective predators, feeding almost exclusively on sponges. Unless you are prepared to duplicate this diet, your Rock Beauty will starve to death. They will eat, often vigorously, and appear to thrive on dried food and shrimp, but both are just stop-gap measures since they only delay starvation rather than stop it. Fed a normal aquarium diet, a healthy young Rock Beauty will normally do well for about two months, then it will begin to look somewhat peaked and thin, often developing a dark area on the forehead. By the end of the third month, it will probably be dead, despite the fact that until almost the last day it will continue to take all food offered.

The other Caribbean angelfish are fortunately more catholic in their diets and will do well, often for years, given standard fare. They do present two generally minor problems, however. First, all, to a certain extent, are prone to develop white-spot disease – *Holacanthus* in particular. Spots usually develop first on the pectoral fins, then spread rapidly to the rest of the body. The speed with which these fish succumb is astounding; within 48 hours of contracting the disease, even large angelfish can die. Fortunately, a standard treatment in copper sulphate is almost 100 per cent effective in combating the parasite. If alone in a hospital or isolation tank, angelfish are very resistant to copper and in particularly virulent attacks, can stand up to double the normal dosage with no ill effects.

The second problem concerns aggressiveness. When very small, all of the species are strongly territorial and will literally fight to the death in the confines of a small tank (witness the pair of tiny French Angels discussed earlier). They also tend to be bullies, especially once established in a tank for some time. Like the Rock Beauties, though to a lesser extent, they will harass the other inhabitants of a community tank and may prevent smaller ones from eating. It is, therefore, a good general rule to keep angelfish only with other fish that are at least as big as they are.

Of the family, one angelfish in particular, *Centropyge argi*, is extremely well suited for spawning in the aquarium. The Cherubfish would seem to have it all. It is small at maturity, active, and does well under normal aquarium care, maintains a small territory on the reef (so a pair will not feel particularly constrained by the small space available to it in the aquarium), and it is normally found in pairs. Indo-Pacific *Centropyge* have already been spawned in the aquarium and, with a little effort, the aquarium spawning of the Cherubfish should present the average aquarist with few problems. In fact, the only real problem is likely to be obtaining a pair if you cannot collect your own fish. The only course available (assuming you are like most of us and cannot afford to commission a professional collector specifically to collect such a pair and ship it to you) is to screen carefully the fish in dealers' tanks. The species is strongly pair-bonded and the members of a pair will usually stay close together and may aid each other in driving off other Cherubfish.

Angelfish are spectacular, beautiful beyond the description of words. At some time in his or her career, every marine aquarist keeps one (at least) and with a little effort, the relationship between the two of you should be a long and pleasant one.

Relevant Literature

Bauer, J. A. & Klaij, G. 1974. 'Pigmy Angels spawn', *Octopus* **1**(5): 7–18

Blasciola, G. C. Jr 1976. '*Centropyge aurantonotus* Burgess, 1974 (Pisces: Chaetodontidae): range extension, and redescription', *Bull. Mar. Sci.* **26**(4): 564–568

Brockman, H. J. & Hailman, J. P. 1976. 'Fish cleaning symbiosis: notes on juvenile Angelfishes (*Pomacanthus*, Chaetodontidae) and comparisons with other species', *Zeit für Tierpsychol.* **42**: 129–138

Burgess, W. E. 1974. 'Evidence for the elevation to family status of the Angelfishes (Pomacanthidae), previously considered a sub-family of the Butterflyfish family, Chaetodontidae', *Pac. Sci.* **28**(1): 57–71

Clarke, R. D. 1977. 'Habitat distribution and species diversity of Chaetodontid and Pomacentrid fishes near Bimini, Bahamas', *Mar. Biol.* **40**: 277–289

Feddern, H. A. 1968. 'Hybridization between the western Atlantic Angelfishes, *Holacanthus isabelita* and *H. ciliaris*', *Bull. Mar. Sci.* **18**(2): 351–382

Feddern, H. A. 1972. 'Field guide to the Angelfishes (Pomacanthidae) in the Western Atlantic', *NOAA Tech. Rept*, NMFS Circ. 369: 10pp

Freihofer, W. C. 1963. 'Patterns of the Ramus Lateralis Accessorius and their systematic significance in Teleostean fishes', *Stanford Ichthyol. Bull.* **8**(2): 79–189

Goldstein, R. J. 1977. 'Angels and Butterflies – introduction', Mar. Aquar. 7(9): 54–58

Moe, M. A. Jr 1976. 'Rearing Atlantic Angelfish', *Mar. Aquar.* 7(7): 17–26

Moe, M. A. Jr 1977. 'Inside the egg of an Angelfish', *Mar. Aquar.* 8(3): 5–12

Moyer, J. T. & Nakazono, A. 1978. 'Population structure, reproductive behavior, and protogynous hermaphroditism in the Angelfish *Centropyge interruptus* at Miyake-jima, Japan', *Japan. J. Ichthyol.* **25**(1): 25–39

Robins, C. R. 1971. 'Distributional patterns of fishes from coastal and shelf waters of the tropical Western Atlantic', *Symp. Invest. Resources Carib. Sea. Adi. Regions, FAO Paper on Fish Resources*: 249–255

Thresher, R. E. 1979. 'Possible mucophagy by juvenile *Holacanthus tricolor* (Pisces: Pomacanthidae)', *Copeia* 1979 (1): 160–162

Chapter 5

Butterflyfish

Of the wide variety of fish found on the coral reef, none is so characteristic of the reef as the butterflyfish, family Chaetodontidae. In part, this is because butterflyfish are largely tropical and, with few exceptions, strictly reef-associated; in part, it is also because of their distinctive and somewhat odd appearance. Butterflyfish are markedly laterally compressed, round in profile, with prominent spines in the dorsal fin and a slender, projecting set of jaws. The last is so drawn out (in a few species) that it generated the common name of 'longsnout' butterflyfish. Most of these species are Indo-Pacific, but the Caribbean also has its own longsnout butterflyfish.

For many years, the butterflyfish were included with the angelfish in the family Chaetodontidae. Recent work on the internal anatomy of the two similar appearing and similar acting groups of fish, however, indicates that their similarity is due more to convergence on a similar lifestyle than to a common ancestry. The present concensus of opinion splits the two groups, leaving the butterflyfish alone in Chaetodontidae and erecting Pomacanthidae for the angelfish. In the field, members of the two groups can be told apart easily on the basis of two features: (1) angelfish always have at least one prominent spine on the rear edge of each gill cover, while butterflyfish always lack such a spine; (2) angelfish usually have a blunt head with relatively inconspicuous jaws; butterflyfish typically have a conspicuous snout, ranging from a short, pointed set of jaws to a long tubular arrangement.

Though the butterflyfish reach their peak abundance and diversity in the Indo-Pacific, the Caribbean has its share of attractive species. These belong to two genera – *Chaetodon*, which has four shallow-water and several deep-water species, and *Prognathodes*, which is monospecific.

Species Account

The species in *Chaetodon* share several characteristics: all tend towards a silvery body sheen; most have some degree of vertical striping; most have one or more spots on the body, if not as adults, then as juveniles; and all are broadly rounded with prominent dorsal fin spines. The various species in the genus can be told apart easily on the basis of colour pattern alone, with the four shallow-water species varying in the intensity and number of vertical stripes and the patterning of spots, if any, on the body.

The two easiest species to identify are virtually self-naming. The Banded Butterflyfish, *Chaetodon striatus*, has four widely separated black stripes on its white body, the first stripe going through the eyes and the last crossing the caudal peduncle, while the Four-eyed Butterflyfish, *Chaetodon capistratus*, has, besides its normal two eyes, a conspicuous 'false eye' on each side of its body. These white-ringed black spots are located just above and ahead of the caudal peduncle. The fish's body is otherwise pale white with fine, dashed diagonal lines crossing it and a single vertical black stripe crossing its real eyes. At night, or when frightened, it can also develop vertical body stripes, similar to those on the Banded Butterflyfish and suggesting a close relationship between the two species. Members of both species are comparable in maximum size (about 6 inches) and have similar differences between the colour patterns of the juveniles and the adults. Juvenile Banded Butterflyfish are coloured like the adults, but have a small white-ringed black spot at the base of the soft dorsal fin. Juvenile four-eyes are also similar to the adults, and also add a white-ringed black spot, a second one, on each side. This juvenile spot is located on the soft dorsal fin, just above the larger spot that will persist into adulthood.

The remaining two shallow-water Caribbean *Chaetodon* are equally distinctive in terms of colour pattern. The Spotfin Butterflyfish, *Chaetodon ocellatus*, is creme white with yellow fins (except for the clear pectorals). The only stripes on the body are both thin, one going through the eyes and the second reduced to a faint blue line that edges the dorsal and anal fins. The species derives its common name from a small, very intense black spot at the tip of its dorsal fin; a second, more diffuse spot is located at

Spotfin Butterflyfish, *Chaetodon ocellatus*, are the largest of the Caribbean butterflyfish; they have been reported as long as 8 inches.

The Reef Butterflyfish, *Chaetodon sedentarius*, is the most attractively coloured butterflyfish in the tropical western Atlantic, and also one of the easiest to keep in captivity.

Adult Four-eye Butterflyfish, *Chaetodon capistratus*, are similar to the juvenile shown, but lack the small spot on the dorsal fin.

Banded Butterflyfish, *Chaetodon striatus*, are common on the shallow reef.

This young adult Cocoa Damselfish, *Eupomacentrus variabilis*, clearly shows the thin vertical lines that most readily distinguish it from the Beau Gregory.

The Honey Gregory, *Eupomacentrus mellis*, is the smallest of the Caribbean damselfish, and also one of the most colourful.

This juvenile Dusky Damselfish, *Eupomacentrus dorsopunicans*, is very different in colour from the all black adult. The function of such juvenile-specific colours are not known.

The three reef-dwelling species of 'Dusky Damselfish' all look much like this *Eupomacentrus diencaeus*, photographed in Florida. They can be separated based on differences in geographic distributions and habitat preferences.

Small Threespot Damselfish, *Eupomacentrus planifrons*, are attractive, but are so aggressive that they are a poor choice for the aquarium.

An adult Threespot Damselfish, *Eupomacentrus planifrons*, in its usual mild-mannered way, threatening the photographer. Such 6 inch fish may defend territories as much as 15 feet in diameter.

the base of the fin. Juveniles are similar in general coloration to the adults, but have a darker, better defined, second spot with a thin black 'tail' running down from it.

The final shallow-water species is the Reef Butterflyfish, *Chaetodon sedentarius*. A golden brown species, paling ventrally, it has only two broad vertical stripes, both very distinct. The first goes through the eyes; the second runs down the rear edge of the dorsal fin, crosses the caudal peduncle, and extends down the rear edge of the anal fin. On juveniles, the rear stripe is restricted to the anal fin and there is a tiny black spot on the dorsal fin.

Along with shallow-water species of *Chaetodon*, there are several closely related deep-water species, rarely found at depths less than 300 feet. The two best-known members of the group are *Chaetodon aya* and *Chaetodon guyanensis*. Both are similar in shape and size to the Banded Butterflyfish and like it, both have black bars on a white body. *Chaetodon aya* has two such bands, one running vertically through the eyes and the other running diagonally from the top end of the eye stripe to the rear base of the anal fin. *Chaetodon guyanensis* is almost identical, but has a third stripe, a short one, above and parallel to the major diagonal stripe. These two deep-water species differ in their distributions and it has been suggested that they may be only sub-species or geographical variants. *Chaetodon aya* is found off the Florida coast, in the Gulf of Mexico, and off the Yucatan peninsula. *Chaetodon guyanensis* is found around the islands of the southern Caribbean.

The western Atlantic representative of the genus *Prognathodes* is thought to be closely related to *Chaetodon aya* and is probably a specialized off-shoot of it. The appropriately named Atlantic Longsnout Butterflyfish, *Prognathodes aculeatus*, cannot be mistaken for anything else in the Caribbean, due to its very slender, definitely elongated snout. Only distantly related to the Indo-Pacific Longsnout Butterflyfish, *Forcipiger* and *Chelmon*, like them it uses its snout to pick food from among crevices in the coral. *Prognathodes* is a small fish, rarely exceeding 3 inches in total length, but is also a very attractive one. The dorsal fin and top of the body are chocolate brown, grading ventrally into golden yellow and, ultimately, into creme white on the fish's underside. A rusty brown line runs along each side of the snout and goes through each eye to run along the forehead. Another line, a black one, runs down the rear edges of the dorsal and anal fins. Juvenile and adult colour patterns are virtually identical.

Field Biology

Butterflyfish in general are benthic species closely associated with live coral and, though never the dominant group, are ubiquitous on Caribbean reefs. Often overlooked in favour of more spectacular fish, they are generally subdued in colour and mild mannered in behaviour. One rarely sees a butterflyfish chasing another fish; nor do they clean, establish cleaning stations, or go through any complex display patterns and colour changes. Typically they keep their distances from divers and, if pressed, will flee rather than hide.

Perhaps because of their mild-mannered nature, Caribbean butterflyfish have not been studied in detail and their biology is little known. Based on gut-content analyses, they feed primarily on benthic invertebrates – worms, some shrimps, and large amounts of coral, gorgonian, and zoanthid tentacles and polyps. With this dietary preference, it is not surprising that as a group, the Caribbean butterflyfish are closely associated with living coral reefs.

In terms of their social behaviour, *Chaetodon* are apparently not territorial in any sense of the word, but rather have a large home range to which they are strongly site-attached. They are seen most often in pairs (sometimes triplets), feeding near one another and moving together, all of which suggests pair fidelity and, perhaps, monogamy.

Juvenile *Chaetodon* are less gregarious than their elders and are usually found as solitary individuals. While on occasion all can be found on the reef, the young clearly prefer inshore areas where they are common around rocks, isolated coral heads, and, in 'civilized areas', jetties, and bridge pilings. The juveniles of the Banded, Spotfin, and Reef Butterflyfish are typically found in shallow areas immediately adjacent to deep water; an ideal spot to find them, for example, is at the end of a long jetty where the bottom drops off sharply from a few to a few dozen feet. Juvenile Four-eye Butterflyfish, in contrast, are common in very shallow areas, often no more than 2 or 3 feet deep at low tide. Each will be closely associated with some particular shelter – a rock, a small coral head, or even an old pipe – on which algae and small encrusting invertebrates, potential food sources, can grow. Their distribution, as well as that of the young of the other species, seems to be limited by a necessity for clean water; in turbid or polluted areas, no more than a few small four-eyes are likely to be present.

Since adult *Chaetodon* are not commonly found in shallow areas, it is likely that some sort of irregular and individual migration off shore occurs for each fish as it matures. Like most aspects of butterflyfish biology, this migration has never been investigated in detail.

Prognathodes differ in many respects from the *Chaetodon*. They are typically found as solitary individuals, even as adults (except during spawning periods, as will be discussed later), suggesting territoriality. They are also more shy than other butterflyfish and, if possible, even more closely tied to living coral heads. Longsnouts rarely stray more than a few inches off the bottom and they are seen most commonly swimming through crevices and under small overhangs in areas of thick coral growth. They prefer deep water (in the northern Caribbean, *Prognathodes* are rarely seen at depths less than 60 feet; in the southern Caribbean, they can sometimes be found close to shore and in as little as 10 feet of water) and vertical drop-offs with lots of caves. On the open reef, for example, a diver is most likely to encounter one dashing from crevice to crevice along the walls of sand channels and similar coraline canyons. They are nowhere really conspicuous and must be looked for even in areas where they are abundant.

Prognathodes feed on items similar to those taken by the *Chaetodon*, with one noteworthy addition. The Longsnout Butterflyfish is one of the few Caribbean fish that feeds regularly on the tiny tube feet of the Long-Spined Sea Urchin, *Diadema antillarum*, and other sea urchins. It is possible that this feeding preference, in fact, accounts for the long snout of the species, an adaptation for reaching between the spines to get at the food source.

Reproductive Biology

Like most aspects of the behaviour of the Atlantic butterflyfish, their reproductive behaviour has never been studied in detail and is known only anecdotally and in scattered bits and pieces. Like the angelfish, all produce large numbers of pelagic eggs, averaging just under a millimetre in diameter, which, presumably within a day hatch into minute planktonic larvae. Late stage larvae are very distinctive: laterally compressed with characteristic large bony plates extending from the posterior portion of the head. The head itself is encased in bony armour. These larvae, called 'tholichthys' are characteristic of butterflyfish (though not angelfish) and are typical of no other western Atlantic group. The duration of the larval stage is not known but at its end, each larva is about the size of a nickel or sixpenny piece, is laterally compressed, and is translucent grey. They settle from the plankton onto the bottom (and any other solid object in shallow water – boat hulls, for example) at night, in some cases by the thousands. Transformation from larva to juvenile is rapid, so that by dawn, each is a miniature but identifiable butterflyfish. The vast majority of these are quickly eaten by the numerous shallow-water predators, while the lucky survivors move into the shelter of small caves and crevices where they remain until they have put on enough size and mass to be relatively safe in the open. Age at sexual maturity is not known for certain, but at least for *Prognathodes*, a small species, anatomical evidence suggests that they mature in less than a year.

Butterflyfish spawning activity, like that of many other reef fish, takes place at dusk. Courtship is prolonged and vigorous, with the fish literally chasing each other about the reef. While typically involving pairs, apparent spawning groups of as many as 11 fish have been observed at dusk, though whether spawning is then promiscuous or still involves stable pairs is not known. Courtship in all four shallow-water *Chaetodon* seems to be similar, involving chasing, head-standing, and lateral displaying between the prospective partners. The pair frequently circle one another, each fish head-to-tail with its mate until one fish breaks and runs, with the other close behind. If approached by a lone fish, the pair will break off courting to chase the intruder, resuming after it has been driven out of their immediate vicinity. Actual spawning has not been observed for western Atlantic species, but is probably similar to that of Hawaiian Butterflyfish, in which the male and female swim up off the bottom, the male slightly below and behind the female, releasing eggs and sperm at the top of a shallow arc before returning to the bottom.

Spawning activity of butterflyfish appears to go on year-round, though probably peaking in early summer in those parts of the world where it remains warm year-round. Off Florida and the northern Bahamas, it is probably temperature limited and occurs from late spring through to early autumn (though pairs stay together year-round). Minimum spawning temperature is somewhere around 74 °F.

Aquarium Biology

The Caribbean butterflyfish vary widely in their adaptability to marine aquaria. Unfortunately, the species most often collected and available in retail stores, the Four-eye Butterflyfish, is the most difficult to keep (and, of course, the easiest species to keep, the Longsnout Butterflyfish, is the one you see the least often). The situation with the Four-eye is a sad one on two accounts; not only are a great many fish killed unnecessarily, but also many novice aquarists, buying this cheap and perky little fish, are doubtless discouraged by their inability to keep what much of the literature calls an 'ideal' aquarium species. Far from being 'ideal', most Four-eyes are difficult even for an expert aquarist to maintain for any length of time.

The problem with this species, and to a lesser extent all of the *Chaetodon*, is their diets. As noted earlier, all depend to a large extent on live coelenterates – corals, hydroids, gorgonians, and the like – from which they crop tentacles, polyps, and probably the mucous such animals often produce. Transferred from the field to an aquarium, 70 to 80 per cent of the juvenile Four-eyes collected will refuse to touch virtually any other food offered them. Even live brine shrimp and tubifex are usually ignored. In Florida and the Caribbean, many hobbyists have found that such fish will do well if provided fresh, live rose coral (*Siderastrea* spp.), a small shallow-water species, on a regular basis, but this is obviously beyond the means of most of us. Without this food, or a comparable substitute, Four-eye Butterflyfish will normally starve to death within a month of capture, give or take a few weeks depending upon the age and condition of the fish when captured.

At this point, I can well imagine some aquarists taking pen in hand to write to me about the Four-eye Butterflyfish they have kept for years with no hassles. To save you the trouble, and the cost of a stamp, let me tell you that I do not doubt it; in fact, I have done the same! Four-eyes vary widely in their feeding habits, as do many reef fish, and for reasons that have never been systematically investigated (it may relate to the specific habitat in which they were collected and the foods available to them in that habitat), a small percentage of the individuals collected eat normal aquarium diets and thrive on them. Unless you collect your own fish or can afford to buy lots of them, and so can waste them in order to find one or two that will do well, I would recommend that aquarists avoid this attractive, and attractively priced, species.

There are, of course, ways to maximize your chances of getting a good fish, if you must keep one. The most obvious way is to buy your fish from a dealer who has many of them, and then pick the one or two in the group that are relatively fat and look like they have eaten since being captured. Or, if you collect your own fish, keep the Four-eyes just long enough to see if they will eat (two weeks should be plenty) and release those that do not.

The remaining species of Atlantic *Chaetodon* are less fussy than the Four-eye and do better in aquaria. Juveniles of the Reef Butterflyfish, *Chaetodon sedentarius*, are beautiful little fish and do quite well. The most suitable aquarium species of the family, however, is *Prognathodes aculeatus*, the sole member of the other Caribbean genus. It is hardy, eats anything, is peaceful, and retains its colours well. It may scrap lightly with angelfish, but usually little, if any, damage is done. Somewhat shy at first, Longsnouts like to have a small, sheltered cave available into which they can retire if bothered. The cave should be orientated such that the mouth is facing away from the front of the aquarium and the fish can enjoy some privacy. Within a week or so, it will be out and swimming happily. Within a month, it will probably be taking food from your fingers. *Prognathodes* is highly recommended for even novice aquarists.

Of all the species, *Prognathodes* is also the one most likely to spawn in an aquarium. Not only is it relatively small at maturity ($2\frac{1}{2}$ to 3 inches), but also its home range is small, and despite its territoriality several can be housed in a single large aquarium if sufficient cover is available. As with any territorial species, it may take some juggling to achieve a stable balance between two or three individuals. It may well be worth the effort, however, as two fish are likely to be of the opposite sex if they are willing to tolerate each other. In this regard, *Prognathodes* are sometimes found in pairs, so that if you can collect your own fish and care to spawn the species, such a pair should be collected rather than scattered individuals.

Relevant Literature

Burgess, W. E. 1974. 'Evidence for the elevation to family status of the Angelfishes (*Pomacanthidae*) previously considered a sub-family of the Butterflyfish family, Chaetodontidae', *Pac. Sci.* **28**(1): 57–71

Clarke, R. D. 1977. 'Habitat distribution and species diversity of Chaetodontid and Pomacentrid fishes near Bimini, Bahamas', *Mar. Biol.* **40**: 277–289

Goldstein, R. J. 1977. 'Angels and Butterflies – introduction', *Mar. Aquar.* **7**(9): 54–58

Hubbs, C. L. 1963. '*Chaetodon aya* and related deep-dwelling Butterflyfishes, their variation, distribution, and synonomy', *Bull. Mar. Sci.* **13**(1): 131–192

Hubbs, C. L. 1965. 'Ecological basis for the distribution of an Atlantic Butterflyfish, *Chaetodon aya*', *Copeia* 1965 (4): 508

Lobel, P. S. 1979. 'Diel, lunar and seasonal periodicity in the reproductive behaviour of the pomacanthid fish, *Centropyge potteri*, and some other reef fishes in Hawaii', *Pac. Sci.* **32**(2): 193–207

The Blue-and-Yellow Damselfish

Lines Indicate Key Features

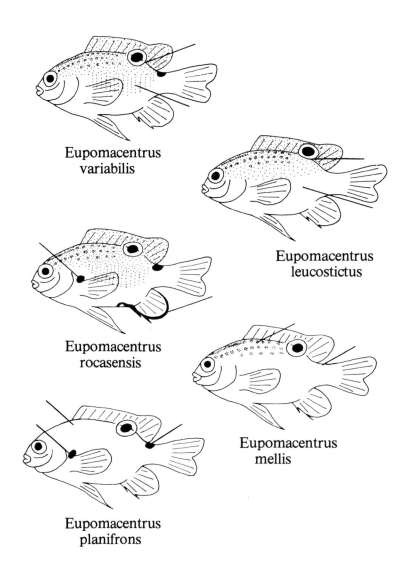

Eupomacentrus
variabilis

Eupomacentrus
leucostictus

Eupomacentrus
rocasensis

Eupomacentrus
mellis

Eupomacentrus
planifrons

Chapter 6

Benthic Damselfish

Although a tremendous variety of fish is found on and around the reef, five families dominate the fauna: the wrasses (Labridae), the gobies (Gobiidae), the angelfish (Pomacanthidae), the butterflyfish (Chaetodontidae), and the damselfish (Pomacentridae). The last are small, often aggressive, and frequently colourful fish usually found close to the reef's surface. Sometimes referred to as 'demoiselles', the damselfish are characterized by a single nasal opening on each side of the head (most fish have two such openings; another family that does not, the Cichlidae, has in the past been thought to be closely related to the damselfish, but such is no longer thought to be the case), a laterally compressed body, large scales, and a small, terminal mouth. The dorsal fin is long and continuous (there is no obvious division between the prominent spiney and soft sections) and, in many cases, the caudal fin is forked. Damselfish are common throughout the shallow tropic seas of the world, and a few, such as the Garibaldi, *Hypsypops rubicunda*, off the coast of California, have even invaded temperate seas.

The damselfish of the tropical western Atlantic can be broadly divided into two groups of ecologically similar fish: the benthic and semi-benthic, usually larger-bodied fish in the genera *Eupomacentrus*, *Microspathodon*, and *Abudefduf*, and the water-column oriented, usually more slender species in the genus *Chromis*. The fish in the first group will be covered in this chapter and those in *Chromis* covered in the next.

Species Account

The most speciose genus of benthic damselfish in the western Atlantic is *Eupomacentrus*, with 11 apparent species. These fall into four clusters of similarly coloured fish: one cluster of two species with a bicolour black-and-white pattern, another of four species with a dusky grey-brown pattern, a third of four species with bicolour blue-and-yellow, and the last with a single black-and-gold species.

In the past, two similar genus names have been used for these fish – *Eupomacentrus* and *Pomacentrus* – and there is still some difference of opinion regarding which is taxonomically correct. The distinction is based on a splitting off of the Caribbean species from the large number of Indo-Pacific species based on a slight difference in dentition. According to the type specimen, *Pomacentrus* have two curved rows of fine teeth in the upper part of the pharynx, while *Eupomacentrus* has only a single row. Otherwise the two genera are broadly similar in most characters, and whether or not to separate the two based on this single character has yet to be resolved. If accepted, some Pacific species will also have to be placed in *Eupomacentrus*. The taxonomic problem is further complicated by a third name that has recently entered the fray. The genus *Stegastes* is now represented by two species of damselfish found in the eastern Atlantic, and it now appears that (a) *Stegastes* and *Eupomacentrus* are one and the same, and (b) that *Stegastes* is the older name. If so, the names of all the Caribbean species (as well as some Pacific ones) may have to be changed to *Stegastes*. To complicate matters further, *Microspathodon*, a clearly distinct genus, also used to be called *Stegastes*. The ultimate fate of these names has yet to be decided and may be argued for some time yet. Needless to say, the taxonomy of the damselfish is far from settled, and re-arranging and re-naming of genera may go on for the next few years.

Returning to the western Atlantic species, the two species in the first cluster are virtually identical in colour pattern, to the extent that there is some question whether their separation at anything above the sub-species level is justified. Throughout the Caribbean and the Bahamas, the sharply black-and-white bicolour damselfish is *Eupomacentrus partitus*, a relatively small (maximum size about $3\frac{1}{4}$ inches), plankton-eating species. As implied, the fish is jet black anteriorly and crisp white posteriorly, with a sharp diagonal demarcation between the two. For reasons not yet understood, some fish also have a

Juvenile Jewel Fish, *Microspathodon chrysurus*, are most common in stands of Fire Coral (*Millepora*) or *Acropora*.

Juvenile Sergeant Majors, *Abudefduf saxatilis*, are common in shallow areas, where they form small schools. The elongate fish at the bottom of the picture is a juvenile Slippery Dick, *Halichoeres bivittatus*.

Juvenile Night Majors, *Abudefduf taurus*, are less colourful than comparable sized Sergeant Majors. They are a common tide-pool fish throughout most of the Caribbean.

Night Majors, *Abudefduf taurus*, are widely distributed, but are not often seen by divers because of their preference for shallow, wave-washed, and often dirty areas.

The Beau Gregory, *Eupomacentrus leucostictus*, is the most common damselfish inshore of the main reef. It can be found in mangroves, around pilings, and even in grass flats.

The yellow spot on the side of this Bicolour Damselfish, *Eupomacentrus partitus*, is a characteristic which varies widely. In some areas, most fish have the yellow spot; in others, none have it. No one knows why.

A male Blue Chromis, *Chromis cyanea*, interrupted while spawning. Note the conspicuous brown spawning tube just ahead of his anal fin. The female is in the background.

Though most common on the deep reef, juvenile Purple Chromis, *Chromis scotti*, can be found in relatively shallow water in the summer. This one was photographed off Florida at a depth of 25 feet.

The Yellowtailed Chromis, *Chromis enchrysura*, is the deepest dwelling of the common species in the genus. This juvenile was photographed at 110 feet.

Adult Olive-backed Damselfish, *Chromis insolata*, lack the bright colours of the juvenile shown. Small juveniles are often found in mixed schools with small Purple Chromis.

A typical pose for the Bluesnout, or Lemon Goby, *Coryphoperus lipernes*. From this position, they swim up to seize plankton drifting by.

The Masked Goby, *Coryphopterus personatus*, is incredibly abundant on reefs at moderate depths. They feed on plankton and, in turn, are fed upon by a variety of small predators.

The Hovering Goby, *Ioglossus caliurus*, is found on sand and rubble patches off the coast of Florida. The virtually identical *Ioglossus helenae* is found in the Bahamas and throughout the Caribbean.

The Grey Chromis, *Chromis multilineata*, is one of two, similarly shaped species of *Chromis* found in shallow water. The Grey Chromis is normally found in large schools swimming well off the bottom.

57

broad yellow swath ventrally at the junction of the two colours. All fish have an electric blue edging on the unpaired fins. The second black-and-white bicolour species is *Eupomacentrus pictus*, thus far reported only from the coast of Brazil, where it is apparently a common species near shore. It is roughly the same size as *Eupomacentrus partitus* and, except for a few minor morphological differences, has the same meristic counts and colour pattern. The status of the two as separate species is based on these slight morphological differences; since the two do not have overlapping ranges, it is not known whether or not, given the opportunity, they will interbreed freely and thereby prove themselves only geographically separated sub-species.

While the question concerning the status of the two bicolours is straightforward, it none the less indicates the taxonomic problems associated with this seemingly simple group. Depending upon with whom you agree, there are anywhere from five to eleven western Atlantic species in *Eupomacentrus*, most involved in clusters of similar species that differ from one another in fine detail, as do *Eupomacentrus partitus* and *Eupomacentrus pictus*. Along with the bicolour pattern, there is the group of chocolate-brown species (*Eupomacentrus dorsopunicans*, *Eupomacentrus diencaeus*, *Eupomacentrus fuscus*, and *Eupomacentrus otophorus*), one of blue-and-yellow fishes (*Eupomacentrus leucostictus*, *Eupomacentrus variabilis*, *Eupomacentrus rocasensis*, and *Eupomacentrus mellis*), and a single gold-and-black species *Eupomacentrus planifrons*. Even in the case of the last species, however, the juveniles look very similar to those in the blue-and-yellow complex.

The Dusky Damselfish, *Eupomacentrus dorsopunicans*, *Eupomacentrus fuscus*, and *Eupomacentrus diencaeus*, are extremely similar in appearance. Between 5 and 6 inches long, adults are a uniform chocolate-brown with fine blue lines edging their unpaired fins and a faint indication of vertical barring. The juveniles of the three species, though strikingly different from the adults, are also similar to one another. Brilliantly coloured, each has a blue to bluish cream body colour, over which lies a rust (occasionally yellow) coloured wash on the forehead and a large blue-ringed, black spot by the rear edge of the dorsal fin. Fine electric blue spots pepper the body. Despite their similar appearances, however, the species can be separated by their geographical and ecological distributions.

Eupomacentrus fuscus has the most restricted distribution, having been found, so far, only off the coast of Brazil (like *Eupomacentrus pictus*). The remaining two species are apparently found throughout the Caribbean, the Bahamas, and off the coast of Florida, but tend to occupy different parts of the reef. *Eupomacentrus diencaeus* prefers shallow water, high energy areas with heavy surge and wave action; *Eupomacentrus dorsopunicans*, on the other hand, prefers calmer and generally deeper areas. The two can also be separated by a few minor morphological differences, the most obvious of which is a relative difference in the length of the anal fin. In *Eupomacentrus diencaeus*, the tip of this fin extends to the rear edge of the caudal peduncle, that is, to the point where it just turns into the caudal fin. On a mature adult, the length of the longest ray in the anal fin is approximately 20–25 per cent of the total length of the fish. For *Eupomacentrus dorsopunicans*, the tip reaches only to the middle of the caudal peduncle, and the longest anal ray is only 10–20 per cent of body length. While great in theory, this difference is most reliable only when you have two preserved specimens in hand with which to make side-by-side comparisons. On the reef, the two species are nearly impossible to tell apart on any basis other than that of preferred areas.

The last member of the Dusky Damselfish group, *Eupomacentrus otophorus*, is both the most restricted ecologically and also the species the vast majority of even experienced Caribbean fish-watchers have never seen. Unlike its relatives, which require normal sea water, this grey-brown species apparently prefers brackish water and so it is found at the mouths of large rivers all along the coast of Central America and off many of the larger Caribbean islands, such as Cuba, Jamaica, and Haiti. Some individuals penetrate quite a way up these rivers and the species seems to be invading the historically unoccupied freshwater streams and ponds of the tropical islands. Because normal freshwater fish (referred to as 'primary' freshwater species) have historically had no way of reaching these islands (before man's intervention, of course), ecological niches are open which have, in part, been filled by a variety of otherwise marine species, including gobies, blennies, snappers, some cardinalfish, and, in the Caribbean, a damselfish. Ichthyologists refer to such species as 'secondary' freshwater fish.

Adult *Eupomacentrus otophorus* range in body colour from dark brown to blue-black, often with an indication of vertical barring. The edges of the dorsal, anal, caudal, and pectoral fins are tinted orange. Regardless of its body colour, the species can always be recognized by the presence of a distinctive blue-black 'earspot' located on the gill cover. Juveniles look like no other damselfish in the area. They are dark black with a series of bright blue spots that form lines running up the forehead and several patches of spots on the gill covers.

The third major colour pattern, bicolour blue-and-yellow, typifies two species which are common in the aquarium trade (plus two others which are not). *Eupomacentrus variabilis*, the Cocoa Damselfish, and *Eupomacentrus leucostictus*, the Beau Gregory, can both be brilliant blue dorsally and bright yellow ventrally, coupled with fine electric blue spots peppering the body and three electric blue lines running up the forehead and overlaying a paler blue wash below. The two species are most difficult to tell apart as small juveniles where, again, relative characters become important. For example, small individuals of both species have an ocellated blue-around-black spot, similar to the one described for juvenile Dusky Damselfish. On the Beau Gregory, this spot tends to be high on the dorsal fin, while on the Cocoa Damselfish, it is lower and extends onto the body. The electric blue coloration of the Beau Gregory also tends to be brighter than that of the Cocoa, while the latter has a strong tendency to develop a series of fine, vertical dark lines on the body, each line following the rear edge of a line of scales. One other character commonly cited as being diagnostic is the presence or absence of a black spot on the top base of the caudal peduncle. This character, unfortunately, is highly variable in its occurence and can appear on juveniles of both species.

The adults of these two blue-and-yellow species are considerably easier to tell apart. Beau Gregories are longer and more slender than Cocoa Damselfish, their dorsal areas are more blue-black than the pale blue of the Cocoa, and their yellow undersides frequently shade toward yellow-orange. Cocoas typically show the vertical banding mentioned above and can range in dorsal colour from dark grey, with yellow highlights underneath, to pale blue and yellow. The two species also differ ecologically. The Beau Gregory is a shallow-water species, commonly found near rocks, submerged debris, and mangrove roots. They are also common in grass beds, usually around an outcrop of rock, coral, or sand, and near small coral heads on rubble flats. The Cocoa, on the other hand, is a creature of the reef and is typically found closely associated with heavy rock and coral cover. It is found from the inshore patch reefs, in 15 to 20 feet of water, out onto the main reef and over the drop-off typical of Caribbean island reefs. It has been reported at depths in excess of 130 feet. While there is considerable overlap in the ranges of these two species, especially near shore, if you catch it in water less than 20 feet deep, it is probably a Beau Gregory; if you catch it in water more than 20 feet deep, it is probably a Cocoa Damselfish.

The third member of the blue-and-yellow complex is an isolated geographical off-shoot of the Cocoa Damselfish, so far as is known, restricted to the Isla das Rocas off the coast of Brazil. The Rocas Gregory, *Eupomacentrus rocasensis*, is dark blue-grey above and yellow below, and has the faint vertical barring and caudal peduncle spot typical of the Cocoa Damselfish. It differs conspicuously, however, in having a black ring around the anus, which continues posteriorly as a black line on the edge of the anal fin. Juveniles are also similar to small Cocoa Damselfish, but like the adults also have the black anus ring and edge to the anal fin (juveniles of an eastern Pacific species, *Eupomacentrus flavilatus* are very similar, but lack the ring around the anus). Aside from its colour pattern and morphology, all that is known about the Rocas Gregory is that it is a shallow-water species (found in rocky areas in water less than 15 feet deep) and that, like its congeners, it feeds on benthic algae and invertebrates.

The final species in the blue-and-yellow complex is called the Honey Gregory, *Eupomacentrus mellis*, and is easy to distinguish from the other three species. Like the juveniles of all three, it has a series of parallel electric blue lines running up its forehead, but unlike them, these blue lines are not on a blue wash, but rather have yellow between them. The only other blue on its body is the standard blue-ringed black spot just at the rear half of the dorsal fin. The Honey does not grow much larger than 3 inches and, like the Cocoa Damselfish, it is a reef species closely associated with shallow-water rock and coral outcrops in areas of clean water. Throughout most of the Caribbean, it can be found immediately offshore, in as little as 4 or 5 feet of water. Off the Florida coast and most of the larger islands, where the water is somewhat dirtier, the species is less common and is restricted to the shallow reef.

The last Caribbean *Eupomacentrus* is uniquely coloured as an adult, but as a juvenile might be confused with the Honey Gregory. The Threespot Damselfish, *Eupomacentrus planifrons*, is a large fish, reaching a length of almost 6 inches. Adults have a large black area in the middle of the body, around which the head, forehead, and fins are a deep golden tan. The underside of the body is usually somewhat pale. The only marks on the body are a very distinct black (sometimes black and blue) spot on the upper edge of the caudal peduncle, a similar spot at the base of each pectoral fin, a bright yellow crescent above each black-in-blue eye, and on smaller fish, the faint remnant of a deeper black spot on the centre of the body. This spot is all that remains of a vivid blue-ringed black spot located just below the soft dorsal fin of the juvenile. The latter are bright golden-yellow, similar in shape, colour, and general behaviour to small Honey Gregories and differing from them by (a) lack of any blue lines on the forehead and (b) possession of one tiny black spot on the caudal peduncle and one each at the base of each pectoral fin. Threespot Damselfish are another reef-associated species, almost invariably found with complex bottom structures − sometimes simply cavernous rocks, but more often large stands of fire coral (*Millepora*), staghorn coral (*Acropora palmata*), or elkhorn coral (*Acropora cervicornis*). Broad stands of elkhorn coral may contain hundreds of these large, territorial damselfish.

The remaining two genera of benthic Caribbean damselfish, *Microspathodon* and *Abudefduf*, are systematically simple. *Microspathodon* has only one Caribbean species (four in the world − one in the eastern Atlantic and two in the eastern Pacific), while *Abudefduf* has two. All three species are found throughout the tropical western Atlantic. *Microspathodon chrysurus*, variously called the Jewel Fish, the Jewel Box (an older name), and the Yellowtailed Damselfish, is unlike anything else in the Caribbean. As adults, each is a large, heavy-bodied fish, roughly 7 to 8 inches long, with a rounded, somewhat blunt head, rounded fins, and rubbery lips. The body colour varies depending upon the motivational state of the animal, but it is generally dull blue-black with a vividly contrasting yellow tail. Juveniles (fish less than 3 inches long) are similar in body shape and general behaviour to small *Eupomacentrus*, but have a distinctive colour pattern. Such fish have been described as resembling a scattering of stars on a deep blue sky. In fact, the body is deep blue, on which tiny sparkling motes of electric blue are dusted. The caudal fin, yellow in the adult, is almost transparent in the juvenile, such that one has to look closely to even see it. Jewel Fish are intimately associated with high energy, wave washed areas that have extensive vertical relief and that usually have broad stands of the fire coral, *Millepora*. Where they are not pushed out by the more aggressive Threespot Damselfish, juveniles are often found on large stands of staghorn coral.

The two species in *Abudefduf*, the Sergeant Major, *Abudefduf saxatilis*, and the Night Major, *Abudefduf taurus*, are both yellow fish with broad vertical black bars. Those of the Sergeant Major are crisply set off from the yellow body and often have a blue tint to them; those of the Night Major look like they have been smudged and the whole fish has a dark cast to it. The two also differ in body shape and preferred habitat. The Sergeant Major is a typical damselfish, strongly laterally compressed, while the Night Major is similar to the Jewel Fish with its heavier, rounded body. The Sergeant Major is found on shallow reefs, around inshore rocks and pilings, in mangrove areas, and in just about every other shallow-water habitat that provides it with enough cover. The Night Major, on the other hand, is restricted to high energy, usually murky areas, frequently in water no more than a few feet deep. Juvenile Night Majors are a common tidepool fish throughout the Caribbean. Both the Sergeant Major and the Night Major have nearly identical counterparts in the eastern Pacific.

Field Biology

Some aspects of the field biology of the various Caribbean damselfish have been mentioned in the section above, especially where such information served to separate otherwise similar species. Yet, a great deal is known about the damselfish; as a group, they constitute what is probably the most intensively studied family of marine fish in the world. In part, this popularity with scientists is due to their ubiquity on the reef, and in part it is due to their complex reproductive and social behaviour.

The bulk of the work to date has centred on the species of *Eupomacentrus*. To some extent, all *Eupomacentrus* are territorial. The vigour of this territorial defence varies widely from species to species, with adult Threespots being the most aggressive and Cocoa Damselfish the least. The Threespot can defend an area as much as 15 feet in diameter (not bad for a 6in fish), chasing from its selected area not only other Threespots, but also a wide variety of related and non-related fish. The pattern of this area defence is termed the 'serial territory', the whole territory being modelled as a series of more or less concentric defence perimeters centred on the spawning site or shelter hole of the damselfish. Other damselfish are chased whenever they cross one of the outer perimeters, while other species, depending on how much their ecological requirements overlap with those of the Threespot, are chased from smaller areas. Vigorously-chased species include angelfish and butterflyfish, surgeonfish and parrotfish, while most serranids, cardinalfish, and grunts are largely ignored. This defence pattern, while especially clear in the behaviour of the Threespot Damselfish, is true for all of the Caribbean *Eupomacentrus* studied to date as well as for several Indo-Pacific species.

At the other end of the aggressive spectrum, the Cocoa Damselfish has a very large home range, up to 500 square feet, but these are only weakly and sporadically defended. As the damselfish wanders about its area, staying close to prominent rocks and caves, it essentially chases an intruder only if the latter approaches it too closely. Again, defence is most vigorous and consistent against members of its own species, and least against fish that are ecologically very different from it. Cocoa Damselfish do, however, become strongly territorial during the spawning season, when males focus their attention on the eggs and spawning site, not only defending the area immediately around these, but also defending with more vigour its entire home range.

The remaining *Eupomacentrus* fall somewhere between the two in the vigour of their space-related defence. The Dusky Damselfish and the Beau Gregory are moderately territorial, defending an area somewhat smaller than that of the Threespot and defending it less vigorously. The Honey Gregory is also territorial, but chases mainly other members of its own species. And finally, the Bicolor Damselfish, *Eupomacentrus partitus*, vigorously defends small territories throughout the year.

The Bicolor has superimposed on its territorial-based social structure a complementary system based on a size-related dominance hierarchy. On any given coral outcrop, there are usually several small Bicolors, each defending its own part of that outcrop. As planktivores, however, each fish frequently leaves the bottom to forage in the water column. The larger the fish, the farther into the water column it roams. While in the water column, the fish form a straightline dominance hierarchy in which the largest fish is the top individual and can chase everyone else. This individual is referred to as the 'alpha'. Below him (the alpha is usually a male) is a 'beta', either another male or a large female, who yields to the alpha, but who dominates all other fish, and then a 'gamma', and so on down the line to the lowest ranking, and usually smallest individual, known as the 'omega', who hides a lot.

Comparable patterns of social organization are established by *Microspathodon* and by *Abudefduf*. The former has both territorial and non-territorial members. Those with territories are spawning fish; those without are roaming individuals who constitute a surplus population. For *Microspathodon*, territories are maintained year-round and serve mainly as spawning sites; food is not a limiting resource for the population and a territory holder will allow any number of roaming individuals to feed in its territory, so long as they acknowledge its dominance. This food consists mainly of algae, plus a scattering of other benthic organisms. *Abudefduf*, in contrast, is basically non-territorial, and is found in schools that roam in the water column above the reef (or, in the case of the Night Major, near shore) feeding on plankton and occasionally on some benthic materials. Yet, like the more bottom-oriented species, males of both *Abudefdufs* become vigorously territorial during the spawning season and, at such time, their behaviour is similar to that of the permanently territorial species.

These social organizations involve a great deal of intra-fish communication and, not surprisingly, the *Eupomacentrus* in particular, and all damselfish in general, have evolved complex repertoires of visual and acoustic signals. A highly aggressive Bicolor Damselfish, for example, changes colour from its normal black anterior–white posterior to a pattern that is all black except for a single, vertical white bar on each side. It poses before its opponent either displaying laterally to it, all fins spread wide, or by tipping, head-down, with its erected dorsal fin and dorsal fin spines towards the opponent. If such displays fail to deter the invader, the damselfish lunges towards it and will bite to drive it away. During this lunge, the damselfish produces a sound known as a 'pop', a single pulsed, short duration sound similar to that produced when you snap your fingers, probably to startle the intruder and scare it off. Similarly well-developed complexes of motor patterns, colour changes, and sounds are used by all of the members of the genus *Eupomacentrus* to communicate not only an aggressive motivation, but also submission and courtship.

Aside from a courting colour, *Abudefduf* does not go through the complex system of communication that the other species engage in. *Microspathodon*, on the other hand, has a series of whole body colour changes that indicate its motivational state. When very aggressive or highly excited, for example, the fish has a very dark blue body, peppered with a few blue spots on the back and forehead, and a bright yellow tail. When subordinate (as when a roving fish is feeding in the territory of a territorial fish), its body turns grey and the tail pales almost to transparency.

Aside from their own social interactions, there is a growing body of evidence that the activities and vigorous territoriality of damselfish have a major impact on the structure and composition of the reef community. One obvious example of such an effect is that certain fish, notably algae-eaters, are excluded from broad areas of the reef where damselfish, algae-eaters themselves, have set up territories and vigorously defend them. Thus, the reef, for a parrotfish, is not a broad open expanse, but rather is a system of safe paths through areas full of damselfish. This effect influences not only the behaviour of the parrotfish (who, as a consequence of damselfish territorial aggression, often form large schools which, because of their size, can invade such territories and for the most part, get away with it), but also the structure of the reef itself. In the centre of their territories, away from the foraging of other reef herbivores, a number of damselfish, and especially the Threespot Damselfish, cultivate 'algal lawns', thick patches of edible algae upon which the damselfish feed. Such lawns also provide sites for the successful attack of organisms that destroy coral colonies, and so, may influence the success or failure of different species of coral on those parts of the reef occupied by the damselfish. It has been suggested, for example, that the activity of damselfish is a prime factor in permitting the dominance of the fast-growing species, *Acropora cervicornis*, the elkhorn coral, on the shallow reef areas around many Caribbean islands. According to the theory, this coral recovers quickly from the effects of bio-eroders, while other, more massive corals cannot recover so well, and perhaps not at all. Thus, the damselfish, by providing sites for the attack of bio-eroders, creates a situation favourable to *Acropora* and detrimental to the other corals that compete with it.

Reproductive Biology

All damselfish are benthic spawners, typically depositing their eggs on a piece of coral or rock which the male has previously cleaned and which afterwards he guards vigorously. For normally non-territorial species, such as *Abudefduf*, the males alone become territorial at this time while the females continue to roam and approach nest-guarding males only when ready to spawn. For those species which are territorial all year round, the territories of both males and females tend to expand during the spawning season, and the vigour of territorial defence by the males increases markedly. During this time of the year, 6in damselfish will fearlessly attack groupers, barracuda, and even divers.

As in the case of aggression, the motivation for spawning is signalled in these fish by a change in the colour pattern of the male and special motor patterns and sounds. In a typical spawning sequence for one of the *Eupomacentrus*, courtship and spawning is initiated by the female who swims slowly towards the male, or males, if several are close together. The males approach her and assume a distinctive spawning colour, different for each species (except possibly the Dusky Damselfish). Male *Eupomacentrus partitus*, normally half black and half white, blanche, leaving only a black area around the eyes and another near the base of the caudal fin. The Threespot Damselfish also blanches, leaving a broad black mask that extends in a band across the eyes and diagonally down each side of the body to the anal fin; the Dusky Damselfish develop a pale grey body and a golden forehead, and the blue-and-yellow species form a black mask that sweeps upwards to end along the rear edge of the dorsal fin. In his courting colours, the male rises in the water column, while approaching the female, then turns on his side for a second before dashing rapidly for the bottom in what is called the 'dip'. After dipping, he again rises in the water, then dips again, and again, his dipping becoming more and more rapid as the female approaches his selected spawning site. During each dip, the male emits a short staccato sound, a series of quick pulses known as a 'chirp'. Like courtship colours, the chirp produced by each species is unique in terms of the duration and number of the pulses in it. If the female is indeed ready to spawn, she follows the male, who by now is dipping rapidly immediately in front of her, back towards his nest. At this point, the male often begins exaggerated swimming motions in the direction of the nest, apparently leading her to it. She approaches the spawning site, and then begins to lay the first of several thousand eggs. The male follows close behind, fertilizing the rows of eggs as they are being deposited. Total spawning time takes from 10 to 20 minutes, after which the male drives the female away. Thereafter, he vigorously guards the spawn and cares for them by fanning with his caudal and pectoral fins, mouthing them, and picking out those that develop fungus.

The eggs are eliptical, roughly 0.9mm long and 0.5mm in diameter. Hatching time varies depending upon water temperature, but averages 4 to 6 days, at which time a relatively advanced planktonic larva, lacking a yolk sac, emerges. Larvae are long and slender with big heads, large eyes, a large mouth with many fine teeth, and stiff dorsal and anal fins. They are active and within a few hours feed on a variety of small planktonic animals and algae. The duration of this larval stage is not known, but at its end, the grown larvae look essentially like tiny, long, and slim damselfish. During the night, they settle to the bottom and, given the proper stimulus (usually a suitable spot for a territory), they transform within a few hours into 10–15mm long juvenile damselfish.

The spawning behaviour of *Abudefduf* is similar in most respects to that of the *Eupomacentrus*. During the spawning season (summer in the northern Caribbean, year-round in the south), males assume a dark metallic blue coloration which they retain throughout courtship, spawning, and care of eggs. Similar spawning movements are used, though in this species, the dip is replaced by a 'signal-jump', in which the male starts close to the bottom and then dashes up and down in a rapid loop. Females may lay as many as 20,000 red-purple eggs at a time, typically in a tight cluster on the side of a rock. Males court virtually every female that passes, and can wind up with as many as four separate clusters of eggs, all close together in the nest site he has prepared. The eggs are eliptical, about 0.9mm long, and coloured red to orange when first laid. As they mature, they gradually become clear until, shortly before hatching, they develop a greenish tint from the developing eyes. Hatching occurs in about 7 days, during which period the male stays with, cares for, and defends the eggs. Newly hatched larvae are approximately 2mm long, are elongate, and have continuous dorsal, anal, and caudal fins. Even at hatching, the mouth is well-developed. They are active swimmers and feed voraciously on small plankton.

Spawning activity of the Night Major is less well studied, but females are known to place as many as 10,000 red eggs in a closely packed clutch in an area cleared by the male. As in the Sergeant Major, male Night Majors guard the eggs until hatching.

Though its larval development appears to be similar to that described above for the *Eupomacentrus*, the spawning of behaviour of *Microspathodon* differs from theirs in several respects. Based on a study conducted in Puerto Rico, both male and female Jewelfish are territorial, but male territories are always located in deep water and female territories in the shallows. At dawn each day, the females leave their territories and approach the males. While moving, the females have a very intense colour pattern, deep blue with a bright yellow tail. The males, in contrast, are light grey and remain this way throughout the spawning sequence. When the female approaches the territory of the male, he displays to her by making rapid figure-eight swimming motions between her and the nest. During the in-going part of the cycle, she follows close behind. As she comes close to the nest site, a dead branch of staghorn coral, *Acropora palmata*, or a gorgonian stalk picked clean by the male, he begins a series of rapid signal jumps. She then approaches the spawning site and deposits her eggs. After fertilization, she is driven off by the male and he defends and cares for the eggs, much in the manner of that described above for the *Eupomacentrus*. Hatching takes from 4 to 5 days.

Aquarium Biology

For the most part, damselfish do well in captivity. Unless you have a very large tank, however, say 200 gallons or more, you will do best to stay away from the adults and concentrate instead on the juveniles of the various species. These are invariably the most colourful fish, at any rate, and many have gained some popularity as aquarium fish. One especially, the Beau Gregory, is commonly available from retailers and has gained wide notoriety for being colourful, active, and hardy.

Unfortunately, it has also gained wide notoriety for its aggressiveness. As discussed above, all the damselfish are territorial to some extent, and the Beau Gregory is one that maintains a strongly defended, moderate-sized territory. This territoriality is transferred into the tank, where one small damselfish can raise havoc in an established community tank. I saw one graphic demonstration of this when a small Bicolor Damselfish was put in a tank with about a dozen peaceful fish, all of which were about twice its size. Within 24 hours, the damselfish was happily patrolling the entire tank as its territory while the tank's original inhabitants huddled miserably in the corners, their colours blanched and their fins shredded.

Because they are so colourful and active, many aquarists justifiably desire to keep these fish despite their aggressiveness. If you are one of these, several hints may help keep things at least a little peaceful. First, choose small damselfish, essentially as small as possible considering whatever predators you might already have. These smaller fish are the most colourful anyway, and their perky behaviour will quickly make up for their lack of size. Second, keep damselfish with ecologically very different fish, such as nocturnally active species, cleaners, small predators, and plankton pickers. Putting one in with a parrotfish or tang, both algae-eaters like the damselfish, is asking for trouble. Finally, select less aggressive species if possible. The juveniles of the Cocoa Damselfish and the Beau Gregory are virtually identical in colour pattern, but the former is much less vigorously territorial than the latter. Cocoas are frequently shipped north either as or mixed in with Beau Gregories and a careful screening of the 'Beau Gregories' offered for sale may well reveal a few of the more peaceful species. After the Cocoa, young Bicolors and Honey Gregories should be selected. Both Jewelfish and the Threespot Damselfish can be hellions in a tank, and only very small ones should be kept.

Other than their general aggressiveness, damselfish do well in aquaria. The Honey Gregory tends to fade rapidly (turning grey), but the others retain their colours well, feed readily, and are quite bold. Small *Abudefduf* school in an aquarium and, in a large tank, are quite attractive. All of the species feed on algae to some extent, so all do best if provided with some greens in their diet, either in the form of a special food for them, or as algae-covered rocks at which they can pick. Finally, all require shelter of some kind and it is important that suitable small caves and refuges can be provided for them. If you find it aesthetically pleasing, a slightly overturned conch shell is ideal for many.

To date, many damselfish have been spawned in aquaria and a few, those in the genus *Amphiprion*, have been reared successfully. One of the Caribbean species has also been spawned in captivity, but the conditions required to do so largely preclude the average aquarist from duplicating the feat. Male Bicolor Damselfish, *Eupomacentrus partitus*, courted females as described above and eggs were laid variously on either the walls of the tank or on rocks. The fish were spawned, however, only in very large aquaria (over 300 gallons) and were part of a colony of such fish. As many as seven and no fewer than four were always present in the tank, along with several wrasses to serve as outlets for pent-up aggression. Getting this many fish to coexist well enough for spawning to occur is difficult and consumes both time, and fish. Many were killed while trying to stabilize the system.

If you must try to spawn them, I would suggest at least a 50-gallon aquarium (75 or 100 would be better) and several very small Bicolor Damselfish. Provide lots of shelter in the tank and let them grow up together in it. For a 50-gallon tank, four fish is probably the maximum number you can handle successfully. Within a year or so, the fish should have grown large enough to begin courtship activity, providing you are lucky enough to wind up with a male and a female, after the battles have ended. Having a few wrasses in the tank to draw their fire will probably help.

Relevant Literature
Albrecht, H. 1969. 'Behavior of four species of Atlantic Damselfishes from Columbia, South America

(*Abudefduf saxatiles*, *A. taurus*, *Chromis multilineata*, *C. cyanea*; Pisces, Pomacentridae)', *Zeit für Tierpsychol.* **26**: 662–676

Brinley, F. J. 1939. 'Spawning habits and development of Beau-gregory (*Pomacentrus leucostictus*)', *Copeia* 1939 (3): 139–140

Clarke, R. D. 1977. 'Habitat distribution and species diversity of Chaetodontid and Pomacentrid fishes near Bimini, Bahamas', *Mar. Biol.* **40**: 277–289

Cummings, W. C. 1968. 'Reproductive habits of the Sergeant Major, *Abudefduf saxatilis* (Pisces: Pomacentridae), with comparative notes on four other Damselfishes in the Bahama Islands', unpublished Ph.D. dissertation, University of Miami, Miami, Florida

Emery, A. R. 1972. 'A new species of Damselfish (Pisces: Pomacentridae) from the eastern coast of South America', *Copeia* 1972 (2): 330–335

Emery, A. R. 1973. 'Atlantic bicolor Damselfish (Pomacentridae): a taxonomic question', *Copeia*, 1973 (3): 590–594

Emery, A. R. 1973. 'Comparative ecology and functional osteology of fourteen species of Damselfish (Pisces: Pomacentridae) at Alligator Reef, Florida Keys', *Bull. Mar. Sci.* **23**(3): 649–770

Emery, A. R. & Burgess, W. E. 1974. 'A new species of Damselfish (*Eupomacentrus*) from the Western Atlantic, with a key to known species of that area', *Copeia* 1974 (4): 879–886

Fishelson, L. 1970. 'Behavior and ecology of a population of *Abudefduf saxatilis* (Pomacentridae, Teleostei) at Eilat (Red Sea)', *Anim. Behav.* **18**: 225–237

Greenfield, D. W. & Woods, L. P. 1974. '*Eupomacentrus diencaeus* Jordan and Rutter. A valid species of Damselfish from the Western tropical Atlantic', *Fieldiana Zool.* **65**(2): 9–20

Gronell, A. M. 1978. 'Home-ranging behavior of the Cocoa Damselfish, *Eupomacentrus variabilis*, off the Coast of Florida', unpublished Master's dissertation, University of Miami, Coral Gables, Florida

Kaufman, L. 1977. 'The Threespot Damselfish: effects on the benthic biota of Caribbean coral reefs', *Proc. Third Internat. Coral Reef Symp.* **1**:559–564

MacDonald, C. 1973. 'Reproductive behavior and social dynamics of the Yellowtail Damselfish *Microspathodon chrysurus* (Perciformes, Pomacentridae)', unpublished Master's dissertation, University of Puerto Rico, Mayaguez, Puerto Rico

Myrberg, A. A. Jr 1972. 'Ecology of the bicolor Damselfish *Eupomacentrus partitus* (Pisces: Pomacentridae): a comparative analysis of laboratory and field behavior', *Anim. Behav. Monogr.* **5**(3): 199–283

Myrberg, A. A. Jr & Thresher, R. E. 1974. 'Interspecific aggression and its relevance to the concept of territoriality in reef fishes', *Amer. Zool.* **14**: 81–96

Rivas, L. R. 1960. 'The fishes of the Genus *Pomacentrus* in Florida and the western Bahamas', *Quart. J. Fla. Acad. Sci.* **23**: 130–163

Shaw, E. S. 1955. 'The embryology of the Sergeant Major, *Abudefduf saxatilis*', *Copeia* 1955 (2): 85–89

Topp, R. W. 1970. 'Redescription of *Pomacentrus otophorus* Poey 1860, a valid species from the Caribbean (Pisces: Pomacentridae)', *Breviora* **342**: 1–16

Thresher, R. E. 1976. 'Field analysis of the territoriality of the Threespot Damselfish, *Eupomacentrus planifrons* (Pomacentridae)', *Copeia* 1976 (2): 266–276

Chapter 7

Chromis

Damselfish come in a wide variety of shapes, colours, habits, and dispositions. The last is perhaps most important as few aquarists are willing to tolerate a fish, no matter how attractive, which attacks every other fish in the tank, even those several times its own size. Many damselfish, as discussed in the last chapter, are every bit as this aggressive. Fortunately, they are not all like this; at least two groups of damoiselles are not only colourful, active, and interesting, but also relatively mild mannered. These are the species of the *Amphiprion* complex, which are strictly Indo-Pacific, and those of the genus *Chromis*.

Chromis is a circumtropical genus, with only a few species venturing into cooler temperate waters (such as *Chromis punctipinna* off the coast of California). Over 50 species are found around the world, with most in the Indo-Pacific and a few in the tropical western Atlantic. Throughout their range, the various species of *Chromis* tend to be similar in their biologies. All are plankton-feeders, swimming in the water column above the reef. Well adapted to this free-swimming mode of life, they tend to be elongate, streamlined fish, generally non-territorial except during reproductive periods.

The features that separate *Chromis* from other damselfish are largely anatomical and difficult to discern without a detailed examination in the laboratory. The key characters include differences in the teeth pattern, scale patterning on the head, structure of the caudal fin, and pattern of fine teething on the gill covers. They are most closely related to the genera *Dascyllus* and *Acanthochromis*, both of which are like *Chromis* in being primarily plankton-feeders.

Species Account

In the tropical western Atlantic, there are definitely five, and probably six, species of *Chromis*. These fall into two groups, based on body shape and distribution on the reef, with two species in one group, the sub-genus *Forcaria*, and at least three, and probably four, in the other, the sub-genus *Heliases*. Although in the Caribbean they are distinctive, in the Indo-Pacific these two groups generally grade into one another and thus there is no valid reason to consider them separate genera.

The two species in the first group are *Chromis cyanea* and *Chromis multilineata*. The two are pretty much the same in shape and size; they are elongate, slender fish, laterally compressed, with forked caudal fins and dorsal and anal fins that end in a point. Each reaches a maximum size of approximately 4 inches (with *Chromis multilineata* being the slightly larger of the two). Colourwise, they have one common marking – black stripes that edge the top and bottom of the caudal fin. Otherwise, their colours differ greatly. *Chromis cyanea* is brilliant blue with a black forehead and dorsal edge of the body. Tiny black dots pepper the body, and the dorsal fin and the leading edge of the anal fin are also trimmed with black. *Chromis multilineata* is less colourful, though still attractive. It is generally greyish-green, shading to lighter silvery-grey below. Aside from the black caudal fin markings mentioned above, its only other distinctive markings are two black dots, one at the base of each pectoral fin, and a creamy white spot on the top edge of the caudal peduncle.

These two fish are called, respectively, the Blue and the Grey *Chromis*, for obvious reasons. Unfortunately, a few authors in the past have referred to them as the 'blue reef fish' and the 'grey reef fish', names which should be avoided like the plague. 'Blue reef fish' can legitimately refer to any fish, living on or near the reef, which is wholly or partially blue. In short, the name is so ambiguous it is totally worthless. The use of the latinized scientific names avoids such confusion and, while initially taking a little more effort to learn, are much to be preferred.

The members of the second group of Atlantic *Chromis*, the sub-genus *Heliases*, are invariably deep-water fish, which probably accounts for their lesser familiarity to the average aquarist or diver. Like the first group, body shape and size are conservative among these fish (all are rounded, eliptical fish, laterally compressed, and all reach a maximum length of approximately 3 inches), but they differ markedly in colour pattern, especially as juveniles. Unlike the Blue and Grey *Chromis*, the deep water species change colour as they mature; the adults are usually duller in colour than the juveniles. For the aquarist, however, this hardly represents a hardship as it is these juveniles that are most likely to be available. Similarly, juveniles are often found in water more shallow than that frequented by the adults and so they are more likely to be seen by divers.

Chromis insolata is the most colourful member of the group. As a juvenile, it is bright yellow above, greenish rose below, and has an iridescent blue stripe running through the eyes and along the mid-line of the side of the body. At a length of 1½ to 2 inches, its colours fade, the yellow changing to dull green, the underside becoming silvery grey, and the blue stripe being reduced to a bluish area between the eyes and the forehead. It is the adult pattern from which the fish derives its common name of Olive-backed Damselfish. *Chromis enchrysura*, the yellowtailed *Chromis*, undergoes a similar transformation at approximately the same size. As a juvenile, it has a slate-blue body (which becomes increasingly blue with age until transformation) and a yellow caudal peduncle, caudal fin, and trailing halves of the dorsal and anal fins. An electric blue line runs from the forehead through the eyes and then forms a shallow arc along the back, ending at about the beginning of the dorsal fin. In Bermuda, the caudal and ventral fins are white, rather than yellow, and the blue may be restricted to the front and dorsal part of the fish. The line through the eye remains distinctive however. After transformation, the basic colours are dull blue or grey above, silvery-grey below, with only a hint of the yellow areas to the rear. The blue line remains on the adult, though it is less obvious. Finally, there is *Chromis scotti*, the purple *Chromis*, which changes the least of the group. Throughout its life, it is entirely blue (another 'blue reef fish') – iridescent blue as a juvenile, dull blue as an adult.

The validity of these species has sometimes been in doubt. Originally, *Chromis scotti* was thought to be only a colour variant of *Chromis insolata*, and while they are now considered separate, all three species are so similar that they are referred to occasionally as the 'insolata complex'. This picture is further complicated by two additional names in the literature, one of which apparently refers to a valid fourth species in the subgenus. *Chromis flavicauda* has been described from a few specimens and several submarine dives into very deep water off Jamaica and Belize. It was recently collected in fair numbers in slightly shallower water (still at depths of 150 feet and more) off Bermuda. Juveniles are sharply bicolour, iridescent blue to the front and glowing yellow to the rear, with a green wash on the forehead. The dorsal and anal fins are edged with yellow as well. Based on the few pictures yet taken of it, it appears to be one of the most attractive fish in the Caribbean. Adults are deeper blue with the yellow restricted mainly to the fins. Specimens are now being examined and in the near future the species will probably be redescribed as valid. At the same time, another already described species, *Chromis bermudae*, will probably be demoted to a junior synonym of *Chromis flavicauda*.

Field Biology

The two slender species of western Atlantic *Chromis*, the Blue and the Grey *Chromis*, are both shallow-water fish, often found on reefs as shallow as 10 or 15 feet. Of the two, the Grey *Chromis* prefers slightly deeper areas, and does not usually reach its peak abundance in water much less than 40 feet deep.

The two species differ somewhat in their biology on the reef. *Chromis multilineata* is an open-water fish, usually found well above the bottom in schools ranging in size from six or seven to several hundred individuals. Usually, the school fans out over the reef area and, facing into the current, the individual fish weave in and out of each other's paths, performing what looks like a complicated underwater ballet, as they pick from the flowing water the small planktonic crustaceans on which they feed. The impression of a ballet is heightened by the scissoring of each fish's black-edged caudal fin before it makes a sharp turn – almost as if the fish is signalling its partner.

Blue *Chromis* are more closely tied to the reef, rarely moving more than a few feet off the bottom. They are also more solitary fish, often seen alone or in groups of two or three individuals. Blue *Chromis* feed in much the same manner as *Chromis multilineata*, picking both copepods and large amounts of pelagic algae from the water.

As juveniles, both species remain close to the bottom, where there are more hiding places should a predator approach. They assemble in small, often mixed schools. The juveniles eat pretty much the same things as the adults and are similar in colour and shape to them (though, of course, they are smaller).

All of the species of the subgenus *Heliases* are deep-reef fish. Most are uncommon-to-rare in areas less than 90 to 100 feet deep, but below this depth the three deep-bodied species become very common and largely replace *Chromis cyanea* and *Chromis multilineata*. Occasionally, juveniles of all three species, newly metamorphosed from their planktonic stages, are found in as little as 20 feet of water, but this is only a summer phenomenon; whether they are eaten, die, or migrate to deeper water as they mature is not known. Only one of the three, *Chromis scotti*, can be found with any regularity as adults in these shallow areas, but it too is relatively rare.

Chromis insolata and *Chromis scotti* are similar in their general biology. Both remain close to the bottom, both as adults and juveniles, rarely moving more than a few feet above it. They are usually found in small groups, often both species together. As juveniles, they have an especially strong tendency to school, most often with other members of their own species, but occasionally with other species of *Chromis*. Neither as adults nor as juveniles do these fish move around the reef to any great extent; one can often return to the same spot on the reef even after considerable lengths of time and find what appear to be the same fish seen previously. Thus, while these species do not appear to be territorial (that is, each fish does not chase members of its own or other species from its own private part of the reef), they are apparently home-rangers, choosing an area and remaining there for long periods, possibly for life.

Chromis enchrysura, the Yellowtail *Chromis*, differs from the other two common deep-water species in its preference of habitat, especially as a juvenile. Rather than remaining in areas of coral or rock outcrop, the young Yellowtail *Chromis* are common on the broad sandy areas around and between coral outcrops. They associate with any obstruction on the bottom – small coral heads, sponges, and tilefish burrows – all of which have around them small schools of juveniles. Even shallow depressions in the sand, offering only the minimum in cover from predators and current, usually contain several of these fish. Beyond the sand plain, on the very deep reef (180 feet plus), they occupy a niche similar to that of the juveniles of *Chromis insolata* and *Chromis scotti*. Adult Yellowtail *Chromis* are also similar in behaviour to these other two species, except that they tend to be higher in the water column when they feed. In this regard, they parallel the shallow-water *Chromis multilineata*. Throughout its life, *Chromis enchrysura* dwells deeper on the reef than the other common species in the genus; it is rarely seen in water shallower than 130 feet and has been collected as deep as 500 feet. Only the tentative species, *Chromis flavicauda*, is generally found deeper, being uncommon at depths much under 200 feet and going down to at least 400 feet.

All of these deep-water species feed in the same manner as the shallow-water *Chromis*, facing into the current and picking from it their planktonic food. This food consists primarily of copepods, algae, and, especially for *Chromis insolata*, the pelagic tunicate, *Oikopleura*.

Reproductive Biology

While all five species of *Chromis* roam over at least small areas of the reef during their non-reproductive periods, spawning itself invariably occurs in a small territory vigorously defended by the male. Other than this single unifying principle, the spawning behaviour of the various species differs widely.

Chromis cyanea is a solitary spawner, each male maintaining a solitary breeding territory on the reef. On northern reefs, this territory is temporary; on southern reefs, it is maintained year-round. From this spot, he courts passing females, signalling to them by two means. First, his colour changes. The narrow band of black on his back grows larger, until it covers the entire dorsal half of the fish; meanwhile, the bottom half becomes very pale. The total image is of a horizontally bicolour *Chromis*. The male wears this colour pattern throughout his courtship activities. The second signal used is a distinctive motor pattern common to many damselfish, called the signal jump. At the approach of a female, the male, close to the bottom, dashes up into the water and in the general direction of the female, then, looping over, returns to the bottom. The more excited the male, the faster these signal jumps. Once a female is attracted, the male leads here to a prepared spawning site where she lays her eggs (through a small, round tube extended from the body for only a brief period, specifically for spawning). The male follows close behind, fertilizing the eggs through his more pointed breeding tube. Having spawned with several different females, the male then guards the eggs and fans them until they hatch into planktonic larvae (after about 3 days).

The Grey *Chromis* breeds in a similar manner, but there is little colour change in the male (he becomes slightly greener) and spawning is usually a group, rather than a solitary affair. A number of males, ranging from less than a dozen to over a thousand, establish small breeding territories near one another on a rocky outcrop. Females congregate in this area and are courted by the males. Each male will spawn with many different females; one male was observed to spawn more than 30 times in less than 45 minutes. Following spawning, the eggs are guarded and cared for until they hatch (after approximately 3 to 4 days at 75 to 77 °F) after which the territory is abandoned. Such colonial breeding occurs throughout the summer, usually at intervals of about a month, each spawning bout lasting about 3 days.

The species in the subgenus *Heliases* are apparently solitary spawners, much in the manner of *Chromis cyanea*. The males develop a white-blotched appearance during courtship. The territories they defend are smaller than those of *Chromis cyanea* and the signal jumps they make are shorter and faster. In general, the breeding behaviour of all of these deeper water species is little known compared with the two shallow-water species. Dives to these depths are infrequent, and of short duration, so that observations of spawning of these species are not common.

Regardless of the species, all *Chomis* lay eliptical demersal eggs, roughly 0.6mm long and 0.4mm across, each containing a single large oil globule. The duration of the planktonic larval stage is not known.

Aquarium Biology

All five common species of *Chromis* readily acclimate to the aquarium, especially as juveniles. All feed well on a variety of common foods, all are active fish, usually preferring the upper portions of the tank, and all are largely non-aggressive towards members of other species. Unfortunately, they are still damselfish and are often aggressive among themselves. Such aggression takes the form of a dominance hierarchy, in which one fish (usually the largest) is boss, another is second in rank, and so on down the line. Each fish picks on those of lower rank than itself, with one fish at the bottom (called the 'omega' by scientists) which everyone picks on. If a number of fish are together, aggression is spread out and no single fish suffers to any extent. But if only two or three *Chromis* are present, the omega fish may be harassed to the point where it constantly hides, may not eat, and may eventually starve to death. Obviously, schools of four or more individuals are to be preferred.

The only other problem with these fish is loss of colour. The Blue and the Grey *Chromis* are largely colour-fast, but the other species fade to some degree in the aquarium. This is probably the result of two factors: an incomplete diet and, perhaps more important, a light-coloured aquarium. These are deep-water fish, living in areas of relatively little light. Given the bright lights of most aquaria, it is little wonder that they fade, attempting to match the background illumination. It is likely that any serious effort to match the conditions these fish encounter in the field will be rewarded by maintenance of the original bright colours.

Rather surprisingly, only one of the five species of western Atlantic *Chromis* is particularly well known to aquarists. *Chromis cyanea* has long been available from dealers and is commonly kept. The reasons for the lack of popularity of the other species are probably two-fold. First, the other common, shallow-water species, *Chromis multilineata*, is relatively drab in coloration. Its green and grey colours may not be flashy enough to attract attention from wholesalers and dealers. This is unfortunate since they are quite attractive in schools of small fish, especially when mixed with a few *Chromis cyanea*. The contrasting blue and grey, otherwise identical, fish in a single school is striking.

The *insolata* group *Chromis*, on the other hand, should be popular aquarium fish. They are beautiful and often delicately coloured; they are very abundant in some areas; and they are easily captured and maintained. The culprit here is doubtless their preference for deep water where, in the past, they have been difficult to capture, or even see. Thus, there has historically been no interest in them and wholesalers simply have not bothered to collect and ship fish for which no ready market exists.

As an added bonus for the deep-water species, they should spawn readily in a standard aquarium set-up, provided they are given a degree of protection from larger, bullying fish and are well fed. On the reef, they are relatively sedentary and breeding territories are small, such that in an aquarium of 35 to 40 gallons or more, they should feel at home and not crowded. The best procedure to attempt spawning any of these species would probably involve keeping a half dozen or so adult fish in their own tank, hoping that with heavy feedings (including some live food), one male will stake out a territory and begin to court females in the main school.

Relevant Literature

Albrecht, H. 1969. 'Behavior of four species of Atlantic Damselfishes from Columbia, South America (*Abudefduf saxatiles*, *A. taurus*, *Chromis multilineata*, *C. cyanea*; Pisces: Pomacentridae)', *Zeit. für Tierpsychol.* **26**: 662–676

de Boer, B. A. 1978. 'Factors affecting the distribution of the Damselfish *Chromis cyanea* (Poey), Pomacentridae, on a reef at Curacao, Netherland Antilles', *Bull. Mar. Sci.* **28**(3): 550–565

Emery, A. R. 1968. 'A new species of *Chromis* (Pisces: Pomacentridae) from the western north Atlantic', *Copeia* 1968: 49–55

Emery, A. R. 1973. 'Comparative Ecology and Functional Osteology of fourteen species of Damselfish (Pisces: Pomacentridae) at Alligator Reef, Florida Keys', *Bull. Mar. Sci.* **23**(3): 649–770

Chapter 8

Gobies

If one sat down and made a list of the species of fish found on and around the reef, one would soon discover that one family far outnumbered all the others in number of species. Typically small, elongate, and often cryptic, gobies (family Gobiidae) literally swarm over the reef, as well as on the surrounding sand and mud flats, and mangrove swamps. There are more than 7,000 species of goby in the world and more than 70 in the Caribbean alone, almost 10 per cent of the entire Caribbean reef fish fauna.

As would be expected from such a speciose group, many species are either drab, large (or both), or have such specialized requirements that they will not do well in aquaria. There are however, quite a few relatively small (2–3 inches), colourful and hardy species that are seen commonly on and around the reef, that can be readily identified, and that do well in captivity. One large block of these, the Neon Gobies, genus *Gobiosoma*, subgenus *Elacatinus*, will be treated in a separate chapter as they form a natural unit with many unique features. The remaining fish will be covered in this chapter. Because even these remaining species are still so numerous, the chapter will concentrate on the more common, more colourful, and more interesting members of the family.

Gobies are typically benthic, that is, bottom resting, fish characterized by having blunt or slightly pointed snouts, small mouths, and two dorsal fins. They can be easily separated from the rubbery blennies and blenny-like fish by the stiffness of their bodies. The gobies are also characterized by pelvic fins that tend to be fused into a sucking disc used for clinging to hard substrates. In the past, gobies have been divided systematically based on the completeness of this fusion; gobies with completely fused fins have been placed in the family Gobiidae, and those with largely unfused fins placed in the family Eleotridae. Though such a division seems to be a reasonable way of splitting up this immense number of fish, in fact, it does not work out in practice. There are many otherwise similar and apparently closely related species, sometimes even in the same genus, that differ widely in the degree of pelvic fin fusion.

Most of the species to be covered in this chapter are clearly gobiids; only one common reef-dwelling genus, *Ioglossus*, would be considered an eleotrid.

Species Account

Rather than provide a descriptive list of a number of different species, then go back to try and relate each to a particular field situation, the gobies will be treated differently from the less speciose groups and will be handled in terms of habitats. Each habitat has associated with it several characteristic species and these will be discussed as a unit.

(1) *The Rocky Inshore Habitat* This first habitat is one strongly swept by waves and tide and, because of this, is one that is often dirty. In this frequently rough area, often no more than a foot or two deep, a surprisingly large number of fish thrive, most relatively small and capable of either squeezing into crevices to avoid the heavy surge action or hanging on tightly to ride it out (thus the gobies and their suction discs). Four gobies of note, including a species that must rank as one of the most colourful fish in the Caribbean, are commonly found in this area: *Gobiosoma multifasciatum*, *Gobiosoma macrodon*, *Ginsburgellus novemlineatus*, and *Bathygobius soporator*.

Gobiosoma multifasciatum, the Greenband Goby, can only be described as beautiful. It is generally lime green, over which lies a series of parallel fine green bars that start just behind the pelvic fins and end at the base of the caudal fin. A bright scarlet band accents the head, running from the mouth, along the forehead and through the eyes to end at the top of the first vertical green bar. *Gobiosoma macrodon*, the Tiger Goby, is also green and barred, but is less spectacular than its near relative. Rather, it is generally dark green with a series of fine black bars starting just behind the head and ending at the caudal fin. Both of these *Gobiosoma* reach a maximum length of about 2 inches and are common in very shallow water. The Greenband, in fact, can often be found in wave-washed rocks, only a few inches below the surface, living in holes bored by the sea urchin, *Echinometra*. A skittish, generally shy fish, the Greenband is usually seen sitting just at the base of an urchin, often right in its tube feet (which they are suspected of eating now and then). Tiger Gobies are found in slightly deeper water, though still less than 10 feet, and they are seen frequently in pairs sitting on amorphous sponges and isolated coral heads, or in crevices under the sea urchin, *Diadema*.

Like the Greenband, the Ninelined Goby, *Ginsburgellus novemlineatus*, is vertically striped and is typically found in *Echinometra* bore holes. It is a small species, rarely reaching more than an inch in total length, with nine narrow neon blue lines vertically crossing its bluish-black or brown body. Like the Greenband, the Ninelined Goby is suspected to feed on the tube feet of the urchins.

In contrast to these small and colourful species, *Bathygobius soporator* is large (up to 6 inches), grey or grey-brown, and heavily scaled. A tide pool fish usually seen scooting among rocks and debris at low tide, *Bathygobius* is commonly collected by aquarists and will thrive in even the worst conditions. Like many other tide pool fish, it is particularly rugged and so it is well suited for even novice aquarists.

(2) *The Reef Habitat*   Moving into deeper water and onto the reef itself, one encounters a wide variety of small, translucent gobies hovering and scooting around on coral heads and rocky outcrops. Most are nondescript and difficult even for a specialist to key out, but a few of the more common and more attractive species are readily identifiable. Of these, the most common (and possibly the most common fish in the entire tropical western Atlantic) is the Masked Goby, *Coryphopterus personatus*. Literally thousands of these small, translucent reddish-brown fish hover in small-to-large groups (up to 70 or 80 fish) inside caves and along rock walls at depths from 30 feet on down. Its common name is derived from a wash of black across the eyes and along the side of its head. It also has several, short, cream-coloured lines along its venter. This attractive little fish (maximum length approximately $1\frac{1}{2}$ inches) may well be the single most important component of the diets of many small predators. The goby itself feeds mainly on plankton, which it picks out of the water with short darting movements.

In the southeastern portion of the Bahamas, a second hovering goby can often be seen swimming in clusters near groups of Masked Gobies. Somewhat more depth restricted (85 to 110 feet), this second goby, *Vomerogobius flavus*, is long and slender, even for a goby, and is brilliant yellow-orange with a contrasting blue wash across its head. Only reaching a length of an inch or two, *Vomerogobius* is more retiring than the Masked Goby and is usually found deeper in caves than is the latter. Like the Masked Goby, *Vomerogobius* feeds mainly on small planktonic organisms.

While these two species rarely rest on corals, the third common goby is almost invariably found sitting on large heads of live coral, often *Montastrea* or *Colpophylia*. Another small (2 inch maximum), translucent species, the Blue Snout Goby, or Lemon Goby, *Coryphopterus lipernes*, is pale yellow with a vivid blue wash across its eyes – an altogether attractive and active fish. They are commonly found in pairs, suggesting a monogamous mating system, on large coral heads at depths in excess of 40 feet. These heads are often shared with a number of Neon Gobies. Unlike them, however, the Blue Snout Goby is not a cleaner, but rather obtains most of its food from the plankton.

The last common species of goby found in this habitat is the Rusty Goby, *Quisquilius hipoliti*, a translucent rusty-red, faintly barred species that more often than not is found sitting upside down on the roof of a small cave. It is a short, chunky-bodied fish, with, for a goby, a wide mouth. It feeds, like the other species, mainly on plankton, which it captures with lightning quick dashes (again, usually while swimming upside down) out of its cave. The Rusty Goby has a wide depth distribution and can be found from immediately below the low tide level to at least 150 feet.

(3) *Mixed Sand and Rubble Habitat*   The reef is hardly a solid sheet of coral. Rather, its surface is broken up by canyons and by pockets of mixed sand and rubble such that in some areas a reef may have more sand than coral heads. A number of gobies are specialized to live in these areas of mixed sand and coral rubble. The two more common of these are both heavy-bodied fish that are translucent white with flecks of darker white, grey, and brown peppering them. The longer, heavier, and more common of the

two is the Bridled Goby, *Coryphopterus glaucofrenum*, which reaches a maximum length of approximately 3 inches. The second species, *Gnatholepis thompsoni*, the Goldspot Goby, is similar to it, but can be identified by a short black vertical line that runs down from each of its eyes and by a black-ringed gold spot (from which the species derives its common name) located just above the pectoral fins. The habitat preferences and behaviour of the two species overlap broadly, such that it is not uncommon to find both in the same sand patch. Both are loosely territorial (against conspecifics and one another), each fish centering its territory on a small cave under a rock or a piece of coral. These caves are sometimes natural, but more often they are excavated by the gobies, the sand being carried out by the mouthful. Both species feed by 'sand filtering', the goby scooping a mouthful of fine sand and slowly filtering it through its mouth and gill chambers for detritus and small organisms while the cleaned sand pours out its gill openings. Though broadly similar in most respects, *Gnatholepis* seems to be more tolerant of silt than the Bridled Goby and is often the only species present close to shore.

The final set of common sand-dwelling gobies is the eleotrid genus, *Ioglossus*, which contains two very similar species in the tropical western Atlantic. *Ioglossus helenae* is found throughout the Bahamas and the Caribbean, while *Ioglossus caliurus*, virtually identical to it in every respect, is restricted to the Florida coast. Commonly known as *the* Hovering Goby, the *Ioglossus* are similar in size and general behaviour to the Indo-Pacific ptereleotrids – long (up to 7 inches) and slender with a blunt head and up-turned mouth at one end and a long pointed caudal fin at the other. For both species, the body is generally pearl white, overlaid with purple and rose highlights. The same colours dominate the fins. *Ioglossus* are usually found in pairs, generally on the same sand and rubble flats around the deeper reef preferred by the Yellowhead Jawfish, *Opistognathus aurifrons*. Like the jawfish, they spend most of their time hovering a few feet off the bottom while feeding on drifting plankton. The normal posture is roughly horizontal with the head slightly lower than the tail; when approached the fish gradually sinks head-down towards one end of a u-shaped burrow dug in the bottom and finally dashes into it head first. Juveniles are commonly found in the summer scattered among the parents and are similar to them, but lack the pointed caudal fin and the intensity of the adults' coloration.

(4) *The Mud Flat Habitat*   The gobies found on mud flats are similar in many respects to those found on sand patches. Most are sand-sifters or plankton-feeders and most dig burrows in which to live. Three genera are commonly found in such areas – *Nes*, *Gobionellus*, and *Microgobius*. The first is represented by *Nes longus*, a long, slender, and heavily scaled species, grey with a series of gold spots along its side and a long, pointed caudal fin. In behaviour, it is most like *Gnatholepis thompsoni* in that it scoots along over the mud, stopping to rest on it frequently, and feeds by sifting silt through its gills for the organic detritus it contains. Unlike *Gnatholepis*, though, the Orangespotted Goby lives in a symbiotic relationship with another dweller on the mud flats, a large species of snapping shrimp in the genus *Alphaeus*. On the flats, the most pressing need for a fish, or any small motile animal, is for shelter from the ubiquitous roving predators. Many species dig burrows in which to hide, but *Nes* bypasses such digging itself and shares the extensive burrow systems constructed by the bulldozer-like shrimp. In exchange for shelter, the fish supposedly serves as a watchdog for the busy shrimp. While not proven, this trade-off seems likely as one usually sees the fish perched on the top of a mud pile near the burrow, apparently acting as a sentry, and both it and the shrimp dash into the burrow when approached. The relationship between the shrimp and the fish is a close one and even a small shrimp invariably has an equally small goby sharing its burrow.

The other two genera contain fish much like *Ioglossus* in shape and behaviour. The largest member of the group is the Spotfin Goby, *Gobionellus stigmalophius*, whose common name is derived from a large black spot on the rear edge of the first dorsal fin. It is an attractive species, growing to just over 6 inches. The basic body colour is bronze, with gold worm-like markings on the head and gill covers and a series of large gold spots running down each side of its body, ending just ahead of the long, pointed caudal fin. A sand sifting species, it lives in a u-shaped burrow dug in part by carrying silt out by the mouthful and in part by washing it out with a steady current of water generated by the fish vigorously beating its tail at the mouth of the burrow. *Gobionellus* is most frequently seen hovering a few inches off the bottom, just ahead of its burrow, an area which it vigorously defends from other members of its species. The Spotfin

Goby is only one of a large number of mud-dwelling *Gobionellus* species, but most are smaller and considerably drabber in overall appearance. One other, reasonably common species, the Dash Goby, *Gobionellus sepaepaellens*, looks and acts a great deal like the Goldspot Goby, *Gnatholepis*. Aside from habitat, the two can be readily distinguished by the series of short black horizontal 'dashes' running down the centre of each side of the Dash Goby.

Like *Gobionellus*, *Microgobius* also contains a large number of small and generally nondescript species, only one of which is colourful. This delicately attractive species, *Microgobius signatus*, is long, slender, and, in terms of colour, sexually dimorphic. Both males and females are golden-yellow, while the female has, in addition, two electric blue marks – a series of blue scrawlings on her gill covers and an electric blue slash that starts under the leading edge of the first dorsal fin and curves down to a point just forward of the pectorals. Like many other gobies, *Microgobius signatus* has an elongated spine near the front of the first dorsal fin. *Microgobius* are mid-water hoverers, like *Ioglossus*, spending most of the day several feet above their *u*-shaped burrows. At dusk, they may range as much as 5 or 6 feet into the water column while looking for the plankton on which they feed. As the name implies, none of the *Microgobius* grow very large; *Microgobius signatus* is about the largest, reaching almost 3 inches.

Reproductive Biology

While reproduction has been observed for a few species of tropical western Atlantic gobies, detailed observations are rare. There are, however, several features that are common to all. First, many gobies are found typically in pairs – two on the same coral head, two burrows close to one another, and so on – suggesting that such species may be monogamous. Second, as far as is known, all gobies lay oval to elipsoid demersal eggs, somewhere around 1 to 2mm in diameter. Third, the eggs are invariably spawned in some sort of cavity – an old worm tube, inside a coral crevice, under an overturned shell – and are cared for and guarded by the male. Such a male often signals the onset of spawning by becoming territorial, driving away both females and other males from his selected spawning site, an area prepared by scraping and picking the surface clean. And finally, after spawning, the eggs take from 18 to 90 hours to hatch and produce 3 to 4mm-long pelagic larvae.

Aside from the Neon Gobies, which will be discussed in the next chapter, the spawning of only one species of Caribbean goby has been described in detail. *Bathygobius soporator* spawns in the summer off the coast of Florida, though probably year-round in the rest of the Caribbean. A courting male prepares a nest cavity under an over-turned sea shell by scooping and digging a pit under one edge. While courting, his colours pale and he develops a prominent black chin and throat. The female is courted by a variety of means, including both a lateral fin spread display, during which the male vibrates his body and a series of short, low-frequency 'grunts' produced by the male and directed at the female. She, in turn, releases a pheromone (a chemical secreted as a means of communication between individuals) that stimulates him to full reproductive condition. Courtship culminates with the female repeatedly entering the prepared spawning cavity, followed each time by the male, during which as many as 18,000 eggs are attached to its walls and ceiling. The eggs are fanned and guarded by the male and hatch in about 3 days.

Aquarium Biology

As a general rule, gobies do very well in captivity; some, in fact, do so well they can eat you out of house and home. I have successfully kept all the species described for extended periods, so none are beyond the capabilities of the average aquarist. In a pinch, all took live brine shrimp very readily (even the smallest species) and most accepted dried food once they were used to it. Most of the species were fairly bold once acclimated to the tank, but you may have problems in this regard with the mud-dwelling species in *Gobionellus* and *Microgobius* and the two very small and retiring species, *Ginsburgellus novemlineatus* and *Gobiosoma multifasciatum*. The two mud dwellers are prone to dash into cover at the approach of the aquarist and generally take several weeks to tame; to a lesser extent, the same is also true of *Ioglossus*. All three will likely disappear for the first week, or longer, after being introduced into a tank and during this period must be provided with enough live food so that some will still be swimming around when they venture out. While fish will easily stand a moderate amount of hunger, these skittish gobies are slender to start with, and will weaken quickly.

The mud-dwelling species, by the way, do not require mud-bottomed aquaria, though if you desire to spawn them it might be wise to provide one. They do require, however, a narrow tube, cave, or similar sized object that they can use for a burrow. I kept a healthy *Microgobius signatus* for several months in an otherwise barren 5-gallon aquarium by giving it a small conch shell (thoroughly cleaned, of course) under which it slept and dashed when frightened.

The small rock-dwelling gobies present similar problems. The spectacular Greenband Goby, as well as the Nineline Goby and, to a lesser extent, the Rusty Goby, all tend to be shy for the first few days. The Greenband and the Rusty Goby rapidly adjust and soon sit out in the open waiting to be fed, while the Nineline, small as it is, always remains shy. The first two species are highly recommended for any reasonably experienced aquarist, while the last is best left to someone with a more than average amount of patience (and fondness for miniature fish).

Bathygobius, as well as several Neon Gobies, have been spawned in captivity and, in fact, spawn both readily and repeatedly. The keys to their spawning have been a good supply of live food, the presence of a small cave or overturned shell in which to spawn, and enough room for the male to establish a successful spawning territory. Such success bodes well for the other species, and some, such as the beautiful Greenband, should present no problems for a determined aquarist. The larvae of many gobies, however, are very small, even for a reef fish, and will be difficult to rear in captivity.

Relevant Literature

Birdsong, R. S. 'A systematic review of the Gobiid fish genus *Microgobius* with special emphasis on Osteology', unpublished Ph.D. dissertation, University of Miami, Coral Gables, Florida

Böhlke, J. E. & Robins, C. R. 1968. 'Western Atlantic Seven-spined Gobies, with descriptions of ten new species and a new genus, with comments on Pacific relatives', *Proc. Acad. Nat. Sci. Phila.* **120**(3): 45–174

Randall, J. E. 1968. '*Ioglossus helenae*, a new Gobiid fish from the West Indies', *Ichthyologica/ Aquarium Jour.* **39**: 107–116

Smith, C. L. & Tyler, J. C. 1977. 'Redescription of the Gobiid fish *Coryphopterus lipernes* Böhlke & Robins, with notes on its habits and relationships', *Amer. Mus. Novitates* (2616): 1–10

Tavolga, W. N. 1950. 'Development of the gobiid fish, *Bathygobius soporator*', *J. Morph.* **87**(3): 467–492

Tavolga, W. N. 1954. 'Reproductive Behavior of the gobiid fish *Bathygobius soporator*', *Bull. Amer. Mus. Nat. Hist.* **104**: 427–460

Tavolga, W. N. 1956. 'Visual, chemical, and sound stimuli as cues in the sex discriminatory behavior of the Gobiid fish *Bathygobius soporator*', *Zoologica* **41**: 49–64

Teytaud, A. R. 1971. 'Food habits of the goby, *Ginsburgellus novemlineatus*, and the clingfish, *Arcos rubiginosus*, associated with echinoids in the Virgin Islands', *Carib. J. Sci.* **11**: 41–45

Weiler, D. A. 1976. 'Burrow-dwelling fishes in a back reef area and the relation of sediment grain size' unpublished Master's dissertation, University of Puerto Rico, Mayaguez, Puerto Rico

The Sponge-Dwelling Neon Gobies

Lines Indicate Key Features

Gobiosoma
chancei

Gobiosoma
horsti

Gobiosoma
louisae

Gobiosoma
tenox

Gobiosoma
xanthiprora

The Cleaning Neon Gobies

Lines Indicate Key Features

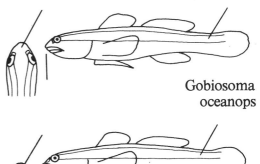

Gobiosoma
oceanops

Gobiosoma
randalli

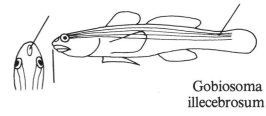

Gobiosoma
illecebrosum

Varies   Varies

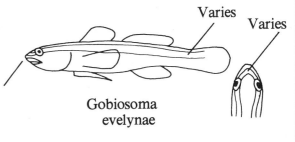

Gobiosoma
evelynae

White   Yellow

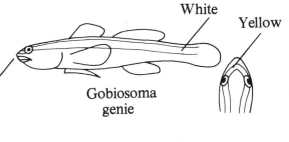

Gobiosoma
genie

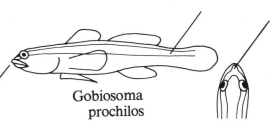

Gobiosoma
prochilos

Chapter 9

Neon Gobies

Neon Gobies are a sub-group of the family Gobiidae characterized by brilliant colours, boldness, a lack of body scales, the presence of some sort of horizontal stripe (and the absence of any vertical banding), a propensity to clean other fish, and a host of specialized morphological and anatomical characters. The neons are a highly variable group, not only in terms of the large number of species and diversity of life styles, but also in terms of colour variation within each species. These tropical western Atlantic fish belong to the genus *Gobiosoma*, sub-genus *Elacatinus* (in the older literature, the latter is sometimes used as the genus name). All have basically the same shape – long and slender; all reach roughly the same size – 2 to 3 inches maximum; and all have a brilliantly coloured horizontal stripe, frequently paired with one or two broader, parallel black stripes. The lateral colour stripe runs from the vicinity of the snout to the caudal fin in most species, but in a few it ends near the middle of the body. The colour, length, and shape of these stripes, plus those of any other colour marks on the body (usually the snout) are key characters in discriminating between the various species.

Species Account

There are presently 12 recognized species of Atlantic Neon Gobies, falling into three natural groups: six species that are commonly seen sitting on coral heads, or occasionally on sponges, and that actively clean other fishes; five more that are invariably associated with massive or tubular sponges; and finally, a single species that hovers in mid water feeding on plankton. The last species can also be associated with live coral, but neither it, nor the sponge-dwelling species, clean.

The species in the first group are all boldly coloured, such coloration doubtless advertising their presence to fish that desire a cleaning. Though specific colour patterns vary between species and between populations within a species, all are combinations of black (usually the base colour), blue, yellow, or white.

The best-known member of the group is *Gobiosoma oceanops*, whose official common name is *the* Neon Goby. This colourful fish possesses a broad electric blue stripe on each side of its body that runs from just ahead of the eyes in a broad swath down the body, to terminate just on the caudal fin. This blue stripe is sandwiched between two broader black lines that meet on the snout and which therefore prevent the two blue lines (one on each side of the body) from meeting (this is an important character in keying this species out; the remaining species in this group either have a distinct 'V' on the snout, where the two colour lines meet, or have a 'pip', a short vertical, coloured line, between the ends of the two lateral stripes). *Gobiosoma oceanops* is common all along the Florida coast and is present at spots along the coast of the Gulf of Mexico (such as the Flower Garden reefs off Texas) and down to the Yucatan Peninsula and Belize. It has not yet been collected from any of the oceanic islands, either in the Bahamas or in the Caribbean proper. The species is common at depths from a few feet to at least 125 feet.

Gobiosoma illecebrosum is one of two cleaning species with a snout 'pip'. It is characterized by the presence of an inferior (as opposed to a terminal) mouth and by a broad pale band sandwiched between the two horizontal black lines on each side of its body. The colour stripe, which depending on the locale can be either electric blue, white, or yellow, runs down the centre of this pale area and so does not touch either black border. These narrow colour stripes extend forward only to the eyes, ahead of which the only colour mark on an otherwise black snout is a very distinct, short, vertical white or yellow slash. *Gobiosoma illecebrosum* is found mainly along the coast of Central America, from the Yucatan Peninsula to Columbia. It is commonly collected in the San Blas islands and other islands immediately offshore of this coast, where it is the dominant cleaning species.

The Yellownose Goby, *Gobiosoma randalli*, is similar in coloration to *Gobiosoma illecebrosum*, including the presence of the snout 'pip', but has several distinguishing characteristics. First, its mouth is terminal, that is, on the very tip of its snout; second, its broad lateral colour stripe is in contact with both lateral black stripes the full length of the body; and third, the lateral colour stripe and snout 'pip' are invariably yellow. The Yellownose Goby is found around the islands off the Venezuelan coast (Curacao, Bonaire, etc.) as well as in the southern portions of the Lesser Antilles. It was reported once from Puerto Rico at a relatively great depth (over 160 feet), but has subsequently not been seen there.

The remaining three cleaning species all have colour stripes that extend through the eyes to meet as a distinct 'V' on the snout. *Gobiosoma genie*, *Gobiosoma evelynae*, and *Gobiosoma prochilos* can be distinguished from each other by the position of the mouth and the colour and shape of the lateral colour stripes.

Gobiosoma genie, known simply as the Cleaning Goby, is closely related to *Gobiosoma evelynae*, the Sharknose Goby, and it is suspected that the two may hybridize in the field. Both have an inferior mouth, but can generally be identified by the colour pattern. *Gobiosoma genie* has only a single known colour form, on which a broad white lateral colour stripe runs between the familiar pair of black paralleling lines along each side of its body; the colour stripes fuse on the snout, while changing colour, to form a distinctly yellow 'V'. The Sharknose Goby has at least three colour forms, none of which matches exactly *Gobiosoma genie*. In the northern Bahamas, *Gobiosoma evelynae* has yellow lateral colour stripes and a yellow snout 'V'; in the southern Bahamas, as well as scattered locations in the northwestern Bahamas, throughout the Lesser Antilles, and off the Venezuelan offshore islands, the lateral stripe is pale blue and the snout 'V' brilliant yellow; and on fish from Jamaica, Swan Island, and a few other mid-Caribbean banks and islands, the lateral stripe is very pale blue-white, leading up to a narrow white 'V'. Both *Gobiosoma genie* and *Gobiosoma evelynae* are widely distributed in the Caribbean and their ranges overlap those of other cleaning species. As a general rule, *Gobiosoma genie* is found in shallower water than *Gobiosoma evelynae* (usually less than 30 feet) and, unlike the latter, is commonly found in small caves and rocky overhangs, as well as on live coral.

The last species in the cleaner complex is the Limpiador (Spanish for 'cleaner'), *Gobiosoma prochilos*, a fairly wide-ranging species with only one colour form. The snout 'V' is always white and often has a short anterior line extending forward from the apex of the 'V'. The lateral colour stripe is white to bluish white, resembling most closely the white form of *Gobiosoma evelynae*. The two can be told apart by the position of the mouth; that of *Gobiosoma evelynae* is clearly inferior and that of *Gobiosoma prochilos* more terminal in position. *Gobiosoma prochilos* is found throughout the Lesser Antilles, off the Yucatan Peninsula and Jamaica, and has tentatively been reported from the northern Gulf of Mexico.

The second group of ecologically similar neon gobies is the sponge dwellers and consists of five species: *Gobiosoma chancei*, *Gobiosoma louisae*, *Gobiosoma horsti*, *Gobiosoma xanthiprora*, and the largely black *Gobiosoma tenox*. All of these species have a very thin lateral colour stripe, being more a line than a stripe, and on two species even these are incomplete, extending through the head and only briefly on to the body. As in the previous group, the size and colour of the lateral stripe, as well as any snout markings, are key features in telling the species apart.

The two easiest species to pick out of the group are *Gobiosoma chancei* and *Gobiosoma tenox*. Both have an abbreviated lateral stripe, extending from the eyes to a point just behind the insertion of the pectoral fins. *Gobiosoma chancei*, known as the Shortstripe Goby, is otherwise dark on top and pale below and lacks any snout markings. *Gobiosoma tenox*, the Slaty Goby, is a uniform dark slate grey, aside from its brief lateral stripe and a short vertical snout 'pip'. The stripes on both species, and the 'pip' on the Slaty Goby, are yellow. *Gobiosoma chancei* is widely distributed from the southern Bahamas throughout the Caribbean, while *Gobiosoma tenox* has thus far been reported from Dominica, Aves Island (southwest of Puerto Rico), and the San Blas islands off the Atlantic coast of Panama.

The remaining three species in the group all have full-length lateral stripes. *Gobiosoma louisae*, a pale coloured sponge dweller, has a very distinct yellow or white snout spot (not a stripe!), a pale white, yellow, or silvery blue lateral stripe, and, at the end of the single parallel black body stripe (below the colour stripe; above the stripe the fish is pale), a large black oval on the caudal peduncle. *Gobiosoma xanthiprora* is similar, but tends to have a brighter, more iridescent colour stripe. It also lacks the dark oval on the caudal peduncle and has a 'pip' rather than a spot on the snout. And finally, the lateral colour stripes of *Gobiosoma horsti* are reduced to fine, electric yellow or white lines and do not extend forward of the eyes. It has, therefore, no snout markings of any kind. *Gobiosoma horsti* is found at scattered locations throughout the Bahamas and the Caribbean, *Gobiosoma louisae* is common throughout the Bahamas and the northern Caribbean (usually in deeper water than *Gobiosoma horsti*), and *Gobiosoma xanthiprora* has thus far been reported only along the coast of Central America and the southeastern states of the U.S.

The final species in the neon goby cluster is a unique one. *Gobiosoma atronasum* has rejected the largely benthic life style of its cleaning or sponge-dwelling relatives and has instead taken up a hovering mode of life in caves and crevices in the deep reef. It looks a great deal like *Gobiosoma louisae*, including even the black spot on the caudal peduncle, but can be identified by its hovering behaviour (often in mixed schools with the Masked Goby, *Coryphopterus personatus*) and by a wash of orange-red about the snout and eyes. *Gobiosoma atronasum* has the most restricted distribution of the neon gobies, being found only in the immediate vicinity of Exuma Sound in the eastern Bahamas.

Field Biology

With such a diversity of species, there is also a great diversity of life style and behaviour. Probably the best known and most easily recognized group of species is the cleaners, which tend to sit on large coral heads, usually *Montastrea*, *Diploria*, and *Colpophylia*, or, in the case of *Gobiosoma oceanops* and *Gobiosoma genie*, in shallow caves and crevices. The areas chosen have two common characteristics — first, they are usually prominent and, second, each has associated with it some type of worm hole or bole hole into which the gobies can retreat and in which the eggs are laid and guarded. All of these species tend to be found in pairs, suggesting monogamy, but large coral heads can have as many as 15 neons on it, sometimes with individuals of different species present, and clusters of four to seven fish are not uncommon.

The boldness and bright colours of these species are largely a function of their cleaning behaviour. These neons will readily swim over to inspect and clean almost any fish that poses for them. Posing involves a stereotyped behaviour on the part of the host. Usually it stops swimming and hovers at the mouth of the crevice or over the coral head, either head-up or head-down, quivering slightly with its fins outspread and often with its mouth open. The neons leap off the bottom and with quick, sure strokes of their pectoral fins approach and begin to inspect the potential food source. Wounded or ragged areas are looked over with special care. Any small external parasites, mainly tiny copepods, on the scales and fins, and for larger fish, such as groupers, in the mouth and gill chambers, are pulled off and eaten by the cleaners. A cleaning session ends either with the host quivering violently, once, apparently signalling the neons to leave, or with the latter simply swimming back to the coral head after satisfying themselves that no more parasites are present.

With a little patience, it is often possible to get neon gobies, especially young ones, to approach and clean one's hand. The hand should be stretched slowly towards the fish, fingers spread, and held steadily. Many times the fish will approach and inspect it just as if it were a posing fish.

As expected, the diets of all six cleaning species of *Gobiosoma* consist mainly of small parasitic copepods and other crustaceans. They also pick plankton from the passing water.

None of the sponge-dwelling species clean and most are shy, dashing into the cavity of their sponge if approached. *Gobiosoma louisae*, more than any of the others, tends to sit on the outside of the sponge, possibly picking out plankton as they drift by. The others can usually be found only by looking into the cavity of tube sponges, such as *Callyspongia* and *Verongia*. The tell-tale mark is a pair of iridescent spots, the forward ends of the lateral stripes, in the sponge as the goby sits, head-up, looking at you.

The sponge-dwelling species are apparently distasteful to most predators, possibly because the gobies pick up noxious toxins present in the walls of the sponges in which they live. While all show a fright reaction when approached by a diver or large fish, when offered to such a fish in aquaria, the gobies are usually ignored or, if engulfed, rapidly spat out, after which the predator frequently makes exaggerated gulping movements, as if trying to clean its mouth. On occasions, the goby will be eaten, but even then the predator usually shows some ill effects, such that it may well regret its decision. While the spong-dwellers are clearly the most protected, tests made with *Gobiosoma evelynae* in aquaria suggest that it too may be somewhat noxious-tasting.

The food habits of all of the sponge-dwelling *Gobiosoma* are similar. By far the most important food item is a polychaete worm, *Syllis spongicola*, that parasitizes sponges. These tiny white worms constitute up to 5 per cent of the weight of some sponges.

The final species of Neon Goby, *Gobiosoma atronasum*, distains both corals, sponges, and cleaning. Except for the brief periods when it sleeps and rests, the goby spends its time hovering in groups of 10 to 40 fish at the mouths of caves on the deep reef. Unlike the other neons, *Gobiosoma atronasum* possesses a large swim bladder, a distinct advantage to a fish that spends most of its time off the bottom. It feeds mainly on zooplankton, mostly small copepods, plucked from the surrounding water as they drift by.

Reproductive Biology

The cleaning species of *Gobiosoma* spawn in worm tubes or bore holes, usually located either in the coral head they inhabit or around its base. Holes left behind by dead serpulid and seribellid feather duster worms seem to be preferred. Spawning takes place when the neons are a minimum 6 to 8 months old and, in the northern portions of their ranges, probably involves year-old fish.

Spawning activity commences with courtship. The male usually darkens (retaining this darker colour throughout spawning and care of the eggs) and courts the female by approaching her, attaching himself to the substrate by means of his pelvic suction disc, and making exaggerated swimming motions. The female, if ready, normally joins in such activity and within a few hours, the pair will retire to the selected hole (which the male has previously prepared by biting and rubbing his body on the spawning site). Eggs are attached to the wall of the hole and project into the water passage. The number of eggs produced varies widely depending upon the age, size, and condition of the female, but several hundred are not unusual. The male guards and cares for the roughly 2mm-long elipsoidal eggs until hatching, a matter, depending on water temperature, of 7 to 12 days. The newborn young are approximately 4mm long, they are transparent, and they have a large yolk sac. The yolk sac is absorbed within 12 hours and the planktonic young begin to feed on a variety of tiny planktonic organisms, striking out at them with a flexed body lunge. Development is rapid and metamorphosis to the benthic stage can occur within 20 days of hatching (though the planktonic stage can last for as long as 2 months). Metamorphosis is signalled by the development of a dark lateral stripe on the floating larva. Post-metamorphic growth is also rapid and fish begin to pair off after as little as 3 to 4 months, though actual spawning is still several months away.

Spawning apparently occurs throughout the day, but seems most common around dawn. *Gobiosoma oceanops* breeds off the coast of Florida from January until May and newly metamorphosed juveniles can be found on the reef from roughly March through August. Other cleaning species spawn in the summer months, although in areas of near-constant water temperature it may occur year-round.

Little is known about the spawning behaviour of the sponge-dwelling species. On several occasions, large male gobies have been found caring for clusters of attached eggs deposited deep in the cavity of the inhabited sponge, suggesting that this is the preferred nest site. Since often only one goby is present in each tube sponge, the females must move some distance to spawn and it is possibly for this purpose that the distastefulness of the species evolved. Development of the eggs and young are similar to those of the cleaning species. Though not known for sure, it is likely that spawning occurs year-round.

To date, the spawning and courtship behaviour of the Hovering Neon, *Gobiosoma atronasum*, has not been observed. It is likely, however, that in most respects it is similar to that of the other neons, that is, they spawn in empty worm tubes, the males guard and care for the eggs, and the eggs develop in a manner similar to that described above.

Aquarium Biology

Neons, as a general rule, are ideal aquarium fish. They are rugged, disease-resistant, peaceful, bold, active, and will eat voraciously practically anything. They have, in addition, two features in their favour not typical of other Caribbean reef fish – they will pick parasites off other aquarium fish and they can readily be spawned in the home aquarium.

Before getting into spawning, it is probably best to review each of the groups in terms of aquarium suitability. First, all of the cleaning species fit the above description perfectly and are ideal fish for the novice aquarist. Mixing species produces few, if any problems, and I have kept successfully for extended periods in the same tank *Gobiosoma oceanops*, the electric blue species, with *Gobiosoma genie* and *Gobiosoma evelynae*, the white forms, producing an attractive contrast. There is occasional chasing and nipping between members of the same species, but this is rarely serious. Such interactions are apparently between members of the same sex and may, in fact, indicate the beginning of a spawning period. As mentioned, one often finds these fish on the reef in pairs and whenever possible, both members of a pair should be collected, kept separate from other such pairs, and housed together in the same aquarium. Aside from being aesthetically pleasing and producing a peaceful tank, this is also the best way to obtain a spawnable pair. If you cannot collect your own fish, the next best procedure is to select your fish from a large group, looking for pairs of fish that are obviously staying close to one another. There is a good chance that these may, in fact, be a mated pair.

The sponge-dwelling species also do well in captivity, but they are more shy than their relatives. Once introduced into an aquarium, they typically disappear and only make brief appearances when being fed. They generally recover within a few days, however, especially if fed in the open area in the front of the tank. The different species vary in the degree to which they will acclimate, with *Gobiosoma louisae* probably the best suited for a community tank.

Because of their tube-dwelling habits, for at least the first few days it is necessary that these fish be provided with suitable shelter. Cavernous corals, such as heads of lettuce coral, *Agaricia*, are ideal. As an alternative, large, empty (and well-cleaned) shells, such as conch, helmets, and tulip shells, are usually accepted; also small pieces of PVC or other dark plastic tubes are ideal. The latter should be stuck vertically into the sand, simulating the natural sponges preferred by the fish.

Though feeding almost exclusively upon polychaete worms in the field, the sponge-dwelling gobies adapt well to standard aquarium diets and will even accept flake foods after a few weeks. During the first week or so, a variety of live foods should be offered to them, not only to tempt them into feeding, but also because such foods, swimming around the aquarium, penetrate far enough into the coral so that the frightened newcomers can feed.

Gobiosoma atronasum is more delicate than its near relatives, but also does well in captivity. Being a plankton-picker, it will readily take live and frozen brine shrimp and prepared foods. Since it is usually found in groups, three or four should be kept together.

Because many species clean and others are noxious tasting, neons can usually be kept safely with even large predatory fish, so long as the latter are well fed. The single exception to this that I know of is the hamlets, genus *Hypoplectrus*, a group of Caribbean serranids covered in Chapter 2. Generalized predators, the hamlets will readily attack not only Neon Gobies, but also other small cleaning species, such as the cleaner shrimps in the genera *Lysmata* and *Stenopus*. The noxious spong-dwelling species are relatively safe, but ěven they may be attacked and, while rarely eaten, may be damaged. The most critical period for the gobies, not only with hamlets, but with other predators as well, occurs just when the gobies are being introduced into the aquarium. At this time, they are usually skittish and a little dazed and this, coupled with the predators expecting to be fed when you approach the tank, produces a dangerous (for the gobies) situation. If such predators are present in your aquarium, neons are best introduced at night (so that they will have a few hours to acclimate) or immediately after the predators have been heavily fed.

As noted, Neon Gobies are frequently spawned in aquaria and, in fact, commercial breeders have now reared several generations of tank-spawned fish. Spawning the various cleaning species requires only the obtaining of a pair (by the means described earlier), offering them a suitable spawning cavity (a rock, a shell, or, even better, a short PVC tube stuck in the sand), and regular feedings with a variety of live foods. Tank temperatures are probably not critical and anything between 70 and 80 °F. is suitable. Spawning can occur any time of the year and its imminent occurence will be signalled by initial territoriality on the part of the male, courtship activity as described above, and a noticeable swelling of the female's venter. Frequently the male will be seen to dig out a spawning hole under a rock or coral, if no other suitable sites are available. Newly hatched larvae are large enough to take rotifers as a first food.

As a final note, like many other small reef fish, Neon Gobies only live for a year or two. If your fish are large adults when you purchase or collect them, you may well find that (a) they are already past their prime spawning period and, (b) they may die in 6 months or less, even under ideal conditions. While these large fish are especially attractive in an aquarium, the aquarist with hopes of spawning the fish will do best to obtain small individuals.

Relevant Literature

Colin, P. L. 1975. *Neon Gobies* Trop. Fish Hobb. Publ. Inc., Neptune City, New Jersey: 304 pp

Valenti, R. J. 1972. 'The embryology of the Neon Goby, *Gobiosoma oceanops*', *Copeia* 1972 (3): 477–482

The Neon Goby, *Gobiosoma oceanops*, is largely restricted to the coast of Florida, but because of its bright colours and ready availability, it is the best known species of neon goby.

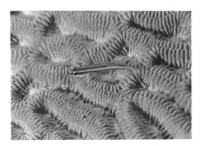

The Yellownose Goby, *Gobiosoma randalli*, is the common cleaner species found off the coast of Central America. Note the snout 'pip'; a similar pip is a diagnostistic feature for several other species of neon gobies.

The Limpiador, *Gobiosoma prochilos*, is a widely distributed species, reported from several areas in the Caribbean proper. The common name is Spanish for 'cleaner'.

A Sharknose Goby, *Gobiosoma evelynae*, cleaning a brown Coney, *Epinephelus fulvus*. Note the pale areas on the grouper; many fishes pale when being cleaned, and it is thought that this makes the parasites more conspicuous to the cleaner.

A small, black Slaty Goby, *Gobiosoma tenox*, sitting on the surface of its preferred sponge, *Neofibularia nolitangere*. Contact with this sponge can cause pain and inflammation in humans.

A typical posture for a sponge-dwelling neon goby, in this case *Gobiosoma louisae*.

The juvenile Clown Wrasse,
Halichoeres maculpinna, does well in
aquaria, but is difficult to catch or, on
the reef, even approach.

Terminal phase T-wrasses, *Halichoeres
garnoti*, are large and colourful. Like
those of most other wrasses, the
terminal phase bears little resemblance
to the more cryptic intermediate phase.
A female Redband Parrotfish,
Sparisoma aurofrenatum, is feeding in
the background.

A male Green Razorfish,
Hemipteronotus splendens,
photographed while patrolling his
territory.

The brilliantly coloured juveniles of the
T-wrasse, *Halichoeres garnoti*, are
common on reefs at moderate depths.
The two smaller fish ahead of it are
juvenile Bluehead Wrasses, *Thalassoma
bifasciatum*.

Terminal phase Bluehead Wrasses,
Thallasoma bifasciatum, have the same
basic colour pattern, but vary widely in
the width and colour of the bands
immediately behind the blue head.
Scientists have recognized individuals
based on this variation.

Chapter 10

Wrasses

The wrasses, family Labridae, are one of the most conspicuous and abundant elements of the coral reef fish fauna. Though most are benthic in their feeding habits, at one time or another all can be seen zipping around the reef, propelling themselves with their characteristic 'pectoral fins only' style of swimming. Wrasses come in a wide variety of shapes and sizes, ranging from a 2in Caribbean dwarf species to Indo-Pacific monsters that can reach a length of almost 10 feet and a weight of several hundred pounds. With such diversity, it is hard to characterize the family, with two exceptions – all swim by pectoral 'wing-beat' propulsion and all have prominent canine teeth, often angled outward, that give many a buck-toothed appearance.

Wrasses are closely related to the parrotfish, family Scaridae (and more distantly to the damselfish, Pomacentridae) with whom they share many features – a complex socio-sexual system involving sex changes, alternate spawning systems, and variable colour patterns, the pectoral fin swimming style, and a terminal mouth. Unlike the strictly tropical parrotfish, however, wrasses have radiated into the world's shallow temperate seas as well as the tropics, though still most speciose and prominent on the coral reef. In the Caribbean, there are eight genera of wrasses (out of approximately 60 world-wide) and almost two dozen species. One large section of these are the hogfish, subfamily Bodianinae, which have a unique biology and will be considered as a separate unit in the next chapter. The remaining Caribbean wrasses fall into two major groups, the cigar-shaped wrasses and the razorfish.

Species Account

The cigar-shaped wrasses include members of 3 genera and 11 species: *Halichoeres* with 9 species, and *Thalassoma* and *Duratonotus* with one each. All are long, slender fish, only slightly laterally compressed, with a terminal mouth and prominent canines. Most can be identified easily on the basis of colour pattern alone, though such identification is complicated by multiple colour patterns for each species. Typically, each has three distinct colour phases: juvenile, small, or intermediate phase, adult (which includes both males and females), and dominant, or terminal phase, adult (usually only males). For the adults, such colour patterns parallel roles in the social system.

In most cases, the various species are also well separated ecologically. Though one can often find several species at any one place, one species typically dominates and may, in fact, be the species characteristic of that habitat. The Slippery Dick, *Halichoeres bivittatus*, for example, is an inshore species, typically associated with mangrove roots, breakwaters, piers, and other sheltered spots, often in water no more than a few feet deep. Although they are sometimes found on the shallow open reef, in such areas they are not as common as closer to shore. Growing to a maximum length of 9 inches, the three colour patterns of this species all centre on a black or brown horizontal lateral stripe. Juveniles are either pale brown or white, depending upon locale, with a single, dark brown, vaguely zig-zagging line running down the centre of each side. As the fish grows, at 3 inches or so, it develops a second, shorter, and usually fainter line below and parallel to the first, generating the intermediate phase adult pattern. Finally, a relatively few, very large fish, 5 inches or more, transform into rainbow-hued dominant males, their bodies becoming green with a pair of black lateral stripes, a broad white area between the stripes, and red worm-like markings on their heads, and on their dorsal, anal, and caudal fins.

Similar changes in colour pattern take place in the Clown Wrasse, *Halichoeres maculipinna*, the species which dominates the shallow reef. Juvenile clown wrasses have a single brown lateral stripe, above which the fish is pale brown and below which it is white. Intermediate phase fish are similar, but the lateral stripe turns black; faint red wavy lines develop on the head around the eyes; and the brown above the lateral stripe develops a golden brilliance. Fish larger than 4 inches take on a greenish cast and lose the lateral stripe, though still remaining pale white below. Dominant adults are entirely green, with a complex pattern of red lines on the head, on the upper part of the back, and on the dorsal, anal, and caudal fins. They also develop two black spots, a large, permanent one near the leading edge of the dorsal fin, and a second, fuzzier one on each side of the body, this spot fading on very large fish. This second spot is backed by a short horizontal yellow bar.

Two other *Halichoeres* can often be found on the shallow reef with the Clown Wrasse. *Halichoeres radiatus*, the Puddingwife, is both the largest of the Caribbean halichoerid wrasses (reaching a length of almost 2 feet) and also the least abundant. The beautiful juveniles, largely orange, scrawled with blue lines, and bearing a pair of blue-ringed black spots at the junction of the dorsal fin and the body, are solitary fish commonly seen swimming about a depression or around a small coral head. Larger fish, similarly coloured, wander over broad sections of the reef and are difficult to approach. The largest individuals are equally shy, but very different in colour, trading the orange of youth for a lime green and yellow, with faint indications of broad vertical white bands.

Puddingwives are very depth-restricted, being rare at depths greater than 40 feet. The third *Halichoeres* commonly seen on the shallow reef, however, the Yellowhead, or 'T' wrasse, *Halichoeres garnoti*, reaches its peak abundance between 30 to 90 feet. Juveniles are strikingly coloured, brilliant yelow with an electric blue line running horizontally down each side. Like those of the Puddingwife, such juveniles are generally solitary fish, though they are seen sometimes in small groups and, rarely, in groups of as many as 50 fish. At a length of 3 inches or so, the blue lateral stripe begins to fade and the body dulls from yellow to reddish salmon, browner dorsally and pale ventrally, with several wavy blue lines running back from the eyes. At 4 to 5 inches, a few develop the yellow head and black 'T' pattern of the dominant adults. The upper half of the head and body, back to the centre of the body, becomes bright yellow and the rear half of the body turns greenish blue, with the two areas separated by a thick black line. This line extends up each side of the body, to meet just below the dorsal fin, then runs down the base of the fin and expands, eventually encompassing the entire caudal fin. Viewed from above, the entire black pattern looks like a 'T', with one arm extending down each side of the body.

On the deep reef, at depths in excess of 40 feet, a species of *Halichoeres* appears that is very different from those thus far covered. The Painted Wrasse, *Halichoeres pictus*, is a plankton picker and is longer, more slender, and more torpedo-shaped than its congeners. It swims in feeding aggregations several feet over the coral, weaving in and out of one another while picking plankton from the currents. Young adults and juveniles are pale brown with a single darker brown stripe running horizontally down the centre of each side. Another, thinner brown stripe parallels the major one and runs along the base of the dorsal fin. Dominant adult painted wrasses are green above and pale blue below, with a prominent black spot at the base of the caudal fin, several alternating rose and green horizontal lines on the head, and wavy red, orange, and blue lines on the unpaired fins.

Two other *Halichoeres* are found even deeper on the reef; one is occasionally seen in water as shallow as 40 feet, but does not become abundant until well over 100 feet, while the other is rarely, if ever, found in water much shallower than 300 feet. Juvenile *Halichoeres cyanocephalus*, the Yellowback Wrasse, are purple, paling slightly on the underside, with a wash of bright yellow starting on the forehead and trailing off along the back to the base of the caudal fin. Adults are green with a broad purple stripe down the centre of the body and live in very deep water. *Halichoeres caudalis*, the deepest dwelling of the known Caribbean members of the genus, is brown with pink and white speckles. Typically collected on the steep wall of the deep reef, it has never been reported from the shallow reef.

The last *Halichoeres* to be covered differs from its near relatives in several respects. The Black-ear Wrasse, *Halichoeres poeyi*, does not live on the reef, but rather inhabits sea grass beds. Like other grass flats fish, it is green. Both juveniles and adults are uniformly lime green with only two markings, a tiny black spot near the rear base of the dorsal fin and a second, larger black spot just above and behind the eye (hence the name 'black-ear'). Terminal phase adults are darker green and have three blue-edged maroon lines on the caudal fin – one bisecting the fin horizontally and the other two running diagonally from the outer tips of the fin to its centre. Black-ear Wrasses can be found in very shallow water, often no more than a few feet deep, but because of their green colour may be hard to discern.

The same is true to an even greater extent for the single species of *Duratonotus*. The Dwarf Wrasse,

Duratonotus megalepis, is another lime green dweller of the grass flats, but because of its small size (maximum 3 inches) and retiring habits, it is rarely seen. A short, somewhat squat wrasse, it has the same prominent canines possessed by its larger relatives, but unlike them has no complicated colour patterning. Over its lime green body, it has only a few pale blue-and-white, indistinct lines and spots on its head and gill covers, and a peppering of tiny red spots on the body. Males, females, and juveniles all look alike.

The final cigar-shaped wrasse in the Caribbean is also the most abundant. The Bluehead Wrasse, *Thalassoma bifasciatum*, can be found almost anywhere in water that is reasonably clear, from near shore among rocks and pilings to deep reef areas at depths well over a hundred feet. It is most abundant, however, on the shallow reef where it is a permanent feature, aggregations of literally thousands of these wrasses foraging across the bottom or picking plankton from the water column. The species is somewhat variable in its colour patterns, in large part because of social controls. Juveniles and intermediate phase adults are yellow (in very shallow water, white) with a single black spot on the leading edge of the dorsal fin. On some occasions, these fish can also show a thick black line running horizontally down each side (juveniles are more prone to this pattern than the adults) and on other occasions, the black lateral stripe is broken into blocks of black on a yellow background. Dominant males are less variable, permanently retaining the gaudy bluehead pattern. As implied in the common name, the head is deep blue with no prominent markings. The rear half of the body is blue-green and between the two areas there are several vertical bands of alternate colours – black, blue (or white), then black again. The width of these bands, as well as the colour intensity and evenness of each, varies from fish to fish so that with a good eye it is possible to recognize dominant male Bluehead Wrasses as individuals.

The remaining slender Caribbean wrasses are in the genus *Hemipteronotus*, a small group of laterally compressed fish with high foreheads, commonly called razorfish. Aside from a marked lateral compression, these wrasses can also be recognized by their habit of diving, head-first, into the sand at the approach of trouble. One species, *Hemipteronotus novacula*, even constructs a low pile of rocks around the spot in which it regularly burrows, perhaps as a means of making it more difficult for a predator to dig it out.

Three species of razorfish are common in the Caribbean and, as adults, all can be identified on the basis of colour pattern. *Hemipteronotus splendens*, the Green Razorfish, is green with red dorsal and anal fins, a red-and-green caudal fin, and narrow dark blue-green lines on a bronze head. Small fish frequently have a series of pale bars on the body. Males and females are similar in appearance, but the former tends to be larger and more brilliantly coloured, and has a blue-ringed, black spot on the middle of the body. The Green Razorfish reaches a length of approximately 4 inches and is common in mixed sand-turtle grass areas in shallow water.

The Straighttail Razorfish, *Hemipteronotus martinicensis*, reaches a larger size than the Green Razorfish, up to 6 inches, but is less brightly coloured. Adults are generally greyish blue, with a small gold marking on each scale. The head is also gold and there are several blue lines about the eyes. Finally, the Pearly Razorfish, *Hemipteronotus novacula*, is the giant of the genus, growing to over 12 inches. Though its colours can vary to match its background, it is most often a uniform pale green and is difficult to see, both because of its cryptic colours and because it tends to remain close to the bottom. Males are drab green on top and pale orange below, with a tiny blue line on each scale. Several larger blue lines run horizontally across the head, the caudal fin, and the anal fin.

Small razorfish do not look like the adults, but rather are short, stocky fish with mottled grey and green colours and usually a prominent, tall spike on the leading edge of the dorsal fin. Such juveniles blend into benthic algae and are difficult to see.

Field Biology

The cigar-shaped wrasses are opportunistic predators, which means that they will eat virtually any small organism whenever the opportunity presents itself. One species in particular, the Yellowhead Wrasse,

Halichoeres garnoti, epitomizes this behaviour. Yellowheads take advantage of practically every disturbance on the bottom to search for food. They are well known for their habit of following goatfish around over the sand flats as the latter grub for benthic invertebrates; the wrasses swim alongside watching for the occasional small fish or swimming crustacean that leaps up off the bottom to avoid the goatfish. Wrasses looking for a free meal similarly follow rays, groupers, and even divers. A triggerfish, attacking a sea urchin, is rapidly mobbed by wrasses of all kinds that immediately converge on the disturbance.

Not all wrasses, however, are quite so continually opportunistic as the Yellowhead. Clown Wrasses, *Halichoeres maculipinna*, feed mainly by picking at the bottom for small invertebrates. Painted Wrasses, *Halichoeres pictus*, and the Bluehead Wrasse, *Thalassoma bifasciatum*, are often seen several feet off the bottom feeding on plankton. Even the Yellowhead Wrasse normally finds its food by peering into crevices and sifting, a mouthful at a time, through bottom sediments for small animals. They can also turn over surprisingly large rocks by clamping on to them with their massive canines and, with a few violent twists of their bodies, heaving them over, at the same time looking under them for food.

The cigar-shaped wrasses, like the majority of reef fish, are strongly site-attached and remain in the same small part of the reef throughout life. Home-range size varies both with the size of the fish (larger fish have larger home ranges than small fish) and with the suitability of the environment (a species in its optimum habitat, such as a Clown Wrasse on the shallow reef, has a smaller home range than a member of the same species in a less suitable habitat). Intermediate phase adults and juvenile fish do not defend these home ranges and often form feeding groups of varying sizes, but the dominant males of several species can be vigorously territorial.

The Clown Wrasse, *Halichoeres maculipinna*, clearly shows the difference in behaviour between these dominant males and the other members of the species. In its preferred habitat, intermediate phase Clown Wrasses move about in large feeding aggregations, as many as 40 fish in a single aggregate. The joint home range of the fish in these aggregations is only a few hundred square feet and the aggregate moves slowly about in this area during the day, constantly picking at the bottom and investigating possible food sources. The aggregations are often joined by fish of other species, including not only other wrasses, but also small surgeonfish (*Acanthuridae*) and parrotfish (*Scaridae*). Swimming about these feeding aggregations, joining any one only for a brief period before moving on, is the single large dominant male whose territory encompasses the home range of the aggregation, and those of several other aggregations. He ignores the juveniles and intermediate phase fish in his territory, and tolerates the few subordinate males present, chasing them only once in a while to reinforce his dominant position, but quickly responds if another dominant male approaches any of the feeding aggregates he 'controls'. The two meet just inside his territorial boundaries and display to one another, threatening each other with open mouths, swimming in parallel back and forth along the boundary, and even chasing one another across the boundary until the intruder yields and returns to his own territory.

While the territories of male Clown Wrasses are permanent, the Bluehead Wrasse has a comparable social system based on temporary spawning territories. At other times, the Bluehead males and the intermediate-phase fish mix freely on the reef. Similar temporary territories also appear to be the rule for the Slippery Dick, *Halichoeres bivitattum*, while the Yellowhead Wrasse, *Halichoeres garnoti*, is strictly a home ranger, with little, if any, territorial aggression even among dominant males. Little is known about the social behaviour of razorfish, though at least the Green Razorfish seems to be permanently territorial.

Unlike *Halichoeres* and *Thalassoma*, which are found in a wide variety of habitats, razorfish are restricted to broad sandy stretches, where they may be the dominant fish species. All of the cigar-shaped wrasses can bury themselves rapidly and many spend the night buried under a few inches of loose sand. The species in *Halichoeres* are especially prone to bury themselves at night and each fish may have a preferred resting spot. If disturbed after burying itself, a male Yellowhead Wrasse will roam about for a few minutes, then circle back to its previous shelter spot and re-bury within inches of it.

Reproductive Biology
The cigar-shaped wrasses have a complex system of reproduction based on protogynous (female to male)

hermaphroditism. As far as it is known for the Caribbean species each has two types of males – primary males, which start off life as males and remain functional males throughout life, and secondary males, which start off as fully functional females, but which, when they reach a large size and social dominance, turn into functional males. Usually, maleness is a characteristic only of dominant fish; if the dominant male in an area dies and is not replaced by a male from another area, then the largest remaining individual, whether already a primary male or a functional female, will assume his position, develop the dominant colours, and, within a few days, be courting and spawning as a fully functional male.

To a wrasse, maleness is something to be desired because it confers a strong genetic advantage to an individual. The production of eggs, because of their large size and the yolky materials they must contain, requires a considerable investment in time and energy. A female will be fortunate to produce enough eggs to spawn once daily. The production of sperm, on the other hand, is relatively easy, since each is so small. A functional male will spawn repeatedly during the day, passing his genetic material on to a much larger number of offspring than can be done by any one female. Because of this advantage, the largest fish in an area will usurp the role of the breeding male and not only suppresses the other fish from becoming males (being a female is genetically better than not spawning at all), but also prevents other males from breeding in his territory.

The Clown Wrasse is a good example of this system. The large feeding aggregations of intermediate phase fish, discussed earlier, consist of both small primary males and females. In general, only the females breed, the males being prevented from doing so by the aggressive behaviour of the large dominant male, which may be either primary or secondary. The dominant male regularly swims from aggregate to aggregate, courting the females and chasing and generally harassing the small males. During actual spawning periods (usually late in the afternoon on an out-going tide), the dominant male, his colours at their brightest, courts virtually every female he comes across, displaying to her with his fins fully spread. If receptive, she swims up off the bottom and the two fish, close together, dash upwards several feet into the water column and then spin for the bottom. At the peak of this spawning rush, the fish release, respectively, their eggs and sperm. In such spawning systems, subordinate males can breed only by 'cheating'. Occasionally, just as the pair begins its rush upwards, another fish, an intermediate phase male, will dash upwards and join them in the actual spawning, presumably shedding his sperm simultaneously with the dominant male. Afterwards, the dominant vigorously chases the 'cheater', but the latter, coloured like a female, quickly loses himself in a feeding aggregation.

For other species, such as the Bluehead Wrasse, this occasional cheating has developed into a spawning system operating in parallel with paired male-female rushes. This alternate system involves large numbers of intermediate phase fish milling about several feet off the bottom and then, en masse, dashing upwards into the water column. At the peak of the rush, each fish sheds its sperm or eggs. After such a rush, one can sometimes see a cloud of gametes drifting off in the current and away from the reef. Paired spawnings, on the other hand, involve strongly territorial dominant males, referred to as 'supermales', each of which has staked out a prominent spawning site from which he courts passing females. Courtship involves approaching the female while dashing up and down in the water column, apparently simulating the spawning rush. If she is receptive, she slows down and the two dash towards the surface to release and fertilize the eggs.

Razorfish spawn in a similar manner. Males are much larger and more colourful than females and roam widely about their territories, briefly chasing and courting potential mates. A receptive female signals her readiness to spawn by hovering, head up, a few feet off the bottom. The male approaches and moves below and to one side of her, then pushes her up into the water column with his snout. Once movement is started, he moves parallel and close to her and they dash a foot or two upwards, to spawn and split apart at the peak of the rush.

Spawning of wrasses occurs year-round in the southern Caribbean and in the summer in the north, and it is generally restricted to a few hours in the afternoon. The planktonic eggs produced during the spawnings develop into planktonic larvae, but the duration of either the egg stage or the larval stage before transformation into the benthic juveniles is not known.

Aquarium Biology

In general, the wrasses do well in community aquaria, though the largest fish, the dominant males, are often aggressive and can do some damage with their prominent canine teeth. Such fish, despite their brilliant colours, should be avoided for all but the largest aquaria.

As is often the case, the best fish for a community tank are juveniles. Fortunately the juveniles of several species are attractive (*Thalassoma bifasciatum* and *Halichoeres poeyi*, for example), while several others are downright beautiful. The juveniles of *Halichoeres garnoti*, yellow and electric blue, of *Halichoeres radiatus*, orange, blue, and black, and of *Halichoeres cyanocephalus*, purple and yellow, are attractive, peaceful, and active fish. They are, however, voracious eaters and, like the juveniles of many species, can starve to death in a matter of a few days if not fed a suitable food often enough. When first introduced into a tank, they should be given large amounts of live brine shrimp. When they are taking these readily, small amounts of frozen brine should be mixed in with the live, over time gradually increasing the proportion of frozen to live food until the fish are taking the frozen shrimp alone. After an acclimation period, all will take dried food and thrive on it. Of the three species, *Halichoeres garnoti* is the easiest to feed; *Halichoeres cyanocephalus* the most difficult.

To some extent, all wrasses gradually fade in colour when put in an aquarium. The Black-ear Wrasse fades almost immediately, while at the other extreme, juvenile Yellowhead Wrasses fade slowly, over a period of several months. Again, the three most attractive species, *garnoti*, *radiatus*, and *cyanocephalus*, are the more colourfast members of the group. Why they fade at all in aquaria is not known.

As a final note, do not panic when shortly after you introduce a wrasse into your tank, it vanishes. Most wrasses immediately bury themselves after being released and may not reappear for several days. They only gradually acclimate to life in a tank and, in all, may take several weeks to finally settle down. Even then they will continue to bury themselves for the night and so may not be seen after sun-down (an important consideration for hobbyists who only get to play with their tanks in the evening).

Relevant Literature

Randall, J. E. 1965. 'A Review of the Razorfish genus *Hemipteronotus* (Labridae) of the Atlantic Ocean', *Copeia* 1965 (4): 487–501

Randall, J. E. and Böhlke, J. E. 1965. 'Review of the Atlantic Labrid fishes of the genus *Halichoeres*', *Proc. Acad. Nat. Sci. Phila.* **117**: 235–259

Robertson, D. R. & Hoffman, S. G. 1977. 'The role of female mate choice and predation in the mating systems of tropical Labroid fishes', *Zeit. für Tierpsychol.* **45**: 298–320

Roede, M. J. 1972. 'Color as related to size, sex, and behavior in seven Caribbean Labrid fish species', *Stud. Fauna Curacao and Other Carib. Islands* (138): 264 pp

Roede, M. J. 1975. 'Reversal of sex in several Labrid species', *Publ. Staz. zool. Napoli* **39**: 595–617

Thresher, R. E. 1979. Social behaviour and ecology of two sympatric wrasses (Labridae: *Halichoeres* sp.) off the coast of Florida. *Mar. Biol.* **53**: 161–172

Warner, R. R. & Robertson, D. R. 1978. 'Sexual patterns of the Labroid fishes of the western Caribbean, I: the wrasses (Labridae)', *Smith. Contrib. Zool.* (254): 1–27

The Hogfish, or Hog Snapper, *Lachnolaimus maximus*, is the largest western Atlantic wrasse, and a popular food and game fish.

The Creole Wrasse, *Clepticus parrae*, is a highly specialized off-shoot of the hogfish line, that has evolved into a mid water foraging planktivore.

Juvenile Spotfin Hogfish, *Bodianus puchellus*, greatly resemble small Bluehead Wrasses, *Thallasoma bifasciatum*. Both are cleaners, which suggests that they may have converged on a common colour pattern to advertise themselves to potential hosts.

A sub-adult Spanish Hogfish, *Bodianus rufus*, showing the typical shallow water colour pattern. Individuals, however, can range from this to almost entirely blue.

Spotfin Hogfish, *Bodianus puchellus*, derive their common name from the conspicuous black spots on the end of each pectoral fin. The function of such spots is not known, but those on several shallow water species of wrasses are involved in courtship.

Juvenile Spanish Hogfish, *Bodianus rufus*, are cleaners, often found on the same cleaning station with several neon gobies.

A large adult Spanish Hogfish, *Bodianus rufus*, exhibiting the normal deep-water coloration – red and yellow. This fish was photographed at 90 feet.

The Diamond Blenny, *Malacoctenus boehlkei*, is the only member of the genus common on the off-shore reef. The yellow head of this pale individual indicates it is a male.

The Spineyhead Blenny, *Acanthemblemaria spinosa*, like its near relatives, spends most of its time peering from a hole in the reef looking for the plankton on which it feeds.

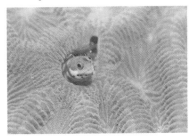

Acanthemblemaria rivasi is the most colourful of the Caribbean 'acanthems', but is restricted to the southern Caribbean.

The Saddled Blenny, *Malacoctenus triangulatus*, frequents algae-covered patch reefs in relatively shallow water. Its basic colour pattern is similar to that of the Diamond Blenny.

An unidentified *Labrisomus*, in the position one usually sees members of this genus. After the photograph, this fish disappeared back into the coral.

An Arrow Blenny, *Lucayablennius zingaro*, in its normal hunting pose. From this position, it springs forward to capture small fish and crustaceans.

The Wrasse Blenny, *Hemiemblemaria simulis*, mimics the initial-phase colours of the Bluehead Wrasse, *Thallasoma bifasciatum*. Only the mimic sits in holes in the reef, however.

Chapter 11

Hogfish

Of the Caribbean wrasses, none are so widely known or so well recognized as those belonging to the subfamily Bodianinae, the hogfish and their relatives. For years, several of the smaller fish have been popular in salt-water aquaria, and one of the largest ones has earned a popularity in its own right as a favourite game and food fish.

The bodianines are an early off-shoot of the main line of labrid evolution. They are morphologically generalized fish with few specialized features of their own and none of the specialized characters that identify the more advanced wrasses. They can, however, be distinguished easily from all other wrasses by the shape of their lateral lines; those of the hogfish are smoothly curved from anterior to posterior, while those of other wrasses have an abrupt turn part way down the body. The bodianines, otherwise, are a diverse group, ranging from the relatively small hogfish kept in aquaria to species that reach several feet in length. The Hogfish, *Lachnolaimus maximus*, is the largest of local wrasses, reaching almost 3 feet in length and weighing over 20 pounds.

There are, around the world, about 10 genera in the subfamily Bodianinae and approximately 70 species. The Caribbean has five species in four genera, two of which are monospecific and are found nowhere else in the world.

Species Account:

The most primitive hogfish found in the Caribbean is also the one about which the least is known. *Decodon* is a genus of round-bodied, parrotfish-like labrids found in relatively deep water in tropic seas around the world. *Decodon puellaris*, the Caribbean representative of the genus, looks very similar to the parrotfish in the genus *Sparisoma*. Adults are broadly yellow, with a red band across the head and back. The dorsal and caudal fins are also yellow. Juveniles have thin dark and light bands on the body. *Decodon puellaris* is rarely found much shallower than 350 to 400 feet and so is rarely, if ever, seen by divers.

The second primitive bodianine found in the Caribbean inhabits much shallower water (sometimes only 10 feet deep) and has developed a popular following among sport fishermen. The Hogfish, or Hog Snapper, *Lachnolaimus maximus*, is both common and quite good eating. *Lachnolaimus*, an endemic monospecific genus, is a large fish, laterally compressed, with a body that is high and round when viewed in profile. It is characterized by a slightly lunate caudal fin, elongate dorsal spines (on males), and a large, protrusible mouth which the fish uses to root around on sand bottoms for the molluscs and crustaceans that make up the bulk of its diet. It is from this snout, and rooting behaviour, that the common name 'hogfish' is derived. Young fish less than 8 inches long, all females, are overall pale grey, brown, or reddish brown, lightening ventrally, with faint indications of barring along the underside. The only distinctive marks are a large black spot at the rear base of the dorsal fin and a bright red iris which, because water absorbs red light so rapidly, is not conspicuous underwater. Large fish, all males, are grey-brown with a strongly lunate caudal fin, a large protruding snout with prominent teeth, a black forehead, and black trim on all but the pectoral fins.

The third primitive Caribbean bodianine, another one endemic to the area, is, though primitive with respect to the main bodianine line, highly specialized in its own right. The Creole Wrasse, *Clepticus parrae*, is the only planktivorous bodianine and, as such, is the most streamlined and best adapted to a rapidly swimming mode of life. Slightly laterally compressed, the fish is smoothly streamlined with a small, slightly upturned terminal mouth, a deeply lunate caudal fin, a long low dorsal fin, and large wing-like pectoral fins that are its main means of propulsion. The caudal fin is used primarily as a rudder, steering the fish through its quick turns in the water column as it hunts the plankton on which it feeds. Like many other fish that live well off the bottom, the Creole Wrasse is blue. Full adults are deep blue with a pale yellow underside and yellow highlights on all but the pectoral fins, while juveniles are paler blue and often have faint x-shaped spots peppered on the body. The Creole Wrasse is an extremely common reef species, found at depths between 30 and 90 feet. It is usually seen in large schools, with as many as several hundred swimming together and feeding in the water currents.

The remaining two Caribbean hogfish are the familiar Spanish Hogfish, *Bodianus rufus*, and the Spotfin, or Cuban, Hogfish, *Bodianus puchellus*. Both are round-bodied, streamlined fish with a terminal mouth, heavy scaling, and, on large adults, thread-like projections trailing off the upper and lower tips of the caudal fin and off the tips of the dorsal and anal fins. Like other labrids, both rely on their large pectoral fins to provide most of the motive power for swimming, the other fins being used primarily as rudders. The two species differ in the maximum size they reach and in their colour patterns. The Spanish Hogfish reaches a maximum length of almost 2 feet and, though its colours vary somewhat depending upon the depth, is typically some combination of blue and yellow. In shallow water, the head and the anterior half of the back are electric blue while the rest of the body is yellow, with a large black spot near the leading edge of the dorsal fin. In deeper water, the pattern of colour is the same, but the blue is often replaced by deep red. Another source of variation in colour pattern, besides depth, is individual variation in the proportions of the body that are dark or light. The majority of Spanish Hogfish are roughly a third blue (or red), but a few may be as much as 90 per cent blue (or red), with only the margins of the fins and the underside of the fish yellow. The significance of this individual variation, if any, is not known.

The Spotfin Hogfish grows to a maximum adult length of approximately 10 inches and is always red and yellow, with black on the trailing edge of the dorsal, anal, and caudal fins, and a black spot at the end of each pectoral fin (hence 'Spotfin'). The forehead and anterior half of the back, the anal fin, its base, and the region of the belly just ahead of the anal fin, are red. The rear half of the back is lemon yellow. Some individuals have a white horizontal band down the centre of each side; again the significance of this variation in colour pattern is not known. Unlike the Spanish Hogfish, which is essentially the same colour throughout its life, the Spotfin has a distinctive juvenile coloration. Juveniles (fish up to about 2½ inches long) are lemon yellow, with a large black spot at the forward edge of the dorsal fin, a red iris, and several fine horizontal red lines running through each eye. Except for the eye coloration and a slightly chunkier body, these juveniles look remarkably similar to small Bluehead Wrasses, *Thalassoma bifasciatum*, and the two can easily be confused.

Field Biology

All of the bodianines are predators; the benthic hogfish prey mainly on molluscs, echinoderms, and small crustaceans (mainly crabs) while *Clepticus* takes primarily planktonic crustaceans.

As discussed earlier, the Creole Wrasse is the most divergent of the group in terms of lifestyle, it being the only species adapted to a completely open-water mode of existence. *Lachnolaimus*, on the other hand, is a large, bottom-associated predator, widely distributed on the edges of the reef and rarely seen in groups of more than a few individuals. They prefer areas of hard sand and rock, and are most common around shallow patch reefs and just inshore and offshore of the main reef. As a general rule, the larger fish are found around the main reef, while the largest number of fish inhabit patch reefs.

The two smaller hogfish, those in the genus *Bodianus*, are both closely associated with the reef itself, rarely being found more than a few feet away from either coral or rock outcrops. The two differ in their preferred depth ranges, however. The Spanish Hogfish is common from close inshore to a depth of 70 to 80 feet; at greater depths, the Spotfin Hogfish is the more common of the two species. The ranges of the two overlap considerably, however, and in some places both can be found swimming about the same coral heads. This is especially true for the juveniles. In the summer, at the height of the spawning season, small, yellow Spotfin Hogfish can be found along rocky ledges in as little as 25 feet of water.

As adults, both species are benthic predators, swimming rapidly about the reef and searching caves, crevices, and sand patches for small molluscs and the like. As juveniles, however, both species supplement this diet by cleaning larger fish, i.e. by picking external parasites, mainly parasitic copepods and isopods, from their skin. Such juveniles establish cleaning stations on the reef, often on a large coral head or at the mouth of a large cave and often in association with other cleaning species, such as one or more Neon Gobies, cleaning shrimps, or, less commonly, juvenile Bluehead Wrasses. Several hogfish will commonly share the same cleaning station, apparently with few, if any, aggressive interactions. Such groups are usually pairs, less often three fish (typically with one fish smaller than the other two), but on occasion can involve as many as 20 fish. Of the two species, the Spanish Hogfish appears to be the more gregarious, but this may only reflect the relatively few detailed observations of the deeper dwelling Spotfin Hogfish.

Reproductive Biology

Like the other wrasses, hogfish are protogynous hermaphrodites, initially female and then, upon reaching large size and, perhaps, social dominance, transforming into functional males. As yet, the social behaviour of the hogfish has only been outlined roughly. In most cases, it appears that the basic social unit is a group of females dominated by a single, larger functional male, a social system referred to (for obvious reasons) as a harem. The male defends the harem and spawns exclusively with the females in it. Spawning apparently occurs during late afternoon and early evening, and involves a prolonged courtship by the male (chasing and lateral displaying to various females) ending in a rapid upwards rush of the two fish into the water column to release the eggs and sperm. Such spawning rushes are typical of both labrids and scarids.

As befitting their unique ecology, the Creole Wrasses also have a unique spawning pattern, involving colour change by the males, aggressive courtship, and a long upwards spawning rush. During spawning, the large males (again derived from females) trade their normal blue colour for a bicolour pattern of dark blue to black anteriorly and yellow-orange posteriorly, with white lips, occasional white blotches on the body, dark black pectoral fins (which are very conspicuous when the fish is swimming), and, frequently, numerous scars on the body. These scars are the results of fights between males over access to ready females during the spawning periods.

Actual courtship involves the male vigorously running down a female in a high-speed chase in the water column over the reef. Spawning is initiated by the male swimming above a female and attempting to touch his underside to her back. If the female is receptive, she slows down and the male moves below her and begins to push her up in the water column using shallow beats of his caudal fin. The female often resists, leading to the two fish circling each other rapidly as the male attempts to maintain his position. Eventually, the female goes rigid and allows herself to be pushed upwards, at the end of which she releases a cloud of eggs which the male fertilizes.

Courtship occurs throughout the year in the warmer parts of the Caribbean, and in the summer in the northern areas. It occurs most often in the afternoon and early evening.

Like all labrids, hogfish produce a pelagic egg which develops rapidly into a pelagic larva. Each egg is approximately 1.5mm in diameter, has a single oil globule, and hatches in roughly 24 hours. The larval stage apparently lasts several weeks. Newly settled juveniles of the Spanish hogfish are approximately half an inch long and are coloured like the adults. Juvenile Creole Wrasses are slightly longer ($\frac{1}{4}$ inch), are very slender, and are largely translucent, with only a faint purple cast. They can be seen in the summer, swimming in small schools close to coral heads and around rock ledges. Juvenile *Lachnolaimus* have an oval profile, are laterally compressed, and have a pointed snout. Mottled red in colour, with indistinct vertical bands, they are fairly common around grass flats.

Aquarium Biology

All of the shallow-water bodianines do well in aquaria, especially as juveniles. Obviously, the adults of almost all (the exception being the Spotfin Hogfish) are suitable only for the largest private aquaria and public exhibition tanks; spawning the species in captivity, therefore, is an unlikely event for the average aquarist. Otherwise, the various species adapt well to aquaria. The two *Bodianus* are especially suitable for community tanks and feed readily, retain their bright colours well, and are generally not aggressive. Small ones may clean other aquarium inhabitants.

The Creole Wrasse presents some special problems for the aquarist. Small, purple individuals adapt well to a mid-sized aquarium (20 gallons or larger), especially if kept in a small school, but the adults are obviously cramped for space in such a tank. This is an active, mid-water foraging species that does best if given enough room to zip around the tank in a small group. Creole Wrasses larger than 3 inches are not recommended for tanks smaller than 50 gallon capacity, despite the hardiness of the species and its willingness to eat practically anything.

Creole Wrasses are also less colourfast than the species in *Bodianus*, generally fading in an aquarium from their normal deep blue to a pale blue-purple with small x-shaped crosses scattered on the body. Though still attractive and apparently healthy, such fish typically never resume their normal colour pattern. Again, this may well be a function of the, for them, cramped living quarters available in even mid-sized tanks.

Relevant Literature

Davis, J. C. 1976. 'Biology of the Hogfish, *Lachnolaimus maximus* (Walbaum), in the Florida Keys', unpublished Master's thesis, University of Miami, Coral Gables, Florida

Feddern, H. A. 1963. 'Color change during growth of *Bodianus puchellus* and *Bodianus rufus* (Pisces: Labridae)', *Bull. Mar. Sci.* **13**(2): 224–241

Randall, J. E. & Warmke, G. L. 1967. 'The food habits of the Hogfish (*Lachnolaimus maximus*), a Labrid fish from the western Atlantic', *Carib. J. Sci.* **7**(3): 141–144

Robertson, D. R. & Hoffman, S. G. 1977. 'The role of female mate choice and predation in the mating systems of tropical Labroid fishes', *Zeit. für Tierpsychol.* **45**: 298–320

Chapter 12

Combtooth Blennies

The fish in this and the following two chapters are members of the order Blennioidei and, in the past, have been treated as members of the single family Blenniidae. All are elongate, generally bottom-dwelling fish with long anal and dorsal fins and prominent eyes. Most are territorial and the vast majority produce large demersal eggs which are laid in a small cave or shelter hole and which are guarded by the male. In recent years, this large cluster of fish has been divided into two closely related families, mainly on the basis of osteological characters (including the number and location of the teeth): the combtooth, or true, blennies, Blenniidae, and the scaled blennies, Clinidae. The latter are sometimes further divided into a third family, Chaenopsidae.

The combtooth blennies, in terms of number of species, are poorly represented in the Caribbean. Roughly a dozen, similar species are found in the area, but only four are common. All are relatively small (4 to 6 inches maximum), elongate, and round-bodied benthic fish with big, blunt heads and fleshy lips. They can easily be distinguished from members of the other major 'benthic small fish' families, the Clinidae and the Gobiidae, by four characters: (1) the pelvic fins of blennies are located anterior of the large pectorals, (2) their bodies are very flexible, (3) they are either scaleless or have very small scales, and (4) in most cases, the dorsal fin is long and obviously continuous.

Species Account

The only species of combtooth blenny commonly found on Caribbean reefs is the Redlip Blenny, *Ophioblennius atlanticus*. Somewhat variable in colour, individuals range from uniformly jet black, through black anteriorly and white posteriorly, to uniform pale white. All colour phases are characterized by red lips, red edges on the dorsal and anal fins, faint red highlights on the pectoral fins, and, occasionally, faint horizontal bars on the head. The fish reaches a maximum size of approximately 6 inches and is heavy bodied with only slight lateral compression. It can be found on much of the reef, but is particularly abundant and conspicuous in shallow, wave-washed areas of high vertical relief and a complex bottom topography. Stands of staghorn coral, *Acropora palmata*, and fire coral, *Millepora* spp., and small patch reefs are preferred, where the fish is often found in the company of small surgeonfish and damselfish (particularly the Jewelfish, *Microspathodon chrysurus*).

Entomacrodus nigricans, the Pearl Blenny, lives in a similar habitat, but is found in shallower water, often no more than two or three feet deep. It is a shy fish and even where abundant it is not conspicuous. Only about 3 inches long, it is unique among Caribbean blennies in the shape of the dorsal fin. Blennies in general are characterized by a long, continuous dorsal fin with, if anything, only a slight notch between the spiny and soft portions of the fin. On *Entomacrodus nigricans*, however, the notch is deep. While it does not completely divide the fin, it nevertheless gives the fish an appearance of two fins. Colourwise, the Pearl Blenny is pale brown with a series of broad, vertical white bands on the body and a scattering of tiny white spots.

The remaining two common species of combtooth blennies have in the past been placed in the genus *Blennius*, along with a wide variety of other New and Old World species. The entire tribe Blenniini, however, has recently been revised, such that the two Caribbean fish once thought to be in *Blennius* have been transferred to other genera. *Blennius* itself is now restricted to a group of fish found in the Old World.

Scartella cristata (= *Blennius cristatus*), the Molley Miller, is the common shore-line blenny. Though rarely, if ever, found in tide pools, it is common just below the tide-line and, in fact, moves in and off shore as the water level changes. A heavy bodied species, it is mottled brown and grey with a scattering of brown-and-black spots and irregularly shaped blotches on its body. *Parablennius marmoreus*

(= *Blennius marmoreus*), the Seaweed Blenny, is slightly slimmer and smaller, and is typically found in slightly deeper water. It prefers scattered rock outcrops and low relief, algae-covered rock areas in the depth range of 5 to 40 feet. The fish is usually pale golden brown with a peppering of darker brown spots on the head and a broad brown stripe down each side of its body. This stripe starts near the eyes, then gradually fades posteriorly, eventually disappearing altogether near the middle of the body. The Seaweed Blenny, however, is capable of a range of colour patterns, such that one occasionally sees fish that are horizontally bicolour (brown above, white below), all brown with only faint indications of markings, and bright golden yellow. The last may be a spawning colour assumed by territorial males.

Field Biology

Blennies are active fish which seem to take delight in scooting around algae-covered rocks and coral heads, particularly on eroded and heavily pitted bottoms. All four species have several common features: they prefer areas of heavy wave or surge action, often in water no more than a few feet deep; feed mainly on benthic algae; are intimately tied to the bottom; and, so far as they have been studied, are all strongly territorial.

The most vigorously territorial member of the family in the Caribbean is the Redlip Blenny, *Ophioblennius atlanticus*. Each fish defends an area of 6 or 7 square feet, chasing off not only other blennies, but also a variety of small fish. Territorial defence involves both active chasing and biting and also a head-bobbing display, seen as a quick shaking of the head up and down when a defender is approached by an intruder. This display is performed most often at one of several 'observation points' located in the territory of each fish. Periodically, the blenny patrols its territory, moving from one high point to another, stopping at each and apparently surveying both its territory and the activities of its neighbours. If the fish are approached carefully and they remain undisturbed, one can often see as many as six or seven blennies perched on observation points scattered about a single large rock outcrop.

The Molly Miller, *Scartella cristata*, is also strongly territorial, but its territoriality is tempered by the tidal rhythm. During high tide, each fish defends an area that centres on a single preferred shelter hole. Defensive behaviour is similar to that of the Redlip Blenny, except that the head-bob display is usually done while sitting in the shelter hole, with only the anterior half of the blenny exposed. As the water-level drops, however, one by one the blennies are forced to leave their territories and they aggregate in large numbers on particularly lush areas of algae (notably *Bryopsis*) to feed. On such feeding grounds, they coexist peacefully. Then, as the water-level goes up again, one by one the fish leave the main group to reoccupy and redefend their areas.

Reproductive Biology

Caribbean blennies are sexually dioecious and produce large, demersal eggs which the male cares for and guards. *Ophioblennius* eggs are slightly flattened spheres, about 0.6mm in diameter, with a single large yellow oil globule in it and a tuft of sticky filaments at one end. Eggs are laid in even rows within small caves in the rock; in the case of the Molly Miller, this cave is the shelter hole the male normally prefers, for *Ophioblennius*, the caves are empty burrows in coral faces. To date the spawning behaviour of only the Molly Miller has been studied in detail. In this species, the male assumes a distinctive courtship colour which consists of a pale mottling of his body and a rose tint to his underside. He advertises his readiness to spawn by vigorously bobbing his head and arching his body towards other blennies. On the approach of a gravid female, the male dashes towards her and leads her back to the shelter hole with an exaggerated swimming motion. He finally stops just before the hole, apparently pointing to its position with his head. The female approaches and enters the hole to deposit her eggs. After she leaves, the male enters and fertilizes them. After spawning, the female is driven away and the male's territoriality becomes particularly vicious. He also stays with the eggs for as long as is possible, leaving them at low tide only at the last possible instant and returning to them as soon as there is enough water to make it back. The eggs, however, are rugged and can even stand short exposures to air while remaining viable.

The eggs hatch in 7 to 12 days, depending on water temperature, and develop into long, torpedo-shaped, silver-coloured larvae, each of which has several large protruding teeth. The duration of the larval stage is not known, but when about $1\frac{1}{2}$ inches long, the larvae settle on to the bottom and gradually develop the shape and colour of the adult.

As stated, the Caribbean blennies are sexually dioecious and, further, are sexually dimorphic. Just ahead of the anal fin, there are two anal spines. On the male, these spines are free and each is capped with a small, fleshy knob; on the female, the spines are encased in a broad triangular fold of flesh. There is some evidence that in the Molly Miller, the fleshy knobs of the male secrete a sex pheromene used to attract the female and stimulate her to spawn.

Aquarium Biology

Blennies are rugged and comical fish that do very well in aquaria. They eat readily, tolerate a wide range of water conditions, and though not strikingly beautiful, liven up a tank with their behaviour. With large, bulging eyes looking around, they scoot from rock to rock, peering around corners and into holes searching for food and imagined enemies. They are constantly active and, more than most other fish, have distinct personalities.

Unfortunately, all are territorial and are prone to be aggressive in captivity. One, in particular, can be a holy terror in a small tank. The Redlip Blenny, *Ophioblennius atlanticus*, seems to take a perverse delight in chasing everyone all the time. They will attack angelfish, serranids, other blennies, and practically anything else that moves, typically dashing out to strike at the 'intruder' and then hightailing it back to the safety of a cave before the other fish can react. After an *Ophioblennius* had completely disrupted his tank and killed several of his fish, a friend swore to me that even the rocks cowered whenever the blenny swam by.

As a general rule, Redlip Blennies should never be kept with fish less than twice their size. Small ones are somewhat less aggressive than large individuals and so should be taken if a choice of fish is available. The other blennies are less aggressive, and though they will chase one another, they do well in a community tank with fish about their own size. These fish, in fact, are so rugged and so adaptable, that they will spawn readily even in small aquaria. Their only requirements are lots of food (virtually any kind will do) and a suitable shelter hole (such as a tube of PVC or some other opaque plastic).

Relevant Literature

Bath, H. 1976. 'Revision der Bleniini (Pisces: Blenniidae)', *Senckenbergiana Biol.* **57**: 167–234

Nursall, J. R. 1977. 'Territoriality in Redlip Blennies (*Ophioblennius atlanticus* – Pisces: Blenniidae)', *J. Zool. Lond.* **182**: 205–223

Smith, R. L. 1974. 'On the biology of *Blennius cristatus* with special reference to anal fin morphology', *Bull. Mar. Sci.* **24**(3): 595–605

Stahl, M. S. 1973. 'The behavior and activity rhythms of *Blennius cristatus* Linnaeus', unpublished Master's thesis, University of Miami, Coral Gables, Florida

Chapter 13

Clinids

For the average diver or marine aquarist, the name 'clinid' triggers virtually no response. Most have no idea what a clinid is and many have never even heard the term. Yet, shown a picture of one, many divers would recognize the fish instantly, even if they could not put a name to it. Clinids are abundant on Caribbean reefs, are active little fish, and are often colourful. Despite their small size, they quickly make an impression on a diver, and should make an equally good impression on marine aquarists.

The basic clinid is a relatively small, slender, blenny-like fish which typically sits on the bottom, feeds on a variety of small organisms, and is brown, black, grey, or some combination thereof, such that it matches its background. Its snout is rather pointed, with a small terminal mouth, its dorsal and anal fins are both long and continuous, and its head is adorned with several clusters of short, hairlike projections, known as 'cirri'. Until a few years ago, the clinids were included in the family Blenniidae, which they resemble and to which they are closely related, and most are still called the 'something' blenny. The two families can be told apart by several characters, however. The Combtooth Blennies, as their common name implies, have teeth located in comb-like rows in the jaws, while the teeth of clinids are clustered in patches. More importantly for field identification, however, the blennies either have very small scales or are completely scaleless, giving each fish a very smooth appearance, while clinids are all heavily and obviously criss-crossed by rows of large scales.

Aside from the chaenopsids, which will be discussed in the next chapter, one other, fairly common blennioid family is present in the Caribbean and looks similar to clinids. The triplefins, family Tripterygiidae, are small (no more than two inches), elongate, and robust fish with heavy scaling. Typically found on rocks and coral heads in shallow, often wave-washed areas, they can be distinguished easily from the clinids by the presence of three distinctly separated dorsal fins, the first two entirely spiney and the last entirely soft; clinids have no more than two dorsal fins, and generally only one. Approximately a half dozen species of tripterygiid are found in the Caribbean, all in the genus *Enneanectes*. All are similar in shape, size, and colour pattern – generally brownish grey with several vertical black bars (the one on the caudal peduncle is the darkest and most conspicuous). The most common member of the genus is the Redeye Blenny, *Enneanectes pectoralis*.

Species Account

There are four genera of common, shallow-water, western Atlantic clinids. Two of these, *Paraclinus* and *Starksia*, consist of small, drab, and often secretive fish found in grass beds and shallow rocky areas. Their major claim to fame is that one, *Starksia*, is a live-bearer, as will be discussed in the section on Reproductive Biology. The two remaining genera, *Malacoctenus* and *Labrisomus*, are both larger and more colourful fish, typically associated with the reef and commonly seen by divers.

Malacoctenus consists of approximately half a dozen common and widespread species, plus several less common ones. All are elongate fish, only slightly laterally compressed, with a pointed snout and prominent, often colourful eyes. Each species in the group has both a characteristic colour pattern (often sexually dimorphic) and a characteristic habitat.

The Diamond Blenny, *Malacoctenus boehlkei*, is the only member of the genus characteristically found on fully developed reefs, especially at depths in excess of 40 feet. It is an active and colourful species, seen scooting among coral crevices and sitting on coral heads. Each fish is pale yellow with six large, dark inverted triangles spaced along its back. These spots are black on the males and red brown on females. Males, especially during the spawning season, have a bright yellow head, peppered with tiny red spots that also extend out on to the back. A small, but distinct, yellow-ringed black spot is located near the leading edge of the dorsal fin. The species can also be identified by its pair of extremely long pelvic fins. When spread, these are so long that a fish sitting on the bottom is completely supported by the tripod formed by these and the caudal fin.

Just inshore of the main reef, on rock and coral outcrops in water 10 to 50 feet deep, a similarly coloured *Malacoctenus* can be found. The Saddled Blenny, *Malacoctenus triangulatus*, also has a series of inverted triangles on its back and a small black spot on the leading edge of the dorsal fin. However, it lacks the yellow body colour typical of the Diamond Blenny and has much shorter pelvic fins. Those of the Saddled Blenny, when folded against the body, just reach to the leading edge of the anal fin, while the longer fins of the Diamond Blenny reach well beyond this point. The Saddled Blenny is probably the most common member of the genus and the species most often seen by divers.

Closer to shore, there are three additional common species. *Malacoctenus gilli*, the Dusky Blenny, is found in water from 2 to 20 feet deep in areas of mixed sand, rock, and coral rubble. Sexually dichromatic, males are dark grey to black, often with a green tint, with sharply contrasting white pelvic fins and two small spots on the dorsal fin. The first spot is black and is located near the leading edge of the fin; the second is black ringed with pale blue and is about two thirds of the way down the dorsal fin, immediately at the base of the fin and overlapping on to the back. Females also have these two spots, but are otherwise generally pale grey or white with a faint indication of vertical barring.

Malacoctenus aurolineatus, the Goldline Blenny, is typical of very shallow, wave-washed, and algae-covered rocks, where it is commonly found peering out of holes bored by sea urchins. Also sexually dichromatic, both sexes are yellow-gold with several brown vertical bars, a yellow or red anal fin, and a thin horizontal gold line on the lower half of the body. Males also have a short horizontal brown bar which crosses the anteriormost three vertical bars. Finally, the Rosy Blenny, *Malacoctenus macropus*, is typical of calm-water areas of mixed sand, rubble, and sea grass. Somewhat variable in colour, males are usually pale red with a brown horizontal band down the mid-line of each side. Females lack the rose colour and are typically grey, grey with brown bars, or grey with a dark back.

Niche separation among the species in the genus *Labrisomus* is less obvious, largely because the fish themselves are less obvious than the bold *Malacoctenus*. Even where common, these large massive-bodied, and blunt-headed species are not commonly seen. Most are what the uninitiated would call ugly, that is, they are usually brown with black or grey blotches (often with faint indications of barring or spotting), have massive heads with big eyes, and bear numerous heavy scales. Most species in the genus have, at most, two colourful spots – an iridescent red eye, conspicuously set in the camouflaged head, and in some species, an ocellated black spot prominent on the gill covers.

Only one of these 'spotcheeked' clinids is common on the reef and it is both one of the most attractive and one of the largest members of the genus. The Frillfin Blenny, *Labrisomus filamentosus*, is characterized by a prominent ocellated spot on the rear edge of each gill cover, prominent brown barring on its body, and on the males, a high dorsal fin which is scrawled with wavy blue and yellow lines. The Frillfin Blenny has been seen as deep as 90 feet and is typical of well-developed coral reefs, though like all members of the genus it is rarely seen. Another large 'spotcheeked' species is found inshore of the main reef, but is less colourful than the Frillfin Blenny. The Hairy Blenny, *Labrisomus nuchipinnis*, lacks the dorsal sail of the previous species as well as the barring, but does have a prominent black spot near the leading edge of the dorsal fin. It is common on patch reefs and barrier reefs near shore which have both heavy surge action and numerous holes and cavities.

The genus *Labrisomus*, rather surprisingly, also contains one of the most attractive of Caribbean reef fish. *The* Spotcheek Blenny, *Labrisomus nigricinctus*, ranks with the Queen Angelfish and the *Liopropoma* in terms of brilliant colours. The blenny is sexually dichromatic, with the males being the colourful sex. Females are green, with alternating vertical bands of dark green and light green that cover not only the body, but also the dorsal and anal fins. Males have the same general pattern of colour, but rather than green, range from electric orange to blood red. A fiery orange male is most spectacular when seen underwater; the fish virtually glows. Both sexes have a prominent ocellated black spot on each gill cover, the outlining ring being mixed shades of red and blue.

The Spotcheek Blenny also differs from its congeners in many respects other than colour. It is laterally compressed, where they are robust; it has a pointed snout where they have a blunt head; and it shows a striking sexual dichromatism where they show little or none. Yet, it is also similar in many respects, notably in its behaviour. Like the other *Labrisomus*, the Spotcheek Blenny is shy, rarely being seen even where common. It lives in the same habitat as the Hairy Blenny – shallow-water patch reefs in high energy areas – and like it, must be actively hunted if it is to be found. Unlike the Hairy Blenny, the Spotcheek Blenny is well worth the effort.

Field Biology

All clinids are benthic fish, closely tied to cavernous rock or coral areas where shelter is readily available. All are also predators that feed on a wide variety of small crustaceans, soft-bodied invertebrates, and, when they can catch them, small fish. Finally, all are also territorial, defending areas against not only conspecifics, but congeners as well. Typically, one sees a single clinid, sitting on a rock or under a coral head, the fish making short dashing hops about its territory while hunting both food and intruders.

Species vary widely in their conspicuousness, with the various *Malacoctenus* being far bolder than members of the other genera. As noted, for a fish as big as some of them become, *Labrisomus* are remarkably shy. To see them regularly, one must be either lucky, or patient. To some extent, all *Labrisomus* are cave dwellers, so that even after waiting for one to make an appearance, all one sees is a bulbous head peering out of the rocks. The slightest movement sends the fish scurrying back into the hollow interior of the reef.

Labrisomus nigricinctus is as shy as any of its congeners and, not suprisingly, most divers and fish-collectors have never even seen the fish, despite its abundance in shallow water and its brilliant colours. Again, one must be patient and search carefully porous rocky bottoms for the fish. They are rarely in the open for more than a minute or two at a time, so that even in areas of abundance it takes a measure of luck to find them consistently. The best areas to search are eroded limestone rock with scattered cavernous coral formations in water less than 15 feet deep. Strong surge action also seems to be a prerequisite.

Most aspects of the field biology of the clinids have yet to be studied in any detail. One aspect of their biology has recently become of special interest, however. Several species of *Malacoctenus* and one *Labrisomus* (*Labrisomus kalisherae*, a small, drab brown, inshore species, lacking a spot on the cheek) are known to seek shelter in the tentacles of the sea anemone, *Condylactus gigantea*, and so may represent an incipient class of Caribbean 'anemonefish'. The relationship between the anemone and the clinids is not obligate, since each is commonly found alone. Nor have the clinids yet developed the complete protection from the anemone's nematocysts (stinging cells) which has been developed by the Pacific anemonefish. If anaesthetized and dropped into an anemone, a clinid will be stung and retained by the anemone, but it will generally not be eaten unless it struggles. Any other species, anaesthetized and dropped in in the same fashion, will be eaten whether or not it struggles. This difference suggests that the clinids have already developed a partial immunity from their dangerous hosts. The nature of this immunity, however, has not yet been investigated.

Reproductive Biology

Most species of clinids have recognizably different male and female colour patterns, the male usually the more brightly coloured of the two. Spawning and courtship behaviour has also not yet been described. What may have been a spawning pair of *Labrisomus* (probably *Labrisomus kalisherae*) was observed at dusk on a shallow patch reef off Puerto Rico. The male was deep brown with a broad white bar running down behind his gill covers; the female was very pale, almost white, with only a few light grey marks. The two fish approached one another closely and the male erected his dorsal fin, presenting its broadside to the female, and then remained immobile. The female approached, but was then interrupted by the presence of the diver and subsequently fled.

Had the activity continued, it is likely it would have led to the female following the male into a shallow hole, in which the actual spawning would have occured. *Labrisomus* produce demersal eggs, laying them in rows inside a small cavity in or under a rock. These eggs are attached by filaments and are guarded and cared for by the male. After hatching, the young emerge as planktonic larvae. Only the larva of one species, *Labrisomus nuchipinnis*, has yet been described; it is slender, streamlined, and lacks scales. The duration of the planktonic larval stage is not known.

Malacoctenus spawns in a similar manner. Spawning occurs during the day and usually takes place under a rock or in the crevice between two rocks. While the male vigorously patrols his territory, and chases from it all intruding fish, the female carefully cements rows of eggs to a cleaned rock surface. Every few seconds, the male dashes in and displaces the female, fertilizing her eggs. After she has finished, the male drives her off and subsequently guards and cares for the eggs until hatching. Eggs are round, approximately 0.8mm in diameter, with attachment threads at either end. They are laid in a single patch and at any one time, a male may be guarding eggs at several different stages of development.

While most Caribbean clinids are egg-layers (oviparous), some members of the family produce live young in the procedure known as ovoviviparity. Males have an intromittent organ and fertilize the eggs inside the female. She then retains the developing eggs in her ovaries until they have hatched. Such reproductive behaviour is typical of the more advanced members of the family, and especially those in the sub-family Clinini, which is found primarily off the coast of South Africa. In the Caribbean, the only live-bearing clinids are those in the genus *Starksia*. Generally small (less than 2 inches), grey, brown, or black fish, *Starksia* are shy and rarely seen in the field, though they are common within rocky outcrops and in the interstices of coral. Like the similar species in the genus *Paraclinus*, they are slightly laterally compressed and have a slightly pointed snout and elongate dorsal fin. Unlike *Paraclinus*, male *Starksia* have a prominent (if you look closely) intromittent organ formed by the union of the first anal fin spine (which is entirely free of the fin) and a fleshy process leading from the genital pore. They have never been observed spawning and their reproductive biology has been deduced entirely from anatomical studies.

Aquarium Biology
Clinids in general do well in captivity, feeding readily on a wide variety of foods, and are relatively hardy. Only the species in *Malacoctenus*, however, are recommended for anyone other than the advanced hobbyist. *Labrisomus* typically disappear when placed in an aquarium and even after several weeks appear only rarely. By temperament, they are not suited for an active community tank. This is true, unfortunately, for the magnificent Spotcheek Blenny, *Labrisomus nigricinctus*, as well as the drabber species. Placed in an aquarium, a male Spotcheek Blenny not only hides, but also pales, almost to white, and never regains colours equal to those in the field.

The *Malacoctenus*, on the other hand, invariably adapt well to aquarium conditions and are active fish which readily learn that the approach of the aquarist generally means food. Within a few weeks of capture, a clinid will often hover patiently just below the water's surface awaiting a hand-out and many can be trained to eat from one's hand. Their only bad habit is a tendency to become bullies, a general characteristic of territorial species. It is probably a good idea to keep clinids only with other bold fish or with larger fish.

One of the major attractions of the clinids is the high probability that they will spawn in the aquarium. They are small at maturity, hardy, and ready eaters, such that even small aquaria should impose no undue strain on the fish. Also, with sex differences in coloration, obtaining a spawnable pair should present no problem. Conditioning a pair for spawning should require little more than a rock-filled aquarium, heavy feeding (preferably with live food), and isolation.

Relevant Literature
Breder, C. M. Jr 1939. 'On the life history and development of the Sponge Blenny, *Paraclinus*

marmoratus (Steindachner)', *Zoologica* **24**: 487–496

Breder, C. M. Jr 1941. 'On the reproductive behavior of the Sponge Blenny, *Paraclinus marmoratus* (Steindachner)', *Zoologica* **26**: 233–235

Hanlon, R. T. & Kaufman, L. 1976. 'Associations of seven West Indian reef fishes with Sea Anemones', *Bull. Mar. Sci.* **26**(2): 225–233

Rosenblatt, R. H. 1960. 'The Atlantic Species of the Blennioid fish genus *Enneanectes*', *Proc. Acad. Nat. Sci. Phila.* **112**(1): 1–23

Rosenblatt, R. H. & Taylor, L. R. Jr 1971. 'The Pacific species of the Clinid fish tribe Starksiini', *Pac. Sci.* **25**(3): 436–463

Springer, V. G. 1959. 'Systematics and zoogeography of the Clinid fishes of the subtribe Labrisomini Hubbs.', *Publ. Inst. Mar. Sci.* (Univ. Texas) **5**: 417–492

Springer, V. G. 1970. 'The western south Atlantic Clinid fish *Ribeiroclinus eigenmanni*, with discussion of the intrarelationships and zoogeography of the Clinidae', *Copeia*, 1970 (3): 430–436

Chapter 14

Chaenopsids

Chaenopsids, or naked blennies, are a specialized branch of the scaled blennies, Clinidae, and are clearly closely related to them. Some ichthyologists prefer to treat the chaenopsids as a sub-family in the Clinidae, arguing that there is a smooth gradation from a heavily-scaled clinid to a naked chaenopsid, with no logical point at which to separate the two. Other ichthyologists feel that the chaenopsids are so specialized and, as a group, are so different from the generally benthic clinids that familial status is justified. Whatever the ultimate status of these groups, clinids and chaenopsids differ in a number of respects. Clinids, for example, are typically heavily scaled and have a well developed lateral line system. Chaenopsids are invariably naked and the lateral line system is reduced, usually to no more than a few pores on the head. The two also differ in terms of skull structure, placement of the teeth, and the patterning of sensory pores on the head.

Chaenopsids are a diverse group in terms of life style and morphology, ranging from blunt-headed and rotund planktivores to pike-jawed and slender piscavores. All are elongate, however, and all have large conspicuous eyes, well-developed jaws, and long, even anal and dorsal fins. The various genera are separated on the basis of the number and location of pores on the head, the size and number of teeth, the number of fin spines and rays, and the size and configuration of the jaws. In total, there are nine genera presently recognized, all represented in the tropical western Atlantic, consisting of approximately 50 species. About half of these species are western Atlantic; the rest are found in the tropical eastern Pacific. Unlike many groups of reef fish, which reach their peaks of abundance and diversity in the Indo-Pacific, the chaenopsids are entirely restricted to the tropical American seas.

Species Account

Two main lines of chaenopsid evolution have developed from a cluster of similar and generalized species. The most common, widespread, and easiest to recognize of these generalized fish is the Sailfin Blenny, *Emblemaria pandionis*. In many respects, it is typical of these generalized species – elongate, small, robust, blunt-headed, and dark in colour. The Sailfin Blenny is typically found on rocky and mixed sand and rubble areas at depths of 5 to 20 feet. Each fish sits in a narrow hole in the bottom, generally an old worm-tube or the borehole of some mollusc, with only its head, gill covers, and pectoral fins protruding. Males are jet black and have a broad, black dorsal fin, the 'sailfin' from which the species derives its common name. Females are mottled grey and brown and have a much smaller dorsal fin. The dorsal fin of the male is used in courtship and aggression, both of which will be covered later.

Several other, generally similar chaenopsids are found in the Caribbean, none of which are as strikingly sexually dimorphic as the sailfin blenny. Aside from several other species in *Emblemaria*, these fish include species in *Ekemblemaria*, *Emblemariopsis*, *Protemblemaria*, and *Coralliozetus*. Separation of these genera is based primarily on internal characteristics.

From this cluster, a line of small, non-sailfinned species has evolved. The species in the genus *Acanthemblemaria* are elongate and slender fish with round bodies, blunt heads, and large eyes. Most do not exceed 2 inches in maximum length (and ¼ inch in cross-section!) and many are colourful. The members of this genus can be readily distinguished from other chaenopsids by the shape of the head. Though both the 'acanthems' and *Emblemaria* et al. have blunt heads, those of the former are covered with numerous, minute spines and papilla, giving each a 'rough-headed' appearance. The heads of fish in the other genera are smooth, aside from occasional cirri over the eyes.

There are approximately a dozen species in the genus *Acanthemblemaria*, of which about half are found in the tropical western Atlantic. The only easy way to tell these fish apart is by colour pattern. *Acanthemblemaria aspera*, the Roughhead Blenny, is a common reef species, easily identified by a black anterior (for the males; females are mottled brown), a dark smudge on the leading edge of the dorsal fin (often obscured on the generally dark males), and a bright orange iris around each pupil. *Acanthemblemaria chaplini* is pale brown with flecks of darker brown and white on the body, a dark leading edge to the dorsal fin, and only blunt papilla (as opposed to spines) on the head. It is commonly found on wave-washed, rock bottoms in shallow water. *Acanthemblemaria rivasi* lives in the same environment, but is found only in the southern Caribbean. Its colours are also distinctive. The head is brown with white 'cheeks', the body is mottled brown with conspicuous banding, and each eye is outlined by a red ring. The remaining two species are widely distributed in the Caribbean, the Secretary Blenny, *Acanthemblemaria maria*, and the Spinyhead Blenny, *Acanthemblemaria spinosa*, are both mottled grey and brown and both live in shallow water. Inside their holes, they are difficult to tell apart; but when outside, the Secretary Blenny can be seen to have conspicuous vertical bands lacked by the Spinyhead Blenny.

The other line of chaenopsid evolution has led to fish morphologically and behaviourally very different from the generally planktivorous 'acanthems'. *Chaenopsis*, *Lucayablennius*, and *Hemiemblemaria*, the only known members of the line, are all predators and have evolved the large jaws typical of predators. They also share with other chaenopsids the elongate body, long dorsal and anal fins, and large eyes characteristic of the family, as well as a pronounced tendency to sit in holes.

Chaenopsis, the Pike Blennies, like the 'acanthems' and *Emblemaria*, spend most of their time sitting in such holes. For the Pike Blennies, the preferred holes are abandoned worm-tubes that dot shallow-water regions of mixed sand and rubble. Typically found in clusters of several individuals, the fish peer from these tubes in search of likely prey – mainly small crustaceans. These are pounced on with a quick dash out of the tube.

All Pike Blennies are very slender and long, some reaching a length of 5 inches. The dorsal and anal fins of these fish have merged with the caudal fin to create a single long fin that completely encircles the posterior edge of the body. The leading edge of the dorsal fin is enlarged into a 'sail' similar to, but smaller than, the 'sail' of the Sailfin Blenny. Finally, the jaws are long and pointed, a miniature version of the jaws of a barracuda or a pike. It is from these characteristic jaws that the fish derive their common name.

There are just over half a dozen species in *Chaenopsis*, of which two are common in the tropical western Atlantic. *Chaenopsis ocellata*, the Bluethroat Pikeblenny, and *Chaenopsis limbaughi*, the Yellowface Pikeblenny, are closely related and very similar fish. The Bluethroat Pikeblenny is less gregarious than the Yellowface Pikeblenny, tends to be found in shallower water (back reef areas rather than around the open reef), and has a dark black head and anterior half of the body (males only; females are mottled grey and brown). It also has dark blue gill membranes, conspicuously exposed when the male is displaying. Yellowfaced Pikeblennies, in turn, have a yellow wash on the head, black gill membranes, and a brown, horizontal stripe running down each side of the body. Both species have a small black spot, outlined with white and orange, on the leading edge of the dorsal fin.

Lucayablennius and *Hemiemblemaria* are both monospecific and restricted to the western Atlantic. The former looks like a shortened Pike Blenny, with a snout slightly more pointed and a distinct caudal fin. The Arrow Blenny, *Lucayablennius zingaro*, is found on the deeper reef, generally 70 feet deep or more, where it is typically seen hovering a few inches off the bottom while moving in short jerks around coral heads and rocky outcrops. Only one to two inches long, this translucent red-brown fish swims with its body 'cocked' in the shape of a fish-hook, its head at the eye of the hook and its tail at the point. Propelling itself by means of its pectoral fins, the chaenopsid stalks small fish and crustaceans, launching itself at them by snapping its body straight and springing forward. Arrow Blennies spend little time in bore-holes, resting there only at night, after feeding, and when guarding eggs (males only).

Hemiemblemaria simulus, like *Lucayablennius*, is a piscavore, but has evolved a very different means of hunting. Unlike the patiently stalking Arrow Blenny, *Hemiemblemaria*, the Wrasse Blenny, mimics in shape, colour, and swimming style the yellow phase of the ubiquitous Bluehead Wrasse, *Thalassoma bifasciatum*. A heavier bodied and larger species than its near relatives, with blunter, though equally

Spotted Jackknife Fish, *Equetes punctatus*, are so-called not because of the spots on the fins, but rather because of the dark smudge on the tip of the snout. This dark smudge is the best way to distinguish between juveniles of this species and those of the Jackknife Fish.

The flowing lines of the Jackknife Fish, *Equetes lanceolatus*, immediately distinguish it from any other fish on western Atlantic reefs. Adult Jackknife Fish are usually found in fairly deep water.

The Highhat, or Cubbyu, *Equetus acuminatus*, is the shallow water representative of the genus. Though hardier than its relatives, it is not as attractive as an adult.

The Swordtail Jawfish, *Lonchopisthus micrognathus*, is found in silty, back-reef areas, where it digs an unlined, pit-like burrow.

Yellow Jawfish, *Opistognathus gilberti*, are a deep-water species, found in small groups on sand-covered ledges.

The Mottled Jawfish, *Opistognathus maxillosus*, is the most common of the similar appearing 'dusky' jawfish in shallow water.

The Smooth Trunkfish, *Lactophrys triqueter*, is the most colourful member of its family in the Caribbean, and is also the only one commonly found on the reef.

A number of rather drab puffers are found in grass beds inshore of the reef. The most common of these is the Bandtail Puffer, *Sphaeroides spengleri*.

The Balloonfish, *Diodon holocanthus*, is one of the few fish distributed as the same species circumtropically.

Sharpnose Puffers, *Canthigaster rostrata*, are ubiquitous, slow-swimming omnivores found throughout the tropical western Atlantic.

The Orangespotted Filefish, *Cantherhines pullus*, is a relatively large fish that is occasionally seen around inshore reefs.

The Queen Triggerfish, *Balistes vetula*, is extremely variable in yellow; all colour phases, however, have the electric blue lines around the mouth and eyes.

The Sargassum Triggerfish, *Xanthichthys ringens*, derives its common name from the floating algae that the pelagic larvae associate with. Adults are found on the reef, usually in deep water.

Black Durgon, *Melichthys niger*, are difficult to approach. They normally forage in the water column and flee at the approach of a diver. If pressed, they retreat into crevices and erect the dorsal spine to lock themselves in place.

expansive jaws, the Wrasse Blenny has three colour patterns, between which it can shift in seconds. These colour patterns duplicate comparable patterns on the Bluehead Wrasse. In the most common pattern, both wrasse and blenny are solid yellow with a conspicuous black spot on the leading edge of the dorsal fin. The wrasse has a horizontal red band across each eye which is lacked by the chaenopsid, but the mimic does have a red iris, partially duplicating it. The wrasse also has a colour phase that includes a broad, horizontal black line running down each side of the body, and another similar phase in which the line is divided into black squares. The chaenopsid can faithfully duplicate each. Model and mimic can be distinguished most readily by two means: the chaenopsid has a large, well-developed set of jaws (so well camouflaged that it takes a careful look to see it), and the chaenopsid, like the Arrow Blenny, occasionally sits in holes in the reef, with just its head showing. Many divers have seen these fish, mistaking them for oddly acting Blueheads, never realizing that they were not seeing a Bluehead Wrasse at all.

While swimming about in an aggregation of wrasses, the chaenopsid is nearly impossible to detect, unless it has eaten and its stomach is bulging. It feeds mainly on small fish (including wrasses) and by mimicking the wrasse, it can approach these small fish without causing them to flee. The prey are captured with a quick lunge, from a 'fish-hook' position similar to that used by the Arrow Blenny. Like the wrasses, Wrasse Blennies are common on patch reefs in water 15 to 60 feet deep.

Hemiemblemaria develops its mimetic colours only at maturity. Small juveniles are transparent with a thin, black line down the centre of each side of the body. As the fish matures, it first develops a yellow tint, then the black spot on the dorsal fin, and finally looses the horizontal black line. Such young Wrasse Blennies are not mimics, but rather stalk prey in a manner similar to the Arrow Blenny.

Field Biology

The behaviour and ecology of the chaenopsids, as a group, are more variable than those of almost any other family of reef fish. *Emblemaria*, its near relatives, and the 'acanthems' are primarily planktivores, 'popping' out of their holes to engulf copepods and other crustaceans as these drift by. *Acanthemblemaria maria*, in addition, feeds on the short, close-cropped algae that often grows around its holes, leaving shelter for several minutes at a time to forage nearby. If approached, the chaenopsid dashes back to its burrow, entering it tail first.

Chaenopsis and its near relatives, in contrast, are voracious predators. While the planktivores rarely leave their holes, except to spawn or to usurp another's hole, *Hemiemblemaria* and *Lucayablennius* spend little time in their shelters. Each roams widely in search of prey.

Chaenopsids in general are territorial, the more sedentary species defending their shelter holes and the more active fish defending the hunting area about the hole. The dynamics of such territoriality have not been studied, but it appears that there is a fair amount of movement even among the tiny 'acanthems'. One occasionally sees a larger fish displace a smaller one from its hole, forcing the smaller to seek shelter elsewhere. Such an interaction usually begins with the intruder approaching a resident, its jaws agape in aggressive display. The resident reciprocates. Pike Blennies also spread their dorsal fins during this display. If defence is successful, the intruder slowly backs away, displaying steadily. If not, it approaches the hole closely and the two fish push their jaws against each other in what is apparently a test of strength. If outclassed, the defender will withdraw partway into its tube, but the intruder persists and eventually drives it out.

The only species which does not appear to be regularly territorial (males may be when guarding eggs) is the Arrow Blenny, *Lucayablennius zingaro*. Groups of several fish are commonly seen on the reef and some ichthyologists have suggested that these predators even hunt in packs. Several blennies have been observed to encircle an aggregation of their favourite prey, the Masked Goby, *Coryphopterus personatus*, and apparently herd the gobies into a blind cave. Finally, one at a time, each rushes in to sieze a prey. Whether or not such behaviour is intentional, coordinated hunting and not simply fortuitous cooperation has not yet been determined.

Reproductive Biology

Chaenopsids, like clinids and combtooth blennies, have demersal eggs which are spawned in either a bore-hole in rock or coral, or in a worm-tube, and which are cared for and guarded by the male. Courtship by the Sailfin Blenny and the Pike Blennies, the species with the large, sail-like dorsal fins, is frequently observed. Males of both display to a female by spreading the dorsal fin and directing it broadside towards her. The display is a quick one, repeated four to eight times on a single bout of displaying. The male rears up out of its hole (usually coming half to two-thirds of the way out), then flicks his dorsal fin out and in, again and again, each time coming further out of his hole. When excited by the presence of a female, a male Sailfin Blenny may end a bout of displaying as much as 2 feet off the bottom.

Spawning by the Pike Blennies has not yet been observed, but in the Sailfin Blenny it is initiated by the cryptically coloured female leaving her hole and approaching a displaying male. On her approach, the male freezes with his dorsal fin spread to its fullest and oriented broadside to her. He pales and may quiver slightly. Still with his 'sail' fully spread, he exits his hole and the female enters, tail first. Within a few minutes, she emerges and the male enters, again tail-first. Upon emerging, he drives off the female if she has not already left (which is usually the case) and subsequently fans and guards the eggs until hatching. Eggs are spherical, approximately 0.9mm in diameter, and grey in colour. Length of time until hatching, duration, and appearance of the larvae, and even the spawning season, are not known.

While details of spawning by the Atlantic species have not been reported, the spawning behaviour of one eastern Pacific *Acanthemblemaria*, *A. macrospilus*, has been observed and is probably similar to that of the Atlantic species. Spawning occurs in the morning, within a few hours of dawn, and is initiated by the male, who darkens and 'bobs' in and out of his hole much like *Emblemaria*. Bouts of 'bobbing' continue intermittently and eventually attract a drab-coloured female. She leaves her hole and dashes quickly to that of a male, backing into it tail-first, on top of the male already in it. She spends about a minute with him, then dashes to the hole of another male to repeat the performance. Each female apparently spawns with several males before returning to her shelter hole. Each male, in turn, courts and spawns with as many females as possible. The eggs are cemented to the sides of the male's tube, where he guards and fans them until hatching.

Aquarium Biology

All chaenopsids will do well in captivity, though their requirements vary widely depending upon the species kept. Both *Emblemaria* and the *Acanthemblemaria* require only a suitable shelter hole (either a natural bore-hole in a rock or coral head, or one drilled in the rock for them) and regular feedings with thawed brine shrimp and flake food. Both may spurn such offerings initially, and may require temporary feedings with live brine shrimp, but within a week or so all will adapt to prepared foods. Even small 'acanthems', only an inch or so long, have large mouths; though it may take some time and effort, even they will choke down whole brine shrimp. For 'acanthems', the only special effort required is to ensure that the food drifts so close to their holes that it can be seized by the fish. Unless very hungry, they will not leave their holes to feed. Sailfin Blennies, on the other hand, learn quickly about frozen brine shrimp and dash into the centre of a mass of food to engulf a mouthful before retreating to the shelter hole.

Chaenopsis, the Pike Blennies, are similar in their requirements to *Emblemaria* and typically adapt well to captivity. In place of the worm-tubes they normally inhabit, they will readily accept straws partially buried in the sand.

Lucayablennius and *Hemiemblemaria* are more demanding in captivity and, unlike their relatives, are recommended only for experienced aquarists. The former, especially, will eat only live brine shrimp and small fishes which it can stalk. Provided with this food, it does well; denied it, it quickly starves to death. The Wrasse Blenny normally refuses anything but live food initially, but can usually be weaned over to thawed brine shrimp and pieces of fish within a few weeks. As in the other species, both of these should be provided a suitable shelter hole somewhere in the tank.

The Flamefish, *Apogon maculatus*, is both the most colourful and the largest of western Atlantic cardinalfish. It is also common in shallow water.

The Squirrelfish, *Holocentrus rufus*, is a nocturnal predator that hovers near the mouths of small caves during the day. They defend these caves from other squirrelfish.

The Glasseye Snapper, *Priacanthus cruentatus*, is the shallow water representative of the genus, and can commonly be seen during the day hovering over a small hole in the reef. Often the hole is too small for the fish to escape into, and after a few futile attempts to enter, the fish usually flees the approaching diver.

The Longspine Squirrelfish, *Flammeo marianus*, is a beautifully coloured species that does well in captivity, but is not often seen because of the relatively great depths it prefers.

Small groups of Blackbar Soldierfish, *Myripristis jacobus*, can often be seen during the day nervously dashing in and out of caves in the shallow reef. At night, they spread out to forage in the water column.

The Cardinal Soldierfish (Squirrelfish), *Plectrypops retrospinis*, is a very shy fish, found well back in large caves in the reef. Despite its bright colours, it is not often seen by divers.

The Bigeye, *Priacanthus arenatus*, is virtually identical to the Glasseye Snapper, but is found only on the deeper reef.

Sweepers, *Pempheris schomburgki*, are copper-coloured fish that aggregate in large numbers in caves during the day. They forage in the water column at night.

Until recently, the Caribbean Flashlight Fish, *Kryptophanaron alfredi*, was thought to be found only on the very deep reef, at depths well below those that could be reached with conventional diving equipment. We now know that they can be found in relatively shallow water, if looked for in the right places and in the right way.

At night, sparisomine parrotfish develop a cryptic colour pattern and settle on to the reef. The scarines, however, develop a conspicuous mucous coat, the function of which is not well understood.

The Spotted Moray, *Gymnothorax morigua*, is the most common moray on western Atlantic reefs.

The Goldentail Moray, *Muraena miliaris*, is frequently seen foraging by day, which suggests that it may be more of a day-time active predator than other morays.

Males of the Princess Parrotfish, *Scarus taeniopterus*, are usually found in the company of several females, suggesting a social system based on male-dominated harems.

The females of the Princess Parrotfish, *Scarus taeniopterus*, like those of other parrotfish, are drab when compared to the gaudy males.

Relevant Literature

Colin, P. L. & Goman, M. F. 1973. 'Notes on the behavior, ecology, and distribution of *Lucayablennius zingaro* (Pisces: Clinidae)', *Carib. J. Sci.* (1–2): 59–61

Randall, J. E. & Randall, H. A. 1960. 'Examples of mimicry and protective resemblence in tropical marine fishes', *Bull Mar. Sci.* **10**(4): 444–480

Robins, C. R., Phillips, C., & Phillips, F. 1959. 'Some aspects of the behavior of the Blennioid fish *Chaenopsis ocellata* Poey', *Zoologica* **44**(2): 77–84

Robins, C. R. & Randall, J. E. 1965. 'Three new Western Atlantic fishes of the Blennioid genus *Chaenopsis*, with notes on the related *Lucayablennius zingaro*', *Proc. Acad. Nat. Sci. Phila.* **117**(6): 213–234

Smith-Vaniz, W. & Palacio, F. J. 1974. 'Atlantic fishes of the genus *Acanthemblemaria*, with description of three new species and comments on Pacific species (Clinidae: Chaenopsinae)', *Proc. Acad. Nat. Sci. Phila.* **125**(11): 197–224

Stephens, J. S. Jr 1970. 'Seven new Chaenopsid Blennies from the Western Atlantic', *Copeia* 1970: 280–309

Stephens, J. S. Jr, Hobson, E. S., & Johnson, R. K. 1966. 'Notes on the distribution, behavior, and morphological variation in some chaenopsid fishes from the tropical Eastern Pacific, with descriptions of two new species, *Acanthemblemaria castroi* and *Coralliozetus springeri*', *Copeia* 1966 (33): 424–438

Chapter 15

Jackknife Fish

The jackknife fish, members of the genus *Equetus*, cannot be confused with any other fish found on or near the reef. The combination of magnificent, flowing fins and stark black-and-white colours marks them as some of the most spectacular of all reef fish. Because of this, they have long been a favourite group for marine aquaria, even back in the days when marine fish were generally considered difficult to maintain.

Jackknife fish *per se* are found only in the tropical western Atlantic and are a unique sub-group of drums, family Sciaenidae, that has invaded the reef environment (though a similar species is found in the eastern Pacific). Drums, in general, are large, heavy-bodied, and massive-headed fish, found in tropical and temperate estuarine environments around the world and characterized by the possession of an inferior mouth which, in some species, has several short sensory barbels. These barbels are used to search for food as the drums forage by grubbing through bottom mud and sand. Most drums, or croakers (the males of several species can make grunting noises by vibrating their swim bladders), are drab species – typically grey or brown with a silver cast. The Caribbean reef and its associated environment has its share of such species, along with the more brilliant jackknife fish. Two, in fact, are fairly common on silty reefs – *Odontoscion dentax*, the reef croaker, and *Umbrina coroides*, the sand drum. Both are retiring species found by day in the shelter of caves and crevices and at night foraging off the sand flats often located near the reef. Another common and well-known drum, not usually found on the reef itself, is the Weakfish, any one of a number of species in the genus *Cynoscion*, which have adapted to an open water, predatory mode of life and are outstanding gamefish.

Species Account

From the basic line of sciaenid development has arisen the three fish of interest here: the Jackknife Fish, *Equetus lanceolatus*, the Spotted Jackknife Fish (or Spotted Drum), *Equetus punctatus*, and the Cubbyu (or High Hat), *Equetus acuminatus*. As 9 to 10in adults, all three are similar in body shape and colour configuration. Each has a large, somewhat blunt head, with big, well-developed eyes, and a slender tapering body that ends in a slightly pointed caudal fin for the Jackknife Fish and a blunt one for the other two species. Each fish has two dorsal fins, the first tall, stubby, and flag-like, the second long and low. The pectoral and pelvic fins, and the anal, are pretty much normal in shape and size. In terms of colour pattern, all three species have an underlying cream colour, over which each has laid a distinctive pattern of black lines and spots.

The most striking of these patterns is that on the Jackknife Fish itself. The cream-coloured body and fins are divided by three black, or brown, lines: the first runs vertically through the eyes, the second runs diagonally from the forehead through the base of the pectoral fins and ends on the leading edge of the pelvics, and the third, the longest, runs from the leading edge of the first dorsal down the centre of the body to end at the tip of the slightly pointed caudal fin. The Spotted Drum, *Equetus punctatus*, is similar, but along with the three lines, also has a number of faint, incomplete black lines above and below, and parallel to, the main body stripe. The Spotted Drum also differs in that its pelvic and pectoral fins, unlike those of the Jackknife Fish, are deep black, while the unpaired fins are black peppered with irregularly shaped white spots. And finally, at the tip of its snout, the Spotted Drum has a large smudge of black, lacking on the Jackknife Fish. This is not only the most reliable feature for telling the two species apart (especially as juveniles), but is also the source of the Spotted Drum's common name.

The last western Atlantic species in the genus *Equetus* is the Cubbyu, or Highhat, *Equetus acuminatus*. It is the least attractive of the three species, but it is also the most common and the easiest to catch — it is therefore the species most often available in the retail trade. The Cubbyu lacks the broad, sweeping lines of its congeners, but has instead only a series of thin, smudged horizontal black stripes which run along each side and cross the snout in parallel. Both the head and the fins tend to be darker than the body proper. Colour patterns on the Cubbyu vary, in part geographically, which has led to the suggestion that more than one species may be involved. If so, and the distinction is far from generally accepted, fish with white or pale-coloured fins, coupled with the parallel black lines on the snout, would be the original *Equetus acuminatus*. Those with darker fins, and usually having the stripes forming a 'V' on the snout would be *Equetus umbrosus*. This latter species is apparently restricted to Florida (mainly the west coast). There has also been a move to transfer both of these fish into another genus, *Pareques*, distinct from *Equetus* (which would then be limited to the two jackknife fish), combining them with a similar species found in the eastern Pacific — *Pareques viola*. This re-assignment has yet to be widely accepted, and is based mainly on differences in the number and length of the bones supporting the dorsal fin.

Because of its spectacular colour pattern, the Jackknife Fish itself is occasionlly sold as an adult, but more often the juveniles attract the most attention. Like many reef fish, the juveniles of these species bear only faint resemblance to the adults. Fresh out of the plankton, baby Jackknife Fish are tiny black dots enveloped by four streaming, black-and-white fins each many times the length of the body. The first dorsal fin, the caudal fin, and the two pelvics are wildly exaggerated and give the tiny swimming creatures a bizarre appearance. At this stage, the fish are found under coral heads and rocks, are poor swimmers, and can be easily captured.

As they mature, the relative length of the fins decreases, though still remaining long and flowing, and all three species develop the streaming bands of black and white on the body characteristic of the adult Jackknife Fish. Juvenile *Equetus lanceolatus* are often yellow-orange with black stripes, a pattern which unfortunately is lost as the fish matures.

At $1\frac{1}{2}$ to 2 inches, the Cubbyo splits off from its congeners and begins to develop the stocky body, short fins, and horizontal lining of the adult. The remaining species, however, retain the flowing dorsal fin and sinuous body and caudal fin until reaching a length of about 4 inches. The long pelvics are lost first, then the body begins to thicken and the caudal fin shortens, leaving for last only the long banner-like dorsal fin. As the fish matures, this too is eventually resorbed and broken off.

Field Biology

The Jackknife Fish and Spotted Drum are strictly reef-associated species, seen by day swimming slowly about inside a hollow coral head or within a cave. They are nowhere common, but on the other hand, they are not really rare; rather, they are simply fish that are often overlooked. The two species are fairly discrete depthwise, with the Spotted Drum being the shallower dwelling of the two. It is usually found near the base of the reef in a depth range of 15 to 50 feet. Below 50 feet, Jackknife Fish begin to replace the Spotted Drums, until the former is the only species present at depths in excess of 90 feet. Juveniles follow the same general pattern of distribution as the adults, with one exception. Very young Jackknife Fish are frequently found in shallow inshore waters, far from the deep reef haunts of the adults. The fate of these shallow-water fish is not known, but since the adults are not found in this area and a migration of such poor swimmers, though possible (several drums migrate in and off shore to spawn), is unlikely; such juveniles probably die off for lack of a suitable habitat. Why some juveniles settle in these shallow areas is not known.

The Cubbyu is found on the shallow reef, but unlike its congeners, is more characteristic of inshore areas, frequently being found in water less than 3 feet deep. Small juveniles can be collected usually under any sort of overhang or small crevice in the area, including under rocks, under cuts in grass banks, and in debris. Further unlike its congeners, the Cubbyu is extremely common, with as many as 20 or 30 fish often found together in a single large cave.

All of the drums are predators and those in the genus *Equetus* are no exception. Like their relatives, they are mainly nocturnal feeders, hovering in sheltered and dark areas by day and moving out over the reef flats to forage at night. Their primary food items are small crabs and shrimps, some molluscs, and a variety of soft-bodied invertebrates. These are located by means of the chin barbels. These sense organs literally taste food as the fish passes over it and trigger a strike downwards.

Reproductive Biology

There is only one reported observation of spawning in any of the jackknife fish. A pair of *Equetus acuminatus* in an aquarium were seen to swim in tight head-to-tail circles, spinning ever faster and closer together. The spinning culminated in a mutual quivering when the fish were quite close together and the visible release of eggs and sperm. The fish, each between 5 and 6 inches long, spawned several times in the same day.

Based on the collection of their pelagic eggs and recruitment patterns of the juveniles, *Equetus* seem to breed all year round, with some suggestion of a spring peak. The eggs of *Equetus acuminatus*, and probably those of the other species as well, are large for a pelagic egg, roughly 1.5mm in diameter, and hatch quickly. Newborn pelagic larvae are correspondingly large and grow rapidly. Settlement to the bottom as 4 to 6mm long post-larvae can occur in as little as 3 days. Such larvae, observed under rock and among the spines of the sea urchin, *Diadema*, have large heads, slender bodies, and a long dorsal fin. Even when very small, the beginnings of the exaggerated first dorsal and pelvic fins are visible. Post-larvae and juveniles are voracious eaters, feeding mainly on plankton, and grow rapidly. Age at sexual maturity is not known for any of the species.

Aquarium Biology

Jackknife fish are spectacular additions to a marine aquarium, especially as juveniles. Unfortunately, the two most attractive species, the Jackknife Fish and the Spotted Drum, are prone to be problem fish and are not recommended for the casual or novice aquarist. Using their chin barbels to taste food before they eat it, both can be very picky eaters. Though readily taking live brine shrimp, or practically anything else live, most will just as steadfastly refuse even the freshest prepared foods. Frozen brine shrimp, flake foods, and chopped shrimp are all usually rejected. A friend had luck feeding a Spotted Drum with chopped crab meat, but other fish rejected that as well. It is therefore best not to contemplate keeping members of either species unless a reasonably steady supply of live food is available. The Cubbyu, fortunately for the many hobbyists who collected their own fish along the Florida coast, is more adaptable in its feeding habits and will accept practically anything within a day or two of capture.

Equetus in general are also sensitive to water quality and should be handled and moved as little as possible. Even when moved carefully in a container of the water in which they have been living, the trauma of being handled is often more than these fish can take. Again, the Cubbyu is much less sensitive in this regard than its deeper-water relatives.

Finally, the most attractive feature of the genus is the long, flowing dorsal fins of the juveniles. These are, unfortunately, great targets for more aggressive fish in a community tank and can be rapidly cut to ribbons. It is therefore best to keep these drums with relatively mild-mannered individuals.

Relevant Literature

Loisel, G. (in preparation). 'Biology and systematics of the Western Atlantic species in the genus *Equetus*', unpublished Master's thesis, University of Florida Atlantic, Boca Raton, Florida

McPhail, J. D. 1961. 'A review of the tropical Eastern Pacific species of *Pareques* (Sciaenidae)', *Copeia* 1961 (1): 27–32

Powles, H. & Burgess, W. E. 1978. 'Observations on benthic larvae of *Pareques* (Pisces: Sciaenidae)

from Florida and Columbia', *Copeia* 1978 (1): 169–172

Straughan, R. P. 1968. 'First spawning of High Hat', *Salt Water Aquar.* 4(3): 73–74

Chapter 16

Jawfish

If a vote were taken for the most popular fish in the Caribbean, the Yellowhead Jawfish, *Opistognathus aurifrons*, would win by a landslide. Probably no other fish combines so well the delicately beautiful coloration and engaging personality which attract so many to the jawfish. The Yellowhead, however, is only one of approximately a dozen shallow-water jawfish (family Opistognathidae) found in the tropical western Atlantic. Though few species match the Yellowhead in beauty, all are fascinating and attractive fish. Most are benthic predators and are best known for their construction of elaborate rock-lined burrows.

Jawfish are characterized by bulbous heads, large jaws (which on some species even extend beyond the rear of the eyes), long undivided dorsal fins, and pelvic fins inserted ahead of the pectorals. Morphologically they most resemble the species of *Gramma*, the basslets (to which they may be closely related), but their strikingly different behaviours permit easy discrimination between the two. Atlantic jawfish are not large; none exceed 8 inches in total length and many grow to no more than 3 or 4 inches.

There are approximately 60 species of jawfish around the world, in three genera (*Stalix*, *Lonchopisthus*, and *Opistognathus*). The first is found only in the Indo-Pacific.

Species Account

There are two genera of Atlantic jawfish – *Opistognathus*, which contains 14 species, and *Lonchopisthus*, with only four. The latter genus consists of fish that live in relatively deep water and that are rarely seen except under unusual circumstances. They differ from *Opistognathus* in having hard spines on the gill covers, scales on both gill covers and cheeks, a more laterally compressed body than is typical for the round-bodied species in *Opistognathus*, and a lanceolate caudal fin.

The only species of *Lonchopisthus* seen commonly in shallow water is the Swordtail Jawfish, *Lonchopisthus micrognathus*, a laterally compressed fish with graceful, flowing lines and a long, lyre-like caudal fin. Largely pale olive-green with a series of faint, pearl, vertical bands on the body, its delicate colouration and flowing fins make it an attractive, though subdued, species. Reaching a length of approximately 5 inches, it is probably widespread in the Caribbean, but is restricted to mud bottoms in deeper water (40 to 70 feet minimum) where it hovers several feet off the bottom while searching for plankton. The two other broadly distributed species are *L. lemus*, which is found in the southern Caribbean and off South America, and *L. higmani*. The former is chunky bodied with a short caudal fin, while the latter has conspicuous black spots on its gill covers.

The shallow-water species of the second genus, *Opistognathus*, fall into three more-or-less distinct types – the distinctive *Opistognathus aurifrons*, the small, deep-reef species, *Opistognathus gilberti*, and the cluster of fish collectively referred to as 'dusky' jawfish. The first, the Yellowhead, is the most attractive member of the genus and is a slender, delicate-appearing fish which reaches a total length of approximately 4 inches. Its body shimmers pale yellow while its flowing fins are faintly tinged with blue highlights. As the common name implies, specimens from areas such as Florida have a bright yellow head, with tear-drop shaped black pupils set in blue irises. There is, however, a fair amount of geographic variation in the colour pattern of the Yellowhead. In areas such as the Bahamas, the head is not yellow, but rather is white with a dark grey 'halo'. These 'haloed' fish are those most often sold on the retail market.

Opistognathus gilberti, the Yellow Jawfish (not to be confused with the Yellowhead Jawfish), is another unique Caribbean member of the genus. This small fish (4 to 5 inches maximum) is a burrow dweller found on sand slopes and ledges along the deep vertical reef wall that surrounds most Caribbean and Bahamian islands. The species is rarely seen by divers, or by collectors, because of its preference for deep water; it is rare at depths less than 90 to 100 feet and is common only below 150 feet. It is also unusual among the Caribbean jawfish in that it is sexually dichromatic, the female being a uniformly pale yellow fish, while the male combines a dusky body with snow-white dorsal, anal, and pelvic fins. The male also has two black spots — one near the forward edge of the dorsal fin and the other in the centre of the caudal fin. In both sexes a thin iridescent gold line, most apparent on the male, runs below the dorsal fin and part way down the back.

The remaining shallow-water species of *Opistognathus* are lumpy fish, characterized by heavy bodies, massive heads, bulging eyes, and mottled brown-and-grey colour patterns. As a group, they are collectively referred to as the 'dusky' jawfish. The three species common in shallow water are similar in general colour pattern, shape, and habitat preference, but can be told apart by a combination of minor characters. *Opistognathus macrognathus*, the Spotfin Jawfish, has alternating black and white bands on the roof of its mouth (probably a social signal of some kind, perhaps used in courtship) and a black spot located high on its dorsal fin and between the sixth or seventh and the ninth dorsal spines. *Opistognathus maxillosus*, the Mottled Jawfish, is similar, but lacks the banding inside the mouth and the spot on its dorsal fin is low, almost touching the body. Often pale coloured, it is the species of 'dusky' jawfish most often encountered in shallow water. Finally, *the* Dusky Jawfish, *Opistognathus whitehursti*, has the dorsal fin spot located farther forward on the fin (between the second and the fourth or fifth spines) and the spot is usually blue to greenish blue rather than black. The last species is also the smallest of the group, less than half the length of an adult Mottled Jawfish (maximum length approximately 5 inches) and a third that of the Spotfin Jawfish (maximum length around 8 inches).

Several other jawfish are typically found below diving depth in the Caribbean. *Opistognathus lonchurus*, a pale gold species with a blue line along its upper jaw, is common on deep-water mud and sand flats off shore of the reef line. Several 'dusky' jawfish, superficially similar to those described, are found in extremely deep water and are unlikely to be encountered by anyone but a professional ichthyologist.

Field Biology

Jawfish are closely tied to sand and silt bottoms, each fish digging a slender, tubular burrow in which it sits, peering out at the world and awaiting the approach of suitable prey — small crustaceans and fish. The structure, orientation, and location of the burrow vary from species to species. 'Dusky' jawfish typically build their burrows on sand patches and line the entrance with small rocks, shells, and pieces of coral collected from the surrounding area. These shy fish, when approached, back down into their burrows, usually tail first, and seldom leave it except to spawn or to strike at passing prey. The Yellow Jawfish, *Opistognathus gilberti*, is similar in general behaviour, but feeds on plankton which it engulfs during brief lunges out of its burrow. Clusters of Yellow Jawfish are usually found on the same sand ledge. Such clustering may not indicate any real gregariousness on their part, however, but may reflect, rather, the limited surface area available on the deep sand ledges where the fish is found.

In contrast to the previous species, both the Yellowhead and Swordtail jawfish are hoverers, their long flowing fins serving to keep them in position a few feet off the bottom and immediately over their burrow. Hovering vertically, their eyes constantly sweep the surrounding water column for the plankton they catch with short lunges from a vertical position. In a steady current, a number of Yellowheads, weaving in and out about one another, are a beautiful sight.

Lonchopisthus dig vertical, unlined burrows, resembling pits, in muddy areas and are most common on the deep mud flats on the lee sides of some Caribbean reefs (such as are found off Martinique and Puetro Rico) at depths in excess of 40 feet. Yellowheads are found on mixed sand-and-rubble bottoms almost everywhere the water is clean. They have been reported in areas as shallow as 10 feet and as deep as 150 feet, and from the vicinity of inshore patch reefs to relatively flat shelves on the deep wall. The two hovering species also differ with respect to their social tendencies; *Lonchopisthus* is generally solitary or is found in small groups, while the Yellowhead is very social and can be found in colonies of as many as 70 fish. Solitary individuals are rare and the minimum group size seems to be 3 or 4 fish.

The burrow of *Lonchopistus micrognathus* consists of a central, cone-shaped opening and several, non-conical accessory openings. Burrows are often quite close together, though many are frequently unoccupied. Typically, there is only one fish per burrow. The burrow of the Yellowhead Jawfish, unlike that of the Swordtail Jawfish, is lined with rocks and small pieces of coral, and ends in a roughly spherical cavity, frequently located so as to take advantage of some large buried object that both forms the roof of the cavity and partially supports the burrow itself. The construction of such a burrow is an art with these fish. On an open sand bottom, the first step is the digging of a shallow pit. Sand is carried from the pit by the mouthful and is dropped a few inches away. The fish then drags to the centre of the pit small rocks and pebbles which then form the initial burrow wall. These are arranged in a narrow ring and all sand subsequently dug out is dropped behind the ring, reinforcing it from the outside. The construction of a suitable burrow takes several hours and is a task never completely finished.

Once established, there is little aggression in stable colonies of Yellowhead Jawfish; in most cases, fighting is concentrated on defence of the burrow and directed at other species. Jawfish chase from their burrows the juveniles of many species, including several wrasses and the sand Tilefish, *Malacanthus plumieri*, while they retreat into their burrows, tail-first (or, if pursued, head-first), at the approach of a larger fish or a diver. Jawfish are apparently a delicacy for several large predators which vigorously attempt to dig them out of their burrows. Nassau groupers, for example, have been seen to lie on their sides and with vigorous beats of their caudal fins, totally obliterate not only the entrance to the burrow, but also the surrounding area, then sit back and wait for the buried jawfish to dig itself out. As soon as it breaks the surface, the grouper pounces. Fortunately for the jawfish, groupers often give up their wait after an hour or so, while jawfish have been known to remain buried, with no apparent ill effects, for as long as 8 hours.

Reproductive Biology

Jawfish produce large, demersal eggs, about 0.9mm in diameter and sphere-shaped, which the male (in a few species, also the female) carries in his mouth until hatching. Though not yet documented for all species, oral incubation will probably be shown to be the general rule for jawfish.

For many species, oral incubation by the male is the only external sexual characteristic; in all other respects, males and females are identical. The Yellowhead Jawfish, unfortunately, is one of these species. Several 'dusky' jawfish, as well as *Opistognathus gilberti*, however, are sexually dimorphic. The markedly different colour patterns of males and females of the latter have already been described; for several 'dusky' jawfish (in the Caribbean, *Opistognathus macrognathus*, and a few deep-water species), the relative length of the upper jaw is sexually diagnostic. The upper jaw bone (the maxilla) of the males extends well behind the eyes, while that of the females reaches only to the eye.

Spawning activities appear to be most common at dawn and dusk, though to date, hard data on the behaviour of only the Yellowhead Jawfish had been collected. A male Yellowhead courts a female with a broadside display, arching his back, spreading his fins, and swimming slowly several feet off the bottom. He gradually leads her back to his burrow (in some cases, a third, 'neutral' burrow may be used) which she, and then he, enter. Spawning occurs in the terminal cavity of the burrow and therefore has not been observed, but after a short period, the female emerges, followed by the male who now carries a mouthful of eggs and who holds them throughout the prolonged incubation.

The duration of the larval stage of the Yellowhead Jawfish is not known, but that of the Spotfin Jawfish, *Opistognathus macrognathus*, is about two weeks. The young settle out of the plankton literally as tiny jawfish, about ¼ of an inch long, and immediately dig equally tiny burrows, 2 to 3 inches deep and lacking a terminal cavity. Juvenile Yellowheads are common, scattered among the burrows of the adults, apparently a reflection of the colonial nature of the species.

Brooding male Yellowheads can be found off the Florida coast from late spring to early fall, though settling juveniles do not become common until mid June. In the Caribbean itself, jawfish, like most species, probably spawn year-round, with spawning bouts between a given male and female occuring at roughly two-week intervals.

Aquarium Biology

Jawfish do well in captivity and are recommended for even novice aquarists. They feed readily, are hardy, and they are peaceful, neither bothering other fishes nor, with a few exceptions, being bothered by them. The exceptions are those other fish that also like caves and burrows and are aggressive enough to push a jawfish out. Royal Grammas (*Gramma loreto*) and young groupers (*Epinephalus* spp.) are especially bad in this respect.

When introduced into a tank, jawfish invariably head for the nearest cover – a hollow under a rock, a crevice between rocks, or, if nothing else is available, the corner of the tank. The first sign of its presence usually comes the next morning when you awaken to find shallow pits dug all over your tank, sometimes with a jawfish sitting in one of them. This first busy night for the jawfish is the most critical period in keeping the fish. Jawfish in general, and the Yellowhead in particular, are highly strung fish, prone to gulp at the surface when upset and to jump when panicked. The gulping soon passes as the fish begins to settle down, but the jumping is far more serious. Most jawfish die within 24 hours of being introduced into a tank, invariably because the fish jumped out the first night. During that night, a jawfish will emerge from hiding and try to dig a burrow. In an unfamiliar area, with no cozy burrow to curl up in, the slightest jar to the tank or loud noise will cause the terrified fish to jump, over and over again. The slighest opening in the tank's cover can cost a fish.

After the first night, and especially after the animal constructs a burrow, it quiets down and the risk of losing it drops steadily, though never disappearing altogether. It is a sad truth that most jawfish in captivity, even those that survive the first critical period, are lost not because of disease or starvation, but because they jump out of a tank that an aquarist has complacently left only partially covered.

In the first few days after introduction, jawfish dig several tentative burrows and usually settle in one that almost invariably faces the back of the tank. With repeated feedings in the front, however, it will eventually get the idea and the burrow opening rapidly shifts to a more suitable position. To facilitate burrow construction, four things should be provided for the fish: relatively coarse gravel (some aquarists prefer large crushed shell), a suitably placed rock or shell under which the burrow can be constructed (if more than one jawfish is to be kept, several such rocks should be available), a deep sediment base (at least 3 inches thick) in which the burrow can be dug, and finally, a variety of small pebbles the fish can use to construct the walls of the burrow. A jawfish will scrounge the tank looking for such pebbles, dragging the larger ones back and carrying the smaller ones in its mouth. Two jawfish will steal from one another constantly and a single pebble may go back and forth every few days for months.

The 'dusky' jawfish do as well as, if not better than, the Yellowhead in captivity, but because of their more mundane colours they are less often desired by aquarists. Nevertheless, all are attractive in their own right and have distinct personalities, more so than the vast majority of fish normally kept in aquaria. Advanced aquarists, who are looking for more than just a 'pretty face', will be attracted to these fascinating species.

Like the Yellowhead, the 'dusky' jawfish also require a burrow to survive and require the same four conditions that it does; like the Yellowhead, they are usually lost because they jump out of a tank, though in this respect they are calmer than their relative and settle into a permanent hole sooner; but the 'duskies' can be picky eaters. I have done best with them by feeding a combination of live brine shrimp and bite-sized (remember they have got big mouths) pieces of shrimp and fish. They also take small, live crustaceans and fish with relish.

The remaining jawfish, both *Opistognathus gilberti* and *Lonchopisthus micrognathus*, are rarely kept in aquaria, which is unfortunate since both are attractive and not difficult to maintain. *Lonchopisthus*, with its long flowing fins and delicate colouration, rivals even the Yellowhead in beauty, especially when it's hovering in mid water. It is, however, more shy than the Yellowhead and may take several weeks to settle into a busy community tank. Both *Lonchopisthus* and *Opistognathus gilberti* have requirements similar to those of the more familiar species and do well if given reasonable care. Again, both are prone to jump.

Jawfish will breed in captivity, if fed well and not disturbed. Aside from the obvious problem of obtaining a pair, the major requirement is for a tank with enough bottom space that several fish can set up independent burrows. Though generally peaceful, the burrows are defended and 'dusky' jawfish, especially, must be allowed to space themselves well apart. More gregarious than the other species, Yellowheads will stand more crowding and should be maintained in a small colony (at least 5 fish), so that at least one pair of spawnable fish is likely to be present. Once identified, however, a pair will do well in a smaller tank. Heavy feeding and warm (75°F +) water will induce such a pair to spawn regularly.

Relevant Literature

Colin, P. L. 1971. 'Interspecific relationships of the Yellowhead Jawfish, *Opistognathus aurifrons* (Pisces: Opistognathidae)', *Copeia* 1971 (3): 469–473

Colin, P. L. 1972. 'Daily activity patterns and effects of environmental conditions on the behaviour of the Yellowhead Jawfish, *Opistognathus aurifrons*, with notes on its ecology', *Zoologica* **57**(4): 137–169

Colin, P. L. 1973. 'Burrowing behaviour of the Yellowhead Jawfish, *Opistognathus aurifrons*', *Copeia* 1973 (1): 84–89

Colin, P. L. & Arneson, D. W. 1978. 'Aspects of the natural history of the Swordtail Jawfish, *Lonchopisthus micrognathus*, off southwestern Puetro Rico (Pisces: Opisthognathidae)', *J. of Nat. Hist.* London **12**

Leong, D. 1967. 'Breeding and territorial behaviour in *Opisthognathus aurifrons* (Opistognathidae)', *Die Naturwissenschaften* **54**(4): 97

Mead, G. W. 1957. 'The Western Atlantic jawfishes of the Opisthognathid genus *Lonchopisthus*', *Stud. Fauna Suriname Other Guyanas* **2**: 104–112

Smith-Vaniz, W. F. & Colin, P. L. (in press). 'Systematics and biology of Western Atlantic Jawfish (Pisces: Opisthognathidae)', *Proc. Acad. Nat. Sci. Phila.*

Chapter 17

Plectognaths

The term 'plectognath' translates literally from its Greek roots as 'twisted jaw' and refers to the mouth structure of a variety of related fish common both on the reef and near shore throughout the world's tropical seas. The order Plectognathi, or Tetraodontiformes, contains four families that most observers would hardly believe to be related: the Balistidae (triggerfish and filefish), the Ostraciidae (trunkfish and cowfish), the Tetraodontidae (puffers), and the Diodontidae (porcupinefish). All are characterized, however, by the absence of spiney rays in the dorsal and anal fins and the presence of a small, but very powerful mouth, often with a hard, beak-like set of jaws and prominent teeth. They are believed to be a specialized off-shoot of some surgeonfish-like ancestor.

Most of the Caribbean plectognaths are inshore fish, living in sea grass beds and on sand flats in very shallow water. Only a few species, generally the most colourful, are found on the reef, but despite their small number, these few are so strikingly different from anything else present that they are often noted, and collected for marine aquaria.

Balistidae

The family Balistidae contains the triggerfish and filefish, two groups which, though similar, have in the past often been treated as separate families. Both are characterized as strongly laterally compressed fish, high in profile, that have a somewhat projecting snout, the jaw structure typical of the order, and two dorsal fins. The second dorsal, long and low, is directly opposite an almost identical anal fin, this pair of fins being a balistid's primary means of locomotion. They are flapped in unison back and forth to propel the fish through the water.

Aside from the fact that they generally look different (triggerfish are typically big and colourful, filefish small and drab), the structure of the first dorsal fin of the two groups has been one of the major reasons they have been often treated separately. On the triggerfish, this small fin has three spines and can be 'locked' into an erect position. It is used both as a defence against predators (who might have second thoughts about swallowing a fish with sharp spines that cannot be pushed down) and as an anchoring device. When harassed, a triggerfish will dive into a crevice, wedge itself tightly, and then essentially anchor itself in place by erecting and locking its dorsal fin. The first dorsal on a filefish, on the other hand, lacks spines altogether and has been reduced to a slender and fleshy finger-like projection (the 'file'). Though superficially very different, the colourful, 'locked' fin species and the drab 'file' fin species, in fact, are only the extremes of a continuous cline of fish whose characters run smoothly all the way from one to the other. Because there is no logical break point in this cline, all of these fish have been merged into a single all-inclusive family Balistidae.

Species Account

The triggerfish end of the balistid spectrum includes some of the most colourful fish in the Caribbean, as well as a couple of drab species. Large fish (up to 18 inches maximum length), most of which are commonly seen on the reef, swim either as solitary individuals or in small groups anywhere from a few feet to a few yards off the bottom. As a general rule, they prefer areas of rapid changes in depth – along the edge of the wall, for example, the near-vertical transition from shallow reef to deep reef that rings many Caribbean and Bahamian islands.

All triggerfish have virtually the same shape – marked lateral compression, projecting snout, and large second dorsal and anal fins – but can be readily distinguished by colour pattern. The most colourful of the Caribbean species is aptly named the Queen Triggerfish, *Balistes vetula*. The Queen is somewhat variable in base colour, ranging from all-blue, to blue-and-gold, to all-grey, but invariably has a pair of parallel electric blue lines running under each eye to the snout, several red or brown wavy lines radiating from each eye, and electric blue stripes that outline the dorsal, anal, and upper and lower lobes of the caudal fin. Each fin ends in a long, streaming blue filament, another character diagnostic for the species. Another large, common, and no less spectacular species is the Black Durgon, *Melichthys niger*. Jet black, aside from a few red and green highlights around the base of the head, the black dorsal and anal fins are set off from the body by an electric blue or white line along the base of each. These lines are extremely conspicuous when the fish is propelling itself along with these fins in mid water. The last colourful species is equally distinctive. A smaller fish (maximum length approximately 8 inches), the Sargassum Triggerfish, *Xanthichthys ringens*, is pale blue with numerous dark blue markings on it. Rows of dark blue spots pepper its back, a dark blue line runs along the base of the dorsal fin with another along the anal fin, and several parallel blue slits, as if the fish has just been raked by sharp claws, run below each eye. Its crescent-shaped caudal fin is also distinctive, bearing in its centre a blood-red half moon.

The only other common Caribbean triggerfish is a large grey species whose only distinguishing mark is a black spot at the base of each pectoral fin. *Canthidermis sufflamen*, the Ocean Triggerfish, grows to almost two feet and is abundant near the edges of deep water bordering the reef. It is usually seen as a solitary individual, but sometimes occurs in small groups that frequently include Black Durgons.

Filefish are similar to the triggerfish in general body shape and fin configuration, but they are usually smaller and slimmer. The three most abundant species are all members of the genus *Monacanthus* and are small, grey, and retiring, relying on their drab colours and slow movements to hide them from predators. Distinguishing these species on the basis of anything but habitat is difficult, but fortunately one each is characteristic of three very distinct habitats. *Monacanthus tuckeri*, the Slender Filefish, is the only species common on the reef, where it is found swimming in the slowly waving fronds of soft corals. Its colours camouflage it so well in that environment that its presence is normally only discovered accidentally. A small fish, it grows to only about 3 inches and is more slender than the other two species.

The second common species is the Sargassum Filefish, *Monacanthus hispidus*, which, not surprisingly, is found only in the thick masses of the pelagic seaweed, *Sargassum*, that float about the surfaces of the world's tropic seas. In these masses, by several recent counts, this little Filefish is the most abundant fish present. Finally, the Fringed Filefish, *Monacanthus ciliatus*, is found primarily on or around inshore grass beds and mixed zones of grass, rubble, and sand. Larger than the other two species, it reaches almost 8 inches in total length and is also a little deeper bodied than they are. Males are larger and much more deeply bodied than females.

Several other grey, brown, or grey and brown, generally large filefish are found inshore in the Caribbean, but none are likely to be seen by the average diver or aquarist. The only truly distinctive-looking member of the lot, occasionally seen on the reef, is the Scrawled Filefish, *Alutera scripta*. A monster among filefish, it reaches a length of almost three feet. This large filefish is long and slender, laterally compressed, and has a large caudal fin. When on the reef, it is seen most often swimming slowly with its snout pointed towards the bottom (probably a feeding position, since its diet consists mainly of benthic algae, grasses, and coelenterates). When harassed, however, it quickly straightens out and scoots off, driven by a powerful and rapid beating of its dorsal and anal fins. The Scrawled Filefish derives its common name from the many short, wavy blue lines and small black dots scattered about on its pale brown or grey body.

Field Biology

The diet of the triggerfish varies with the habits of each species. The Queen Triggerfish is the most bottom-oriented of the group and, not surprisingly, its diet consists mainly of echinoderms (including the long-spined sea urchin, *Diadema antilarum*, which it eats shell, spines, and all), molluscs (including conchs), and crustaceans. The other species of Caribbean triggerfish are normally found off the bottom, foraging in the water currents. Their gut contents consist mainly of plankton and drifting blades of sea grass, bits of algae, and an occasional mollusc and echinoderm.

The proportion of planktonic material in the diet of these fish is probably highest when they are young. It is a common observation that one rarely, if ever, finds juvenile triggerfish on the reef. One occasionally sees small ones, but even these are small adults, not really juveniles. Exactly where the juveniles are to be found is still something of a mystery, but it has been suggested that they most probably drift in the plankton, perhaps loosely associated with floating masses of *Sargassum*, until they reach a respectable size. The Sargassum Triggerfish, *Xanthichthys ringens*, in fact, has a mottled green post-larval stage, very different from the adults, which is commonly associated with these *Sargassum* patches (hence the species' common name).

Small filefish are less mysterious, with very small individuals of at least *Monacanthus tuckeri* being found on the reef sporadically. Like the adults, these small fish remain close to the waving fronds of soft corals and are well camouflaged. *Monacanthus tuckeri* apparently subsists mainly on planktonic crustaceans, picking them from the water as they drift close to the coral. Slender Filefish are so closely tied to such corals, that they not only hide in and feed in them, but even sleep in them at night, hovering tightly against the main axis of the coral frond. An almost identical relationship exists between the Sargassum Filefish and the drifting masses of *Sargassum*, the algae not only sheltering the fish, but also providing it with food and protection from the ubiquitous open-water predators.

Little is known about the social behaviour of the balistids. Slender Filefish are commonly seen chasing one another out of soft corals, indicating that the fish is probably territorial against at least other members of its species. Other triggerfish and filefish, though occasionally seen as solitary individuals, are just as commonly found in pairs, triads, and so on, up to groups of as many as 50 fish, all co-existing with little or no overt aggression. Black Durgons and Sargassum Triggerfish probably form loose, size-based dominance hierarchies, as do many other site-attached, planktivorus fish.

Reproductive Biology

Little is known about the reproductive biology of either the triggerfish or the filefish. All appear to produce a sticky, demersal egg which, in some species, is bright green. Presumably, these eggs adhere to corals and algae on the bottom and are effectively camouflaged. There appears to be no care of eggs after spawning.

Based on their lifestyle, it is likely that the triggerfish are polygamous, that is, mating between individual males and females is largely random and no long-term pair bonds are established. What appeared to be spawning has been observed for only one species of triggerfish, the Sargassum Trigger, *Xanthicthys ringens*. Two fishes, located in about 70 feet of water, were observed to race towards one another across the reef, then to cross bodies in the shape of an 'X' and spin together in this position towards the surface. About 20 feet below the surface, the pair split apart, leaving behind a white cloud, presumably the eggs and sperm. The two fishes then disappeared and spawning was not seen again. The fertilized eggs presumably sank to the bottom. Defence of a spawning nest, a shallow depression in the sand, has been reported for a few, non-Caribbean triggerfish, and might be worth looking for among local species.

Where it has been observed, courtship among filefish involves the male hovering nose-down before a female, probably before some form of spawning clasp. For at least a few species, male filefish tend to be larger than the females, have larger anal fins, and are more brightly coloured. The same is basically true for Queen Triggerfish, in which the male is not only more brightly coloured than the female, but also has longer filaments trailing from his dorsal, anal, and caudal fins.

Aquarium Biology

All the smaller balistids do well in community aquaria, with *Xanthichthys* the best of the triggerfish and

Monacanthus tuckeri and *Monacanthus hispidus* the best of the filefish. All three species feed voraciously on practically anything given them and grow rapidly if captured when small. All are active, peaceful fish, though larger *Xanthichthys* can become bullies towards smaller fish, especially if the latter are introduced well after the triggerfish has had a chance to establish prior residency.

The large and colourful triggerfish also do well in captivity, but they are suitable only for very large private aquaria and public exhibition tanks. They tame quickly, learning to eat from your hand in a short period, are colourfast, and hardy.

Breeding the smaller species may be possible for the average aquarist, but with so little known about their reproductive biology it is difficult to predict just when or in what manner spawning would occur. The most likely candidate for aquarium spawning among the Caribbean species is the Sargassum Triggerfish, *Xanthichthys ringens*, which is not only small and gregarious at maturity, but which also adapts beautifully to aquarium conditions. Heavy feeding with a liberal mixture of live foods should be enough to get the fish into spawning condition. The only critical factor is likely to be aquarium size, as the best approach will probably be to keep four or five fish together until pairing can be seen. Based on the single observed spawning of the species in the field, it is likely that a large aquarium, 100 gallons or more, will be required in order to provide the fish with enough room to perform their energetic spawning act.

Ostraciidae

The trunkfish, or cowfish, are the familiar small, round species that are encased in a living box of armour plating. A rigid set of skeletal plates completely covers each animal, except for a few small holes through which the eyes, the mouth, and the fins protrude. Several species also have various spines, bumps, and ridges at different spots on the armour, apparently adding to the protection such plating affords them from large predators. Several species, those in the genus *Acanthostration*, derive their common name from the location of such spines; each cowfish has a long sharp spine jutting forward from the skull just above each eye.

Rigidly encased as they are, normal modes of swimming are clearly impossible for these fish. They have, instead, evolved their own type of swimming, referred to, naturally, as 'ostraciiform' swimming, in which the primary motive power is provided by sculling the dorsal and anal fins, as in the balistids, and beating the pectorals while the body itself remains rigid. Such swimming is slow, but with its solid armour, trunkfish apparently have little need to go fast. When and if extra speed is necessary, however, they can also beat the caudal fin, resulting in a sculling type of motion which can shoot them off with short bursts of speed.

Species Account

There are two common genera of Caribbean trunkfish, *Acanthostracion* and *Lactophrys*, with five species between them. Most are relatively large (1½ to 2 feet maximum length) and common inshore around sand and mud flats and sea grass beds. Only one species is commonly seen on the reef, and that is the smallest of the group. *Lactophrys triqueter*, the Smooth Trunkfish, is a lumpy round animal, peppered by large white spots and blotches on a web-like black background. It grows to a maximum size of approximately 11 inches and is characterized by a flat bottom to its armour (viewed from head-on, the fish is shaped like a broad triangle, point up), large, fleshy lips, and big black eyes. The dorsal and anal fins are both small and fan-shaped and the caudal fin is broad and trimmed with black.

Field Biology

The Smooth Trunkfish is a common reef species, found on sandy and low-profile reefs in depths from less than 10 feet to at least 60 feet. They clearly prefer sandy areas to fully developed reef, such that in the latter areas they are generally found around the edges of coral development. This preference is made clear by the fish's mode of feeding. *Lactophrys* is a suction feeder, sucking sand and detritus off the bottom through its fleshy tube-like mouth, eating the organic material and small organisms in the mass, and then spitting out the remains. They are seen head-standing on the reef, sitting just off the bottom while blowing a strong jet of water into the bottom, scattering the sand and detritus and apparently hunting for the worms and other buried organisms that make up the bulk of their diet.

Like other trunkfish, *Lactophrys* is capable of secreting a powerful poison from glands located on its body and head. This poison, called ostracitoxin, is deadly not only to most invertebrates, but is one of the few that is also toxic to fish. Current thought has it that the chemical is a stress secretion, released when the fish is attacked or harmed, and that it serves to protect the animal further from the large predatory fish that it obviously cannot outswim. If this is indeed the case, then this toxin provides remarkably ineffective protection, since trunkfish have been found in the gut contents of a wide variety of piscavores, including sharks, groupers, and barracuda.

Reproductive Biology
Neither the social behaviour nor the reproductive biology of the trunkfish is known in any detail. Regarding the former, trunkfish are usually solitary, suggesting either large, non-overlapping home ranges or some sort of territoriality. Regarding reproduction, trunkfish produce pelagic eggs, about 1 to 1.5mm in diameter, which hatch in approximately 48 hours. Metamorphosis from planktonic larvae to benthic juveniles takes about a week. Small juveniles are green, oval with transparent fins (they look like swimming peas) and are commonly collected in grass beds. Evidence from a number of species suggests that the males are generally smaller than the females and are more brightly coloured.

Aquarium Biology
Smooth Trunkfish, especially small ones, do very well in aquaria, but are risky fish to keep in a community aquarium, despite their good looks and peaceful manner. The culprit is the toxin they secrete. If stressed for any reason (ill health, not enough food, or harassment by a tank bully), a trunkfish can secrete enough toxin in a matter of a few hours to kill not only the entire tank population (including the invertebrates), but itself also. The effects of the toxin are almost immediate and appear to be largely non-reversible. Even when transferred to clean water, most fish will die within a few minutes of first reacting to the poison.

As a general rule, then, unless you are particularly fond of gambling, trunkfish of any kind, even the tiny juveniles occasionally found drifting about grass flats, should *never* be kept with other fish.

Tetraodontidae and Diodontidae
These two closely related families contain, respectively, the puffers and the porcupinefish. Both are capable of inflating themselves, probably as an anti-predator device (it makes them too big to be conveniently eaten), and both have spines on the body to make them even less palatable. The members of the two families can be readily separated by the length of these spines. Those on the puffers are tiny, amounting to no more than prickles, and many feel smooth; those on the porcupinefish, as the common name implies, are long and sharp. The two families also differ in the structure of their parrot-like jaws; those of the puffers have a division in the front centre of the beak, while those of the porcupinefish are completely fused into a single unit.

Species Account
There are two genera of puffers in the Caribbean, *Sphaeroides* with roughly half a dozen species, and

Canthigaster with one. The members of *Sphaeroides* are relatively large (most reach about a foot) and are generally brown with a white belly and numerous brown and black spots on the body. The most common of these on the reef is the Bandtail Puffer, *Sphaeroides spengleri*, which is characterized by a horizontal row of large black spots running down its side just below the level of the pectoral fins, and by a band of orange red across its caudal fin.

Canthigaster rostrata, on the other hand, is a colourful species, reaching a maximum length of only 4 inches. A squat, round-bodied little puffer, it is brown on top, white below, has a pair of horizontal black lines edging the white of its caudal peduncle, and has a pair of large, shining green-and-yellow eyes. The Sharpnose Puffer is common on the reef, found close to the bottom almost anywhere at depths greater than 5 or 10 feet.

There are also two genera of Caribbean porcupinefish, *Diodon* and *Chilomycterus*, the latter usually referred to as 'burrfish'. The members of the two genera can be readily separated by a study of their spines. Those on *Chilomycterus* are relatively short and are always erect; those on *Diodon* are long and normally lie flat against the body, being erected only when the fish inflates.

The only common member of the family on Caribbean reefs is the Balloonfish, *Diodon holocanthus*. This porcupinefish reaches a maximum length of approximately one foot and is pale brown with a vertical black mask through its eyes, a large black or dark brown spot at the base of its fan-like dorsal fin, and several similar spots scattered on its body. The other Caribbean member of the genus, *Diodon hystrix*, grows much larger (up to 3 feet) and lacks the large black spots.

Field Biology

The Sharpnose Puffer is found in a wide variety of habitats, including reefs. A slow-moving species, it propels itself with its pectoral, dorsal, and anal fins and is generally seen cruising about small coral heads and soft corals looking for food. It often sits, its tail slightly curved and its body angled head-down, hovering in the water a few inches off the bottom, apparently concentrating on its search for food (which is practically anything – the Sharpnose Puffer has an amazingly catholic diet and eats a little bit of everything, including sea grasses, sponges, and small invertebrates). It is apparently a territorial species, as one frequently sees them chasing one another about the reef. Their social organization has yet to be investigated in any detail, however.

Porcupinefish are not commonly seen on the reef, especially during the day. When found, they are usually hiding well back in some shallow cave or crevice and have to be prodded out into the open. They are more often seen in the open during the night and it has been suggested that they are primarily nocturnal foragers. Their food consists mainly of crustaceans, molluscs, and echinoderms, including the long-spined sea urchin, *Diadema antillarum*. Like the Sharpnose Puffer, little is known about their social behaviour.

Reproductive Biology

To date, little is known about the reproductive biology of the puffers. Females tend to be slightly larger and more colourful than males, and at least the Sharpnose Puffer, *Canthigaster rostrata*, is frequently seen on the reef in pairs. Puffer eggs are roughly 1mm in diameter, are weakly adhesive, and sink. Hatching takes place in four to five days, depending upon water temperature. Duration of the planktonic larval stage is not known, but one occasionally collects very tiny Sharpnose Puffers, roughly ⅛ inch long, that are still soft-bodied and translucent, suggesting that these are newly settled juveniles and ⅛ inch is about the maximum size of the planktonic larvae. Such juveniles are found almost exclusively at night, suggesting that this is the period when they settle out.

Among the porcupine fish, only the spawning of *Diodon holacanthus* has been described in any detail. In a public aquarium in Japan, the fish spawned in the late afternoon, with several males simultaneously pushing an inert female to the surface of the aquarium with their snouts. Immediately at the surface, eggs and sperm were released. Observations of *D. holacanthus* spawning in the field in the eastern Pacific are similar, but occurred early in the morning (just after dawn) and involved a single male with each female. Whether the differences represent population differences in behaviour or are artifacts brought about by aquarium conditions, is not known. In either case, the fish produce buoyant, colourless, and spherical eggs, about 1.7mm in diameter. Hatching takes place in about 4 days and the newly hatched larvae are approximately 2½mm long and round-bodied. Larvae less than 10 days old are covered, except for the caudal fin, with a thin shell, similar to that of adult cowfish and trunkfish (perhaps indicating their close relationship). Thereafter, the shell is lost and the larvae develop small spines. Growth is rapid and after about 3 months in the plankton a small porcupine fish, about 100mm long, settles on to the reef. Size or age of sexual maturity is not known.

Aquarium Biology
Puffers and porcupinefish do well in aquaria, but should not be kept with fish that might try to eat them. Aside from the obvious problem of loosing the puffer, one also risks loosing the entire tank. In one case, a friend had both a small grouper and a puffer in a community tank and found one day that the puffer, a *Canthigaster*, had been eaten; not only did the puffer die, but so did almost every other fish in the tank. Only the grouper survived and it was obviously miserable – pale, breathing hard and rapidly, and constantly coughing up. Roughly a day later, it spat up the partially digested puffer. As to the cause of these deaths, puffers concentrate a toxin, known as tetradotoxin, in their viscera, gonads, and liver, and though this toxin is reported not to affect fish, in the confines of the aquarium, the toxin released by the dead puffer may have been so concentrated that it resulted in the death of the tank's other inhabitants.

With this caution in mind, puffers can be kept safely in community tanks for many years. The Sharpnose Puffer is especially attractive and makes a fine addition to the average set-up. As omnivores, they eat virtually anything and are peaceful, hardy, and interesting fish to keep.

Relevant Literature

Milstein, C. B. 1971. 'Puffer Toxin of *Sphaeroides testudineus* (Tetraodontidae) in predator-prey interactions', unpublished Master's thesis, University of Puerto Rico, Mayaguez, Puerto Rico

Palko, B. J. & Richards, W. J. 1969. 'The rearing of Cowfish and related species from eggs', *Salt Water Aquar.* **5**(3): 67–70

Randall, J. E. & Randall, H. A. 1960. 'Examples of mimicry and protective resemblance in tropical marine fishes', *Bull. Mar. Sci.* **10**: 444–480

Sakamoto, T. & Suzuki, K. 1978. 'Spawning behavior and early life history of the Porcupine Puffer, *Diodon holacanthus*, in aquaria', *Japan. J. Ichthyol.* **24**(4): 261–270

Shipp, R. L. 1970. 'The Pufferfishes (Osteichthys: Tetraodontidae) of the Atlantic Ocean and adjacent waters', unpublished Ph.D. dissertation, Florida St. University, Tallahassee, Florida

Thomson, D. A. 1969. 'Toxic stress reactions of the Boxfish, *Ostracion meleagris* Shaw', *Copeia* 1969 (2): 333–352

Chapter 18

Nocturnal Fish

The fish that are most familiar to aquarists and divers are those active by day – angelfish, tangs, damselfish, and so on. These, however, are only part of the fish fauna found on the reef. At dusk, as the diurnal fish slowly withdraw into the shelter of coral crevices and sponge cavities and the predators stalk the reef looking for the unwary, another group of fish rises slowly out of the reef to forage by night. These typically red-coloured and big-eyed fish spread to all parts of the reef complex, feeding on plankton, on nocturnally active invertebrates and, to a certain extent, on each other.

The nocturnal fish are a diverse lot, united mainly by their convergence on those characters best suited for nocturnal hunting. Some reach only a few inches in length while others grow to a foot or more; some school, others are solitary; and some roam well out into the water column while others stay close to the shelter of the reef. The best-known members of this guild belong to four families: the cardinalfish (Apogonidae), the soldierfish (Holocentridae), the sweepers (Pempheridae), and the bigeyes (Priacanthidae). In addition, one very unusual nocturnal fish, in the family Anomalopidae, has recently been rediscovered in the Caribbean.

Cardinalfish

Cardinalfish are so named because of the generally deep-red colour characteristic of the group. These are the smallest and most common of the nocturnal fish, averaging no more than a few inches long. All are laterally compressed and square-bodied in profile, with large eyes, an up-turned terminal mouth, two dorsal fins, and a forked caudal fin. Most are red with one or more vertical black bars or spots. The patterning of these bars and spots is species-specific and is the easiest way to tell the species apart.

The most speciose genus of cardinalfish is *Apogon*. Of the dozen or so species that can be found in shallow water, only three are common and easily recognized. The Flamefish, *Apogon maculatus*, is the most common shallow-water member of the genus, and also the largest, reaching a maximum length of at least 5 inches. Its common name is derived from the fiery red colour of the fish shortly after collection. Its colour marks consist of a short, broad dark stripe across the caudal peduncle, a prominent black spot under the second dorsal fin, and a pair of parallel white lines extending horizontally through each eye. *Apogon binotatus*, the Barred Cardinalfish, is smaller than the flamefish and is found in deeper water. It is generally pale red, almost pink, with two thin, equally wide, vertical black bars, one across the caudal peduncle and the other connecting the second dorsal fin and the anal fin. Finally, the Whitestar Cardinalfish, *Apogon lachneri*, is bright red with a half-black, half-white spot just behind the second dorsal fin. The white portion of the spot is especially prominent. The Whitestar Cardinalfish is of the deep reef, being common on the 'wall', the near-vertical drop-off from shallow water to oceanic depths that rings most Caribbean and Bahamian islands. By day, it is found deep in caves or under ledges; even at night it does not move far from these caves.

There are only two other genera of common Caribbean cardinalfish, *Astrapogon* and *Phaeoptyx*. The former includes the Conchfish, *Astrapogon stellatus*, a black-and-white mottled fish commonly found inhabiting the mantle cavity of the Queen Conch, *Strombus gigas*, in live and dead pen shells (*Pinna*), and in the bivalve *Atrina rigida*. Though, like other cardinalfish, it forages about the reef at night, by day the Conchfish seeks shelter within the living snail. This relationship is known as 'endoecism' – one animal living inside the body of another and deriving from it no benefits but shelter (as opposed to a parasite, for example, which derives both shelter and food). Conchfish remain in their hosts throughout the day and leave them at dusk to forage close to the bottom for planktonic crustaceans. Approximately one hour before sunrise, the fish locates a conch (apparently by visual cues) and enters it through the anterior siphonal canal. The fish show no host specificity and several can often be found in the same shell.

A similar, though less complex relationship exists between the Sponge Cardinalfish, *Phaeoptyx xenus*, and the long, tubular sponges in the genera *Verongia* and *Callyspongia*. Two to three inches long, *Phaeoptyx* are pale yellow or orange with tiny black dots peppering the body, a dusky spot at the base of the caudal peduncle, another on the head, and a silvery sheen on the abdomen. Each fish spends the day deep in the cavities of the sponges, many of which are noxious and probably deter predators from coming into them after the cardinalfish. *Phaeoptyx* leaves its host at dusk to forage in loose aggregations in mid water.

Regardless of their shelter site, all cardinalfish are plankton feeders. Niche partitioning is based in part on habitat preferences and in part on preferred foraging height above the bottom. Flamefish, for example, are common on the shallow reef, often near the sea urchin, *Diadema*, and forage as solitary individuals; each fish roams about a large area around its shelter site, but rarely moves more than a few feet off the bottom. They show a degree of site-attachment, with tagged fish observed in the same cave for as long as two months. The Whitestar Cardinalfish behaves in a similar manner, but is found on the deep reef and seems to be more site attached, staying closer to its shelter site. In contrast, *Phaeoptyx* roam well out into open water to feed and are typically found in loosely coordinated schools.

Other than their general foraging patterns, little is known about the nocturnal behaviour of cardinalfish. Most are shy and when approached by a diver either flee or move into shelter. The scattered distribution of some species, such as the Whitestar Cardinalfish, suggests territoriality, but if so, how such territoriality is maintained and enforced is not known.

Because of their requirement of suitable shelter during the day, cardinalfish have evolved several close relationships with other organisms. The examples cited above of the Conchfish and the Sponge Cardinalfish, are only two of the better known cases. Another such relationship, only recently documented, is between the Sawcheek Cardinalfish, *Apogon quadrisquamatus*, and the sea anemone, *Bartholomea annulata*. During the day, the fish hover deep within the tentacles of the anemone, a precarious position at best since the cardinalfish lack any protection from the nematocysts of their hosts. Many bear external scars and some, doubtless, are killed and eaten by the anemones. Nevertheless, for the majority of the fish the relationship is still a positive one. Cardinalfish shelter in the anemone only on the broad sandy areas where no other cover is available. In such areas, even an occasionally dangerous shelter is better than no shelter at all.

Cardinalfish are also unusual, though not unique, among reef fish in that they 'mouthbrood' their eggs. Fertilized eggs, approximately a millimeter in diameter and containing a single globule of oil, are held in a large clustered ball in the mouth of the male and can usually be seen through his partially open jaws. Little is known about the courtship and spawning of cardinalfish, since both occur either at night or deep in the recesses of caves. The spawning of one non-Caribbean species, *Apogon imberbis*, however, consists of a side-by-side quivering of the male and the female, with the male's anal fin wrapped around the female's abdomen. After several seconds, the pair breaks apart and shortly thereafter the female extrudes a large ball of eggs. (The delay between the spawning clasp and egg extrusion has led to the suggestion that internal fertilization may be occurring, but such has not been experimentally confirmed and it seems unlikely.) The eggs adhere to one another because of threads that emerge from one pole of each. The male quickly engulfs the entire mass and carries the eggs in his mouth until shortly before hatching.

Phaeoptyx has also been observed in the field while spawning. The fish orient with the male perpendicular and facing the body of the female and begin quivering. The pair then move parallel to each other and their venters are brought together. The female extrudes the eggs within a few seconds and the male then turns to engulf them in his mouth. Based on a single observation in the aquarium, the spawning of *Apogon maculatus* differs from this in several respects. Before spawning, the pair swim together in tight circles for several hours, with the male on the inside with his anal fin under the anus of the female. Actual spawning was not seen (it apparently occurred at night), but one morning the male was found with 75 to 100 eggs in his mouth.

Males of some species spawn repeatedly, as evidenced by several masses of eggs, each at a different stage of development, in their mouths simultaneously. The planktonic larvae are elongate with large heads, massive eyes, and only a few pigment spots. Duration of the larval stage is not known.

Cardinalfish vary in their adaptability to captivity, in general making curious, if not active members of a community tank. By day, they stay back in the shelter of coral and rocks and emerge only briefly, even when being fed. At dusk, however, they become slightly bolder and can be seen regularly. They are hardy, disease resistant, and eat readily. Most will accept prepared foods, but they all do best when given live and thawed brine shrimp occasionally. While all species adapt to aquarium conditions, the most attractive member of the family and the one most often collected is the Flamefish, *Apogon maculatus*. For several weeks after its capture, the colours of a healthy Flamefish almost glow and several in an aquarium is most attractive. Unfortunately, this brilliance gradually fades.

Squirrelfish

Members of the family Holocentridae are found in shallow tropic seas around the world, with 9 species in 5 genera found in the shallow tropical western Atlantic. All share a number of characters: short and stocky body, large scales, spine-covered bony plates on the head, one or more spines on the rear edges of the gill covers, a deeply forked caudal fin, two dorsal fins, large jaws, and prominent eyes. The different Caribbean species can be readily identified on the basis of colour pattern and variations in a few obvious characters.

The two species in the genus *Holocentrus* are the only Caribbean squirrelfish with uneven lobes on the caudal fin (the upper lobe is longer than the lower one) and a large, flag-like second dorsal fin, much larger than the anal fin directly below it (on most squirrelfish, the second dorsal fin and the anal fin are approximately the same shape and size). Both *Holocentrus rufus*, *the* Squirrelfish, and *Holocentrus ascensionis*, the Longjaw Squirrelfish, are red with a series of horizontal white stripes on the body. During the day, such striping is not conspicuous as the fish tend to pale. The two species can be readily distinguished by the small, triangular white marks behind each dorsal fin spine of *Holocentrus rufus*, and the absence of such marks on *Holocentrus ascensionis*. The former is also the more common of the two in shallow water and is often seen by day hovering over the mouth of a shallow cave in the reef. If pressed, the Squirrelfish enters head-first, sometimes leaving its caudal fin exposed.

Adioryx are smaller than *Holocentrus*, have even-sized caudal fin lobes and same-sized second dorsal and anal fins, and have a prominent black spot near the leading edge of the first dorsal fin. Otherwise fish in the two genera are similar in shape and colour. Several *Adioryx* are found in the Caribbean, but all are similar in general appearance and none are commonly seen by divers. In contrast, the Longspine Squirrelfish, *Flammeo marianus*, is conspicuous when present. This beautifully coloured fish is similar in shape to *Holocentrus*, but has alternating horizontal stripes of gold and red, a projecting lower jaw, and a very long and very conspicuous white spine leading the anal fin. It reaches a maximum size of approximately 8 inches, but is commonly seen in the 4 to 6in range. *Flammeo marianus* is found almost exclusively on the open reef, generally at depths of 40 feet or more.

The remaining two genera of squirrelfish are each represented in the Caribbean by a single species. *Plectrypops retrospinis*, the Cardinal Squirrelfish, is electric red, short, and very spiney. Its fins are more rounded than those of other squirrelfish and its body heavier. It is also a very shy fish, rarely seen by divers even at night. Found deep in the recesses of large caves in the reef, it is usually seen only as it dives farther back into the darkness to avoid the approaching diver. The Blackbar Soldierfish, *Myripristis jacobus*, in contrast, is a common and abundant shallow-water species, often found in the back reef and around patch reefs. It is the most laterally compressed of the Caribbean holocentrids and is also one of the most colourful. Lacking horizontal stripes, its body is pale red with a darker red diagonal bar (the 'blackbar') just behind the gill covers. The leading edges of the second dorsal fin, the anal fin, the pelvic fins, and the upper and lower lobes of the deeply forked caudal fin are crisp white.

All holocentrids are predators. Some, such as *Myripristis jacobus*, feed in the water column and take predominantly crustaceans; others such as the two species in *Holocentrus*, are oriented more towards the bottom and feed on a wide variety of benthic crustaceans, molluscs, and, occasionally, fishes. Beyond their dietary preferences, little is known about the behaviour and ecology of these fish. Most species are known to produce sounds amd some are apparently territorial. *Holocentrus* have reliably been observed in the same shelter hole for as long as a month, and may remain much longer than this. Longspine Squirrelfish are strongly territorial during the day, slightly less so at night, charging at an intruder while 'grunting', quivering the body, and laterally displaying to the intruder. Along with other Squirrelfish, they also chase off grunts, mullet, and morays.

Sweepers

The sweepers, family Pempheridae, are laterally compressed, deep-bodied fish which in profile are shaped like tear-drops, with the head at the blunt end. They bear only a single, small dorsal fin; the anal fin is long, low, and even; and the caudal fin is only slightly forked. There are two species of sweeper found in the Caribbean, but only one is common. The Glassy Sweeper, *Pempheris schomburgki* is copper coloured with blue highlights, conspicuous scaling, large eyes, and a prominent red line along the base of its anal fin. It is usually found in large schools by day, swimming about inside large caves and hollow coral heads. Schools frequently contain several hundred individuals. The other species of Caribbean sweeper, the Shortfin Sweeper, *Pempheris poeyi*, is rare. It can be distinguished from its more common relative by the relative shortness of its anal fin and by the lack of a red line along the base of that fin.

Little is known about the sweepers. They are a delicate fish with deciduous scales, these falling out even when the fish is handled carefully. Though beautiful in schools and apparently an attractive addition to a large marine aquarium, they almost invariably die within a day or two of capture.

Bigeyes

Bigeyes, family Priacanthidae, are large (up to a foot long), laterally compressed red fish with large, up-turned jaws, big eyes, a squared-off caudal fin, and long and even dorsal and anal fins. The Glass-eye Snapper, *Priacanthus cruentatus*, is common in shallow water, typically seen by day hovering at the opening of a small cave, often one so small that when harassed the fish cannot get into it and must flee. Somewhat variable in colour pattern, Glass-eye Snappers range from uniform dull red to red with prominent partial bands of silver along the back. These bands can fade in and out rapidly and may be signals used in aggression and courtship. The Bigeye, *Priacanthus arenatus*, is more often found in deeper water than is the Glass-eye (usually more than 40 feet) and it is invariably uniform red. Aside from habitat and colour differences, the two species can also be separated by the shape of the gill covers. *Priacanthus cruentatus* has a large spine on the lower corner of each gill cover; *Priacanthus arenatus* lacks this spine.

Little is known about the nocturnal behaviour of the priacanthids. Both feed on large planktonic organisms, such as fish larvae, crabs, and shrimps, and are generally seen foraging a few feet off the bottom. The two species also differ in their foraging strategies, however. The Bigeye is commonly seen in schools of 4 to 8 fish, such a school typically feeding in the water column near a prominent coral head or a particularly large sea fan. The Glass-eye, on the other hand, is a solitary fish. Though it has never been studied in detail, the scattered distribution of individuals and the displays observed between individuals when they do meet suggest that this shallow-water species is territorial.

Flashlight Fish

The Caribbean Flashlight Fish, *Kryptophanaron alfredi*, in the family Anomalopidae, is the sole representative of the family in the western Atlantic and is one of the most distinctive, and least known fish in the area. The fish derives its common name from a pair of blue-green light organs, shaped like beans, one under each eye. The organs are attached at their forward end, and can be rotated slightly so that, combined with a movable flap of skin under the organ, they can be covered. The Flashlight Fish reaches a known maximum length of about 4 inches and, even aside from its light organ, looks like nothing else on Caribbean reefs. It is relatively deep-bodied and laterally compressed with large eyes, well-developed fins, and a forked caudal fin. Its body is black, darker on the head and fins and lighter on the body. There are also lines of white, reflective scales along the bases of the dorsal and anal fins and along the lateral line.

For many years, the only known specimen of the Caribbean Flashlight Fish was one that was found floating at the surface off Jamaica in 1907 and officially described and named in 1926. Despite some extensive searching, additional specimens could not be found and it was assumed that it was a very deep water species, normally found well below diving depths. This assumption seemed to be confirmed when, in 1977, a second specimen, similar to the first, was caught in a fish trap set at 600 feet. Based on the behaviour of other anomalopids (in the Pacific), it was suspected that the fish may approach the surface at night to feed, but despite extensive night diving to as much as 200 feet, none were ever observed – until 1978. Diving on a moonless night, without lights, to a depth of about 120 feet, an ichthyologist looking for the fish found several off the coast of Grand Cayman Island. Since then, they have also been found, in as little as 60 feet, at night, off Puerto Rico and Curacao. It now appears, contrary to earlier beliefs, that the Flashlight Fish is widely distributed throughout the Caribbean and apparently roams over the shallow reef at night while feeding. The reason it has not been previously discovered is that scientists have largely been looking for it in the wrong place, at the wrong times, and in the wrong way. Firstly, the fish are apparently common only on reefs at the edge of very deep, oceanic water. By day, they appear to sink to great depths and hide in caves. Secondly, they are extremely light-sensitive, so much so that even at 100 feet the light of the moon is enough to keep them from coming up. One must therefore look for them either after the moon has set, or on cloudy or moonless nights. And thirdly, because they are so light-sensitive, the presence of a diving light, even as far away as a few hundred feet, is enough to drive them into cover. Most night dives, naturally, are done with dive lights shining brightly (after all, one makes the dive to see things) and divers have probably been swimming by these distinctive and 'rare' fish for years without ever seeing them.

To find them, then, scientists carefully select the time and place of a dive, and then submerge with diving lights off. On the bottom, the paired light organs of the fish are so bright, and so distinctive, that the fish can often be located from as far away as 30 to 40 feet. Approached with lights off, the fish are quite bold and will come within inches. Typically, they are seen darting about the bottom in quick movements, searching out the shrimps, small fish, and other organisms upon which they feed. Prey are located by means of the light organs, used essentially as 'headlights'.

As yet, little is known about the behaviour or ecology of the Caribbean Flashlight Fish, though studies on it are in progress. Captured fish frequently release eggs, so that they clearly reach sexual maturity at 3 to 4 inches. One group of 9 fish milling about one another, was also observed blinking their light organs on and off, in what might have been a spawning group.

For divers interested in locating these fish, it should be emphasized that diving at night on the edge of the deep reef, without lights, is a dangerous practice. Disorientation and extreme nitrogen narcosis are common at even relatively shallow depths, due to the lack of references in the dark. Collection and observation of *Kryptophanaron* is best left to professionals.

Relevant Literature
Böhlke, J. E. & Randall, J. E. 1968. 'A key to the shallow-water west Atlantic Cardinal fish (Apogonidae) with descriptions of five new species', *Proc. Acad. Nat. Sci. Phila.* **120**(4): 175–206

Bright, T. J. 1972. 'Bio-acoustic studies on reef organisms', in 'Results of the Tektite program, ecology of coral reef fishes' (Collette, B. & Earle, S. A. eds.) *Bull. Nat. Hist. Mus. Los Angeles* (14): 45–69

Charney, P. 1976. 'Oral brooding in the Cardinalfishes *Phaeoptyx conklini* and *Apogon maculatus* from the Bahamas', *Copeia* 1976 (1): 198–200

Coleman, R. K. 1966. 'Spawning red Cardinals', *Salt Water Aquarium* 2(6): 144–148

Colin, P. L. 1975. 'Mini-prowlers of the night reef', *Sea Frontiers* 20(3): 139–145

Colin, P. L. & Heiser, J. B. 1973. 'Associations of two species of Cardinalfishes (Apogonidae: Pisces) with Sea Anemones in the West Indies', *Bull. Mar. Sci.* 23(3): 521–524

Colin, P. L., Arneson, D. W., & Smith-Vaniz, W. (in press). 'Rediscovery and redescription of the Caribbean Anomalopid fish *Kryptophanaron alfred*, Silvester and Fowler (Pisces: Anomalopidae)', *Bull. Mar. Sci.*

Dale, G. 1975. 'Observations on the Cardinalfish population of a patch reef in the Bahamas', *Hydrolab J.* 3(1): 67–75

Dewey, R. A. 1975. 'Bigeye or Glasseye?', *Sea Frontiers* 21(2): 91–94

Fishelson, L. 1970. 'Spawning behaviour of the Cardinalfish *Cheilodipterus lineatus* (Gulf of Aqaba, Red Sea)', *Copeia* 1970 (2): 370–371

Pagan-Font, F. A. 1967. 'A study of the commensal relationship between the Conchfish, *Astrapogon stellatus* (Cope), and the Queen Conch, *Strombus gigus* Linnaeus, in Southwestern Puerto Rico', unpublished Master's thesis, University of Puerto Rico, Mayaguez, Puerto Rico

Winn, H. E., Marshall, J. A., & Hazlett, B. 1964. 'Behavior, diel activities, and stimuli that elicit sound production and reactions in the Longpine Squirrelfish', *Copeia* 1964 (2): 413–425

Woods, L. and Sonoda, P. 1973. 'Order Berycomorphi, family Holocentridae' in *Fishes of the Western North Atlantic* ed. Cohen, D. M., 1(6): 331–386 (Sears Found. for Mar. Res., Yale Univ., New Haven, Conn.)

Chapter 19

Eels

The Caribbean, like most shallow seas, abounds with eels of all shapes, sizes, and colours. They emerge from their shelters at dusk and at night to forage, but by day, most are retiring and are rarely seen. Nevertheless, a poison station made on a shallow patch reef may reveal hundreds of eels, where previously only a few scattered individuals could be seen.

Eels in general are an old group, only distantly related to other fish. In part because of their long history, and in part because of their lifestyles, eels have radiated into virtually every marine environment, from rocky shorelines to deep abysmal plains. All are characterized by a very elongate and slender body, either lacking scales or possessing only a few small scales, and by a peculiar planktonic larval stage, known as the leptocephalus (a similar larva is found in related groups such as tarpon and ladyfish). A leptocephalus is leaf-shaped, that is, long and flat, largely transparent, and has minute eyes and a tiny, tooth-filled mouth. These drift in the plankton for varying periods of time, depending upon the species, then transform into a round, more-or-less normal juvenile eel. The difference between the leptocephalus and the adult configurations of a species is striking, to the extent that matching the two (which leptocephalus goes with which adult) is a problem that has been worked on by ichthyologists for many years. Even now, the larvae of some species have not been identified, nor have the adults of some larvae been determined.

Species Account

There are several families of eels in the Caribbean, but only three are likely to be seen by the average diver or aquarist: the morays (Muraenidae), the snake eels (Ophichthidae), and the garden eels (Congridae).

The morays (not moray eels!) are the eels most commonly seen on the reef. They inhabit the numerous caves and holes in and under coral and coral rock and are most often seen as just a head peering out of some crevice. Morays can be distinguished from other eels by a combination of characters: they are heavily muscled, including a bulging 'forehead' of muscles used to close the jaws; they are often laterally compressed; they usually have large and prominent canine teeth; and they lack pectoral fins. The dorsal and anal fins are both long (the anus, located at the forward end of the anal fin, is about half way down the body), and are continuous with a brief caudal fin at the tip of the body.

Four species of moray are common in the Caribbean; three are found on the reef. The most common and boldest of these is the Spotted Moray, *Gymnothorax moringua*, a 3 to 4 foot eel that is pale yellow dorsally, white ventrally, and overlaid with many dark brown spots. The size and number of spots varies greatly, such that some individuals are virtually solid brown with white highlights, while others are almost entirely white with only a few brown spots. The Green Moray, *Gymnothorax funebris*, another ubiquitous species, is, as its common name implies, uniformly bright green. It is the largest Caribbean eel, reaching a verified length of at least 6 feet (with a massive body to match) and has been reported at lengths in excess of 8 feet. A relatively shy fish, despite its size, it usually flees from approaching divers and is probably more common than supposed. The third reef-associated species is the Goldentail Moray, *Muraena miliaris*, probably the most attractive of the Caribbean eels. A small species (maximum length under 2 feet), it is brown, flecked with thousands of gold spots. These spots are minute near the head, but increase in size posteriorly, until the edges of the tail itself may be entirely gold. Though common, the Goldentail Moray is secretive and is seen less often than other morays.

One very different species of moray is also abundant in the Caribbean and in some places can be collected as easily as turning over a rock along the shore. The Chain Moray, *Echidna catenata*, is a shallow-water species which on occasion can be found above the water-line on rocky beaches. In such areas, they survive in the pockets of water under and between rocks and can often be found in great numbers. An attractive, small fish, it is dark brown with fine, interweaving vertical yellow lines, between which the brown shows as blocks of colour. On small individuals, the yellow lines may be relatively wide, creating an eel with alternating bands of brown and yellow. The Chain Moray also differs from other morays in the shape of its teeth. While the others have fine, sharp teeth adapted to eating fish, those of *Echidna* are flat and blunt, adapted for crushing the crustaceans and molluscs that make up the bulk of its diet.

The second major family of Caribbean eels, the snake eels (Ophichthidae), appear to be as common as the morays, but are even more secretive. All are burrowing species, living in the sandy stretches between coral and rock outcrops and emerging from the sand to forage. Round-bodied, well-muscled eels, they have pointed snouts, large bulbous heads (because of a broadly extended set of gill arches under the skull), and pectoral fins. The size of these fins varies from species to species. Most species also have a hard, sharp tail and lack a caudal fin altogether. Because of their shape and their habit of crawling over the reef looking for food, these eels strongly resemble snakes and are the probable cause of 'sea snake' sightings in the tropical western Atlantic.

While several snake eels can be found in the Caribbean, only one, the Goldenspotted Snake Eel, *Myrichthys oculatus*, is seen commonly in shallow water. Reaching a maximum length of approximately 3 feet, it is greenish-brown with a series of brown-ringed gold spots scattered about the body. It is common in turtle grass beds and on nearby reef complexes, where it is usually seen poking about coral rubble hunting for small crustaceans.

The Garden Eel, *Nystactichthys halis*, is unique among Caribbean fish. A plankton-picker, this congrid eel is found in large colonies on fine sand and silt bottoms between coral outcrops. Each fish is long and slender, reaching a maximum length of approximately 2 feet, and sits in a mucous-lined burrow dug in the bottom. The last third of the fish remains in the burrow at all times while the forward two-thirds rears up into the water and is bent, candy-cane fashion, into the current. Often found in immense numbers, the eels form 'gardens' of weaving, bobbing heads as each fish picks from the flowing water the planktonic crustaceans that constitute the bulk of its diet. Colour pattern varies somewhat, but is usually some combination of a black anterior and white posterior.

Field Biology

With the exception of the Garden Eel, all eels are predators. The morays (except for *Echidna*), for example, are fish-eaters – damselfish and cardinalfish being the most common prey items. There is as yet some question of exactly when and how morays feed. The general literature reports them to be nocturnal fish, roaming over the reef at night and peering into crevices for quiescent, day-time active species. Yet, for a supposedly nocturnal predator, a surprisingly small number of morays are actually seen at night. The Goldentail Moray, especially, is generally seen actively foraging during the day. These observations, coupled with the large and well-developed eyes of all species, suggest that morays follow the normal activity cycle of reef predators – feeding opportunistically at any time with periods of peak feeding at dawn and dusk.

The relationship between morays and other reef fish often extends beyond simple predators and prey, however. A moray foraging by day, for example, is usually accompanied on its rounds by a grouper, usually one of the smaller species in *Epinephelus*, which follows the eel from hole to hole as it quietly and unobtrusively slips from one to the other. The relationship between eel and grouper is, in this case, probably one-sided, the grouper following the eel in order to be in a position to pounce on small fishes or crustaceans the eel may scare up on its wanderings.

A somewhat less obvious relationship exists between morays and a variety of daytime-active fish, such as surgeonfish, angelfish, and damselfish. These smaller fish frequently swim well out of their way to approach and display to a quietly sitting moray, sidling up to it and approaching so closely as to push against its jaws. In most cases, the moray either pulls back into its shelter hole or, in cases of extreme harassment, may flee the area altogether. In no case has an eel been observed to strike out at or bite such a displaying fish. Exactly what is happening between the eel and the other species, and what function it might serve, has never been investigated.

Most aspects of the field biology of the morays are in a similar state. Repeated sightings of distinctive, very large individuals in the same cave for several years suggest that at least these larger fish do not move around much. Most, if not all individuals, probably have a limited home range within which they roam and forage. So far as is known, morays are not territorial (fighting between morays has not been reported), but again, since the eels spend most of their time out of sight in crevices, such fighting would rarely, if ever, be seen.

As a final note concerning the reef-dwelling morays, large eels have engendered an immense folklore of being wildly vicious creatures that will attack a diver and hold him underwater in the grip of their 'bulldog' jaws until the diver drowns. Most stories are largely just that – stories. Morays are shy animals that will disappear into their crevices when approached. Most attacks on humans result from idiot lobster hunters reaching into crevices to feel around for the crustaceans, only to put their hands into the mouth of a terrified and trapped eel. Under such conditions, the eel seems to be justified in biting. The bulldog grip is also unlikely since morays have to open their mouths to breathe. Of necessity, they must free any diver who has the sense not to panic. Those that flail around wildly only succeed in further scaring the eel, causing it to bite down even harder. Despite their shyness, however, anything 6 or 7 feet long armed with large, sharp teeth can do considerable damage if provoked and there are several apparently reliable reports of large eels attacking divers. Morays in general are harmless, but large ones are best left alone.

In contrast to the fish-eating species, the Chain Moray, *Echidna catenata*, is an innocuous fish which spends most of its time rumaging under rocks for crustaceans and soft-bodied invertebrates. The former it crushes with its plate-like molariform teeth. Prey are detected by a combination of two systems – olfaction and touch. First, prey are smelled from relatively long distances and are homed in on by the eel. At close range, striking the prey is triggered by the eel touching it with any one of a series of delicate touch receptors on the head. Sight plays little or no role in the entire process, which in part accounts for the poorly developed eyes of this species. Other than its hunting habits and preferred habitat, little is known about the biology of this attractive little eel.

The same is basically the case for the ophichthid eels. They feed primarily on crustaceans, can be found foraging both during the day and at night, and prefer areas of mixed sand, rubble, and sea grass. They are efficient burrowers, apparently able to burrow both tail-first and head-first. Other than these few facts, their biology is largely unknown.

The Garden Eel, *Nystactichthys halis*, is another species that has yet to be studied in any detail; however, two of its near relatives living in the Red Sea have been studied. *Nystactichthys*, *Gorgonasia sillneri*, and *Taenioconger hassi* are all diurnal fish most active when there is a strong current flowing by. At least for the latter two species, males are territorial, displaying to one another both by frontal thrusting and lateral displaying with outspread fins, and by active biting, usually one fish seizing the other just behind the head. Such battles are usually over access to females rather than any defence of the burrow. These burrows are constructed easily by the eel, it literally swims backwards through the sand and drives the hard tip of its tail deep into the bottom with short, powerful flexes of its body. Sand is carried out of the new burrow by a current of water propelled by vibrating the long dorsal fin. The burrows walls are reinforced by a mucous coat secreted by the fish.

Reproductive Biology

Because of their secretive nature, nothing is known about the spawning behaviour of the morays, aside from the fact that they are not hermaphroditic. The same is basically true for the ophichthids, though observations on one non-Caribbean species suggest that the eels may spawn near the ocean's surface at night. (There is at least one report of 'sea snakes' in the Caribbean swarming at the surface at night.) Both morays and ophichthids, like other eels, have leptocephalus larvae. Those of the morays have been caught near the reef, which suggests that spawning by morays occurs on or near the reef, and that the larval stage, for an eel, may be a short one. Newly metamorphosed individuals (probably 3 to 4 inches long) head straight into the maze of tunnels under the reef, hiding there and feeding on small invertebrates until they are large enough to approach safely the reef's surface.

The spawning behaviour of *Nystactichthys* has never been described, but that of its Red Sea relatives has been studied. In these species, males become extremely aggressive towards other males for several days prior to spawning. On the day of spawning, he reaches over and butts a female several times on her side. The two spread their fins broad side towards one another and the male retreats, the female following. The smaller female then wraps a single loop of her body around the male and may hold this position for several hours. During this period, sperm is transferred to the genital opening of the female and her newly fertilized eggs are released into the water. Duration of the leptocephalus stage is not known. Newly settled juveniles, approximately 2 inches long, settle in among the colony of adults. Like most reef fish, they probably reach sexual maturity within a year.

Aquarium Biology

The suitability of the Caribbean eels for captivity varies from group to group. Reef morays, for example, generally do well in aquaria while the related Chain Moray does poorly. The former require only well-aerated water, a hole-filled substrate in which to roam and from which they can peer out, and an adequate supply of small fishes and pieces of shrimp. Like all such predators, they are not adverse to eating smaller aquarium inhabitants, including each other. Almost the only problem with the group is their propensity to escape from a tank, which should therefore be well-sealed. Morays are excellent at wriggling through the smallest holes and, while hardy, do poorly if left for too long on the living-room floor (where they are also prone to give heart attacks to emotionally less stable persons).

In contrast, the little Chain Moray is not recommended for any but advanced hobbyists. Though the small size of this species at maturity makes them a tempting addition to a community tank, they are both very secretive (such that once released in a tank, you may never see them again) and difficult to feed. They will not readily accept either prepared foods or even free-swimming live foods, but rather require small crabs and shrimps.

Snake eels also do poorly in captivity. While individuals vary in their adaptability, as a group they are secretive and poor feeders.

Adult Garden Eels also adapt poorly to captivity, but small ones (4 inches or less) do fairly well. Aside from the obvious requirement of a deep bed of fine gravel in which they can construct burrows, they also require a steady current (such as that produced by a power filter) into which they can face. At least initially, they should be fed live brine shrimp, but they will gradually acclimate to frozen shrimp and prepared foods.

Garden Eels are not generally available on the retail market, largely because they are difficult to catch. Neither anaesthetics nor conventional nets and slurp guns are of any use in capturing these shy, and fast, animals. One technique that will get them is the use of a miniature lasso of monofilament line or thread. Placed around the slightly oval burrow opening and held in place by a couple of small rocks, the loop is quickly drawn tight by a diver (located at the other end of the line, about 30 feet away) just as the eel emerges after its fright. With luck, this quick jerk sometimes snags the eel. Even so, the slightest slack in the line will allow the fish to slip free and disappear back into the bottom.

Relevant Literature

Bardach, J. E., Winn, H. E., & Menze, D. W. 1959. 'The role of the senses in the feeding of the nocturnal reef predators *Gymnothorax moringa* and *G. vicinus*', *Copeia* 1959 (2): 133–139

Gruber, M. A. 1973. 'Defensive and avoidance reactions of Octopuses to the presence of Moray eels', unpublished Ph.D. dissertation, University of Miami, Coral Gables, Florida

Fricke, H. W. 1970. 'Okologische und verhaltensbiologische Beobachtungen an den Röhrenaalen *Gorgonasia sillneri* and *Taenioconger hassi* (Pisces, Apodes, Heterocongridae)', *Zeit. für Tierpsychol.* **27**(9): 1076–1099

Chapter 20

Miscellaneous Fish I
Herbivores

Although many fish on the reef feed wholly or partially on algae, sea grasses, or both, on Caribbean reefs, only the members of two families, Scaridae, the parrotfish, and Acanthuridae, the surgeonfish, are characteristically grazers, roaming across the reef often in large, herd-like schools and foraging on the algae that grows sporadically everywhere. Members of both of these families are extremely abundant; between them, in fact, they virtually outnumber all the other fish on the reef and form the largest part of the reef fish bio-mass.

Though the fish of the two families are similar in their trophic status and, to a certain extent, have evolved similar social systems (both form large schools, for example), they are not closely related and differ in many respects, including body shape, colour, size, reproductive biology, and feeding strategy.

Scaridae

Parrotfish are in many respects similar to the wrasses (family Labridae) to which they are closely related. Both are protogynous hermaphrodites, with similar spawning patterns; both characteristically have several alternate and very different colour patterns within each species; and both tend to swim entirely by the pectoral fins, using the caudal fin only when an extra burst of speed is required. They differ, however, in a number of ways, the most obvious of which is jaw structure. Along with large and heavy scales in even rows on the body and head, a discontinuous lateral line, and a plethora of internal features, parrotfish are characterized by a set of prominent horny beak-like jaws, while the wrasses have jaws with many conspicuous and sharp conical teeth. The close relationship between the two families is well illustrated by two very primitive Caribbean parrotfish, which are intermediate between the two in dentition. *Cryptotomus roseus* and *Nicholsina usta* have fused teeth, the beginnings of beaks, but on the free edge of these teeth there are rows of separate points, rather than the single point characteristic of a beak.

From these primitive wrasse-like species, two main lines of parrotfish evolution have developed – the *Sparisoma* group and the *Scarus* group. *Sparisoma* is apparently restricted to the Caribbean, with species that tend to be small (less than a foot in total length), brown or grey fish (with a few colourful exceptions) that generally forage alone or in small groups, and that are often characteristic of grass beds rather than the reef proper. Scarids, conversely, tend to be large (up to 4 feet), colourful, forage in small to very large schools, and are typically found on or near reefs. The two also differ in jaw configuration: when a *Sparisoma* closes its mouth, the lower jaw lies outside of and covers over the upper jaw; in *Scarus* the opposite is true.

Species Account

Most of the major and common parrotfish in both genera can be readily identified on the basis of colour pattern alone. All have roughly the same shape – elongate bodies, only slightly laterally compressed, blunt heads, and long and even dorsal and anal fins – and, aside from colour pattern, look similar. Regarding colour, identification is complicated by different colour patterns in each species for juveniles, intermediate-phase fish (males and females), and the dominant males, in a manner parallel to that in the wrasses. Unlike the wrasses, however, the identification of juvenile parrotfish is difficult, as most of them look a great deal alike. Small *Scarus* are usually brown with white horizontal stripes; most small

Sparisoma are brown flecked with green, and lack such stripes. Adults, however, can usually be keyed out with little difficulty.

Only two species of *Sparisoma* are likely to be encountered on the reef: the Stoplight Parrotfish, *Sparisoma viride*, and the Redband Parrotfish, *Sparisoma aurofrenatum*. The former is the largest member of the genus, some fish reaching as much as 20 inches, and is also the most common on the shallow reef. Dominant males are a bright combination of blue-green and yellow. The body is solid blue-green, with yellow lines radiating from the mouth, yellow dorsal and pectoral fins, an anal fin that is yellow and edged with electric blue, and a crescent-shaped caudal fin that starts as a yellow spot on the caudal peduncle, then continues with vertical bands of green, yellow, and finally electric blue. Intermediate-phase fish are drab by comparison, red brown above and dull red below with all fins but the clear pectorals red. On both dominant-phase and intermediate-phase fish, the scale rows on the body are conspicuous.

Sparisoma aurofrenatum is both less colourful and smaller (maximum size approximately 1 foot) and is most common on the deep reef, usually seen in groups of two or three fish. Dominant males have a bright green back, a pale streak of yellow running along each side of the body, a red line that runs up from the mouth to cross the head just below the eye, and a small black-and-yellow spot just above each pectoral fin. Intermediate-phase fish are smaller, grey-green with red dorsal and anal fins, and have a conspicuous white spot at the rear base of the dorsal fin.

Six species of *Scarus* are likely to be encountered on the reef, with the two smallest being the most common and the three largest the least. *Scarus taeniopterus*, the Princess Parrotfish, and *Scarus croicensis*, the Mottlefin Parrotfish, are conspicuous species on shallow to mid-depth reefs, sometimes occurring in schools of as many as several thousand individuals. The two species, apparently closely related, are both small (maximum length approximately 1 foot) and have similar colour patterns. Intermediate-phase individuals are especially difficult to tell apart. Both are brown, each with a pair of broad white horizontal stripes running down each side of the body. The only obvious difference between the two is a dark edge on the top and bottom of the caudal fin on the Princess Parrotfish, these edgings being absent on the Mottlefin. Dominant males are more colourful, and they are somewhat easier to tell apart. Both have a broad dark stripe running down the centre of each side of the body, and they are grey-green above the stripe and white below it. The Princess Parrotfish, however, has a conspicuous spot of yellow in the centre of the dark stripe and has even bands of alternating colours on the unpaired fins. Mottlefin Parrotfish also have a yellow mark, but it is reduced and far less conspicuous, and the unpaired fins have a complex mottling of yellow wavy lines on a green background.

A third common reef *Scarus* is intermediate in size between these two smaller species and the three giants. *Scarus vetula*, the Queen Parrotfish, reaches a maximum size of approximately 2 feet and can readily be distinguished by its colour patterns. Intermediate-phase fish are superficially similar to those of the two smaller *Scarus*, but generally have only a single broad white band running down the centre of each side, rather than two thinner bands. Males are green, with several wavy yellow lines running between the jaw and the eyes, a yellow band at the base of the anal fin, and conspicuous yellow upper and lower lobes on the caudal fin. *Scarus vetula* typically does not form the large schools characteristic of the smaller *Scarus*, but rather is seen commonly in loose feeding aggregations of four or five individuals, generally one dominant male and several intermediate phase fish.

The remaining three *Scarus* all reach a maximum length of approximately 4 feet and are seen less commonly in shallow water than their smaller relatives. The Blue Parrotfish, *Scarus coeruleus*, is, not surprisingly, blue – dark blue above and paler blue below. Males and females have virtually identical colour patterns (which is true for all three of these large species), but can be told apart on the basis of the shape of the head. Males typically have a very blunt head, almost flattened in front, while females have the more typical round-headed parrotfish look. Juveniles are pale blue with a yellow wash on the head. The Midnight Parrotfish, *Scarus coelestinus*, is also blue, but is much darker, almost blue-black. There are several patches of lighter blue on the head and around the eyes. Finally, *Scarus guacamaia*, the Rainbow Parrotfish, has an orange head, venter, and fins, while the rear half of the back, and the mouth, are shiny green. Like *Scarus vetula*, all three of the large *Scarus* are seen in small groups, again

Terminal phase males of the Striped Parrotfish, *Scarus croicensis*, are territorial during spawning periods, but in most areas forage with the large initial phase herds during the rest of the day.

The factors that result in the change from yellow to blue in juvenile Blue Tangs is not well understood. It is paralleled by a change in the behaviour of the fish, however – from territoriality to schooling.

Juveniles of the Doctorfish, *Acanthurus chirurgus*, are similar to those of the Ocean Surgeonfish, but are more common closer to shore.

Full adult Blue Tangs are darker than the blue juveniles, and have a yellow line surrounding and emphasizing the 'scalpel' located on the caudal peduncle.

At night, sleeping Blue Tangs develop a barred pattern. Similar bars at night are characteristic of many reef fishes.

Small juveniles of the Blue Tang, *Acanthurus coeruleus*, are yellow, and strongly territorial.

Adult Ocean Surgeonfish, *Acanthurus bahianus*, are characterized by the prominent white band around the caudal peduncle, and by the short blue lines radiating from each eye.

The Coney, *Epinephelus fulvus*, varies widely in colour. This black Coney shows the two features characteristic of all colour phases, however, large red eyes and small blue spots peppering the body.

The Golden Coney, *Epinephelus fulvus*, is a beautiful fish that is far less common that its more drab relatives.

The Red Hind, *Epinephelus guttatus*, is one of several small groupers that are cryptically coloured and that capture prey from ambush.

The Creole Fish, *Paranthias furcifer*, is an unusual grouper that has specialized as a water-column forager. Compare its shape with the similarly specialized Yellowtail Snapper

The Soapfish, *Rypticus saponaceus*, photographed while hunting at night.

consisting of one male and several females.

Field Biology

As stated earlier, all parrotfish are herbivores, roaming over the bottom and scraping algae off rocks and coral with their horny beaks. Unlike their Indo-Pacific counterparts, the Caribbean parrotfish are not thought to eat live coral regularly and deliberately; rather, the coral material injested by the Caribbean species is thought to be incidental to their normal feeding process of scraping algae off coral surfaces.

Roaming as they do over the reef, parrotfish remind one of a herd of cows. At least superficially, the similarity in behaviour between the two very dissimilar groups of animals is striking. Both normally forage in small groups, apparently drifting aimlessly and foraging sporadically on an abundant and constantly growing food supply. Both are also organized into similar social units, that is, small herds dominated by a single male. To continue the comparison, male parrotfish, like bulls, often chase one another and are at least sporadically territorial, while the 'placid' females continue their regular foraging. Finally, like cattle, parrotfish are often organized into huge 'herds' that are, in part, an anti-predator device (the presence of so many parrotfish in one small place is thought to confuse the predators and prevent them from targeting on any one as a prey item; in this respect, parrotfish are a major component in the diets of many reef piscavores) and, in part, a means of overwhelming the defences of smaller, strongly territorial herbivorous species. Many benthic fish, and especially the damselfish, are herbivorous and defend their supplies of growing algae against other herbivores, including parrotfish. Against such vigorous defence, a single parrotfish can do little but flee. However, when several thousand parrotfish descend on a single damselfish territory, the defender, despite its wild and frenzied chasing, can drive off no more than a small number of intruders. The rest contentedly munch on the bottom and effectively strip the area of anything edible, in the process destroying coral and ripping up much of the benthic sessile invertebrate fauna.

Feeding this way, the amount of material parrotfish crop each day is tremendous. One study estimated that in one day, reef fish defecate as much as a ton of calcareous sand particles per acre of reef. The primary agents of such destruction are the parrotfish.

Aside from their ecological role as bio-eroders, the parrotfish are also well known for their sleeping habits. The members of the genus *Scarus*, though not *Sparisoma*, produce a mucous cacoon every evening which completely covers them and within which they spend the night. It has been suggested that this cocoon serves to protect the parrotfish from the nocturnal foragings of morays, which hunt primarily by scent. Theoretically, the cocoon seals in any odour the parrotfish might generate until morning, so that the eels cannot home in on it to the sleeping, and supposedly defenceless, parrotfish.

Reproductive Biology

Spawning in parrotfish, like that of the wrasses, is a complicated affair with two alternate spawning systems available to most species. Intermediate-phase males and females group-spawn, several hundred fish milling about an area and then rushing *en masse* for the surface in close formation. The rush ends a few yards off the bottom and the mass breaks up, each fish heading back to the bottom. Behind them, they leave a cloud of eggs and milt which slowly drift off in the current. Such mass spawnings usually take place in late afternoon and occur around rocky promentories and such on the edge of deep water. The fish, having spent most of the day on the shallow reef foraging, migrate into this deeper water to spawn. Particularly attractive spawning sites may be used year round, day after day, for years.

Dominant males do not partake in such mass spawnings, but rather, like supermale wrasses, individually court and spawn with passing females. Such males are strongly territorial, chasing not only each other, but also other parrotfish. Spawning for such fish is like that of the wrasses, a pair rushing towards the surface together and at the peak of the rush releasing the eggs and sperm. For most species, pair spawning typically occurs late in the day or at dusk.

All parrotfish produce large, pelagic eggs, those of *Scarus* eliptical and about 2 to 3mm in diameter, those of *Sparisoma* spherical and only 1 to 2mm in diameter. Duration of the larval stage is not known.

Aquarium Biology

Though most of the parrotfish are much too large as adults for anything but large public aquaria, smaller ones, and the young of the larger species, adapt well to captivity and can become an interesting, somewhat unusual, addition to a community tank. They readily accept thawed brine shrimp and flake food, but in addition require algae-covered rocks and coral on which they can browse throughout the day. To put a young, growing parrotfish in a sterile aquarium is a cruel act; even if fed several times daily, the fish will soon starve.

Large parrotfish can also be annoying because of the large amounts of fecal material they excrete each day. Parrotfish, feeding constantly, also defecate constantly, and unless this has been taken into account, they can impose a strain on a filtering system.

Acanthuridae

The surgeonfish, or tangs, are high-bodied, laterally compressed fish with small, terminal mouths, long undivided dorsal fins, big eyes, and steeply sloping foreheads. Like the parrotfish, they are grazers, often seen roaming in schools about the reef and foraging upon a variety of plant and animal materials.

Surgeonfish derive their common name from a small, sharp spine which lies along each side of the caudal peduncle and which is referred to as a 'scalpel'. Those of the Caribbean species lie in small slits in the skin, sheathing the spine when not in use, and are hinged anteriorly such that they can be flipped out 'for action'. This spine is used by the fish during fights for dominance or territories, and apparently as defence against predators. The display patterns normally used by the fish invariably focus on the spine and in all species the area around it is enhanced by contrasting colour. During an aggressive encounter, two surgeonfish will circle each other warily, each fish with its fins fully spread and its body flexed so that the scalpel can be aimed at its opponent. Such displays may go on for several seconds before the fish break apart and with a sudden rush go off chasing one another.

Species Account

There is only one genus of surgeonfish in the tropical western Atlantic, *Acanthurus*, with three, widely distributed and common species in the Caribbean. All three grow to approximately 1 foot long and are virtually identical in shape and gross external morphology. They can be readily identified on the basis of colour pattern, however.

The most distinctive of the three species is the Blue Tang, *Acanthurus coeruleus*, which, not surprisingly, is deep blue. Its only colour mark is a thin ring of yellow encircling the scalpel on each side of its caudal peduncle. As juveniles, the Blue Tang is not blue, but is rather bright yellow (younger ones are generally paler than older ones) and is known as the Yellow Tang. The size at which a given fish transforms from the yellow to the blue stage varies widely, such that one can find both 3in Blue Tangs and 6in Yellow Tangs. The factor (or factors) controlling colour change is not known, but is probably social.

The actual transformation is a gradual one, involving first the body and then the caudal fin. Initial transformation starts with the body darkening from yellow towards grey, then to a blue-grey, and finally brilliant light blue. At this stage, the yellow tail of the fish contrasts sharply with the blue body. Finally, the caudal fin changes to blue as well. With maturity, the light blue of the juvenile slowly darkens until it reaches the deep blue of the adult.

The two remaining species of *Acanthurus* are mahogany brown, both as adults and as juveniles, and

The Yellowtail Snapper, *Ocyurus chrysurus*, is commonly seen in small schools over the shallow reef. It feeds in the water column, and so is more streamlined than its bottom-oriented relatives.

Lizardfish, such as *Synodus intermedius*, are voracious predators armed with strong jaws and rows of fine, sharp teeth.

Adult Porkfish, *Anisotremus virginicus*, are one of the more common inshore grunts. They are often found in large schools.

The Bluestriped Grunt, *Haemulon sciurus*, is found on the reef, where it spends its days hovering around coral heads, and its nights foraging over nearby sand and mud flats.

The Sky Snapper, *Apsilus dentatus*, is the juvenile of a large, reddish snapper found below divable depths. Even the juveniles are not common at depths less than 200 feet. This one was photographed at 160 feet.

Sharksuckers, *Echeneis naucrates*, are occasionally seen on the reef, where they attach to parrotfish, snappers, sharks, and, sometimes, divers.

The spots on the side of a Spotted Goatfish, *Pseudopeneus maculatus*, fade in and out, and may serve a function in communication between fish.

The Red Spotted Hawkfish, *Amblycirrhitus pinos*, is a common, but rarely seen inhabitant of shallow reefs. It is the only member of its family found in the western Atlantic.

This young Sand Tilefish, *Malacanthus plumieri*, has not yet developed full adult colours, nor has it begun to build a mound.

Unlike the Spotted Goatfish, which is usually seen either alone or in small groups, the Yellow Goatfish, *Mulloidichthys martinicus*, usually forages in schools.

must be identified from features of the colour patterns. The Doctorfish, *Acanthurus chirurgus*, has a thin faint blue ring, similar in placement and function to the yellow line on the adult Blue Tang, which completely encircles the scalpel on each side of its body, and a squared-off caudal fin. Adults have faint vertical lines on the body. The Ocean Tang, *Acanthurus bahianus*, lacks the white, outlining ring, but has instead an all-white caudal peduncle, just ahead of a brown caudal fin. It also lacks vertical striping on the body, but has instead several wavy blue lines radiating from each eye, an electric blue edge on its dorsal, anal, and caudal fins, and a distinctly crescent-shaped caudal fin.

The two species can also be identified, in part, on the basis of location. Doctorfish are very common along the southeastern coast of the United States, where they are easily the more common of the two species. In the Bahamas and the Caribbean proper, however, the Ocean Surgeonfish is the more common of the two, with the Doctorfish, if present at all, restricted mainly to inshore areas and shallow-water reef and rocks.

A possible fourth species of tropical western Atlantic *Acanthurus* was described from the Gulf of Mexico in 1957, but its validity as a separate species is still in doubt. *Acanthurus randalli* is described as being very similar in shape and colour to the Doctorfish, but it lacks the dark vertical banding characteristic of the latter and also has a relatively longer pectoral fin. It is restricted to the area off the west coast of Florida where, supposedly, the Doctorfish is absent. Based on the widespread distribution of the surgeonfish in general, it seems unlikely that *Acanthurus randalli* is indeed a valid species; more likely, it is a local population of the Doctorfish, slightly isolated from the main body of the species, that varies from it in a few characters.

Field Biology

Though all are grazers, the amount that different species of Caribbean surgeonfish feed on plant material varies. *Acanthurus coeruleus* is a strict herbivore and has the long, thin-walled intestinal tract typical of such animals. The Doctorfish and the Ocean Surgeon, on the other hand, are more catholic in their tastes and injest a wide variety of small organisms along with the plant material that makes up the bulk of their diets. Both species also differ from the Blue Tang in possessing a gizzard-like organ in the intestines, partially filled with sand particles, that apparently helps to grind up food prior to digestion.

Of the three species, the Blue Tang is also the most social, adults often forming large schools which roam about the reef during the day, feeding on benthic algae. These are often mixed schools, typically involving parrotfish and occasionally wrasses. Tangs are also the least bottom-oriented of the three species, frequently seen foraging in the water column, and sometimes immediately at the surface, apparently going after planktonic algae and floating blades of sea grass. In terms of niche separation, then, the Blue Tang is the most distinctive of the group, feeding more on plant and pelagic material than the other two species. The Doctorfish and Ocean Surgeon, however, appear to compete directly in many respects and are separated geographically and, to a lesser extent, in terms of depth preference – the Doctorfish being found in water that is shallower and often dirtier than that tolerated by the Ocean Surgeonfish.

Unlike the gregarious Blue Tang, Yellow Tangs are strongly territorial. Each establishes a home range in shallow water and spends most of its time foraging about this area, occasionally joining small feeding aggregations of wrasses and juvenile parrotfish as they move about. The entrance of another yellow individual, though not a blue one, quickly prompts an attack. Smaller individuals are more aggressive than larger ones and the territorial behaviour is lost altogether about the same time the fish begins to assume its adult coloration.

Reproductive Biology

Spawning by surgeonfish occurs in late afternoon and early evening. For *Acanthurus coeruleus*, such spawning is indicated by a change in colour pattern away from a uniform dark blue to a pale blue anterior, dark blue posterior. Such fish, probably the males, court aggressively either other members of the school, if all are moving across the reef, or passing individuals, if the male has established a temporary spawning territory. This courtship leads to a quick upward spawning rush, similar to that described for the parrotfish, at the top of which eggs and sperm are shed.

Though not yet reported for any of the Caribbean species, based on observations of several Indo-Pacific surgeonfish, including an *Acanthurus*, it is likely that the Caribbean species also group-spawn, again at dusk. What appeared to be a pre-spawning group of milling Blue Tangs was observed off the coast of Cat Cay in the Bahamas, late in the evening; further observations of this and the other species at this time of day will probably reveal such spawning behaviour to be common.

Surgeonfish produce pelagic eggs approximately 0.8mm in diameter, each with a tiny drop of oil in it to provide flotation. Hatching time varies somewhat depending on temperature, but is usually just over a day. Newly hatched larvae are diamond-shaped and laterally compressed, with a triangular head, blunt mouth, large eyes, and prominent pectoral fins. At less than 2mm total length, the dorsal and anal fins are not well-developed (the latter consisting essentially of a few, short anal spines) and the caudal fin exists only as a small flap of skin that merges with the body. Between 2 and 6mm, long and even dorsal and anal fins, a distinct caudal fin, pelvic spines, and scales develop. The scalpel appears at about 13mm. Late post-larvae drift inshore, where they undergo a prolonged and pronounced metamorphosis. These metamorphosing individuals, known as 'acronurus', lose the silver juvenile coloration and turn brown (or, in the case of *A. coeruleus*, yellow), their profile rounds markedly (looking less like a diamond), the scalpel enlarges, the prominent dorsal and anal spines typical of the larvae are markedly reduced, and, in *A. coeruleus*, the snout elongates. Complete metamorphosis takes about a week and results in juvenile surgeonfish approximately 2 inches long.

Growth of newly settled surgeonfish is rapid and sexual maturity is probably reached within 9 months to a year. Spawning, however, probably does not occur until the following spawning season.

Aquarium Biology
Small surgeonfish do well in aquaria, provided they are fed large amounts several times daily or have available a large crop of algae on which they can graze. Like the young of all species, juvenile tangs grow rapidly, and like all herbivores, feed constantly. The combination of these two traits in a single fish results in almost instant starvation if the fish are not fed regularly. Young Doctorfish and Ocean Surgeons are the worst in this respect; even with conscientious care, they usually starve to death within a few days of capture. In general, the smaller the surgeonfish the faster it will starve. Yellow Tangs are less demanding than their congeners and will usually do well if fed two or three times daily.

Small tangs also have a tendency to become bullies, especially after they have been established in an aquarium for some time. Though not equipped with any formidable offensive armour, they will nevertheless threaten other fish with their scalpels and generally harass fish newly introduced into their tank. Such harassment usually ends within a day or so.

Relevant Literature
Barlow, G. 1975. 'On the sociobiology of four Puerto Rican Parrotfishes (Scaridae)', *Mar. Biol.* **33**: 281–293

Briggs, J. C. & Caldwell, D. K. 1957. '*Acanthurus randalli*, a new Surgeonfish from the Gulf of Mexico', *Bull. Fla. State Mus., Biol. Sci.* **2**(4): 43–51

Buckmann, N. S. & Ogden, J. C. 1973. 'Territorial behavior of the Striped Parrotfish *Scarus croicensis* Bloch (Scaridae)', *Ecol.* **54**(6): 1377–1382

Burgess, W. E. 1965. 'Larvae of the Surgeonfish genus *Acanthurus* of the tropical Western Atlantic', unpublished Master's thesis, University of Miami, Coral Gables, Florida

Clavijo, I. E. 1974. 'A contribution on feeding habits of three species of Acanthurids (Pisces) from the West Indies', unpublished Master's thesis, Florida Atlantic University, Boca Raton, Florida

Colin, P. L. 1978. 'Daily and summer–winter variation in mass spawning of the Striped Parrotfish, *Scarus croicensis*', *Fish. Bull.* **76**(1): 117–124

Ogden, J. C. & Buckmann, N. S. 1973. 'Movements, foraging groups, and diurnal migrations of the Striped Parrotfish, *Scarus croicensis* Bloch (Scaridae)', *Ecol.* **54**(3): 589–596

Randall, J. E. 1961. 'A contribution to the biology of the Convict Surgeonfish of the Hawaiian Islands, *Acanthurus triostegus sandivicensis*', *Pac. Sci.* **15**(2): 215–272

Randall, J. E. 1961. 'Observations on the spawning of the Surgeonfish (Acanthuridae) of the Society Islands', *Copeia* 1961 (2): 237–238

Randall, J. E. and Randall, H. A. 1963. 'The spawning and early development of the Atlantic Parrotfish, *Sparisoma rubripinne*, with notes on other Scarid and Labrid fishes', *Zoologica* **48**(5): 49–60

Robertson, D. R. & Warner, R. R. 1978. 'Sexual patterns in the Labroid fishes of the Western Caribbean, II: the Parrotfishes (Scaridae)', *Smithson. Contrib. Zool.* (255): 26 pp

Robertson, D. R., Sweetman, H. P., Fletcher, E. A., & Cleland, M. G. 1976. 'Schooling as a mechanism for circumventing the territoriality of competitors', *Ecol.* **57**(6): 1208–1220

Winn, H. E. & Bardach, J. E. 1960. 'Some aspects of the comparative biology of Parrotfishes at Bermuda', *Zoologica* **45**(3): 29–34

Winterbottom, R. 1971. 'Movement of the caudal spine of some Surgeonfishes (Acanthuridae, Perciformes)', *Copeia* 1971 (3): 562–566

Chapter 21

Miscellaneous Fish II
Predators

The majority of the fish on Caribbean reefs are herbivores, omnivores, or if carnivores, feed mainly on soft-bodied invertebrates or crustaceans; yet, like any complete community, the reefs have their share of piscavores, fish that survive by eating other fish. Many of these are large fish, as adults not suitable for any but the largest aquaria, but as juveniles, many do well in captivity. Even with regard to these, though, there are some necessary reservations to make and a distinct time limit. Like the juveniles of any other fish, young predators grow rapidly, and as they grow, so grow their appetites and the size range of the prey they can engulf.

Groupers

Groupers are moderate-to-large sea basses found on the reef, top level predators characterized by bass-like bodies, small scales, big mouths, and big appetites. All belong to the family Serranidae and most belong to one of two similar-appearing genera – *Epinephelus* and *Mycteroperca*. The two are separated primarily on the shape of the body (*Epinephelus* generally laterally compressed; *Mycteroperca* round-bodied), the number of anal fin rays, and features of skull osteology. *Epinephelus* now contains several species which, in the past, were placed in several other genera, including *Cephalopholis*, *Dermatolepis*, and *Alphestes*. While these are still referred to occasionally in the literature and may reflect lines of grouper evolution, a recent revision of the American groupers indicated that the lines of separation of these various genera are hazy and recommended treating all as sub-genera of a more comprehensive *Epinephelus*.

As they now stand, the *Epinephelus* groupers range from several small species that are ubiquitous on Caribbean reefs to the giant Atlantic Jewfish, *Epinephelus itajara*, which may reach a length of 8 feet and a weight of almost half a ton. Of this diverse group, there are six common and attractive species found on the reef: *Epinephelus striatus*, the Nassau Grouper; *Epinephelus niveatus*, the Snowy Grouper; *Epinephelus fulvus*, the Coney; *Epinephelus cruentatus*, the Graysby; *Epinephelus guttatus*, the Red Hind; and *Epinephelus adscensionis*, the Rock Hind. Though these vary slightly in body shape and habits, the most distinctive feature of each is its colour pattern.

The two larger members of the group are the Nassau Grouper and the Snowy Grouper, both of which are commercially important species that reach maximum lengths in the neighbourhood of 4 feet. Adult Nassau Groupers are dark grey with several black vertical bands on the body, two similar, but smaller, bands running diagonally along the forehead, and several black spots around each eye. Juveniles, the small groupers most often seen and collected by divers, are grey-brown with numerous red-brown spots scattered on the body and a thin white line running up the centre of the forehead. Nassaus are the most abundant of the several species of large Caribbean groupers and can be found anywhere from near shore to the deep reef. They are most common, however, on well-developed coral reefs at depths of 40 to 90 feet, where numerous large caves are present to provide them with shelter during the day. The Snowy Grouper is less often seen in shallow water, but is often available from tropical fish dealers because of its attractive colours. Juveniles are chocolate brown with a pale yellow caudal fin, a large black spot on the top of the caudal peduncle, and several vertical rows of large white spots banding the body. The adults are restricted to deep water and are coppery gold with a series of narrow and wavy vertical bands on each side of the body.

The remaining species in the genus are small at maturity (maximum size approximately a foot) and usually very common. On some reefs, dozens can be seen around every coral outcrop, peering from crevices and skulking about the reef. The most common of these small predators in the Bahamas and the Caribbean proper is also the most diverse colourwise. The Coney, *Epinephelus fulvus* (= *Cephalopholis fulva*) ranges in colour from bright golden yellow to brown, red, and horizontally bicolour – brown above and white below. All colour phases have two features in common, however – fine blue spots that pepper the body and a pair of larger, black spots on the top of the caudal peduncle. Transformation of a fish of one colour phase into another occurs only twice: first, all dark fish, when excited, can shift to the horizontal bicolour phase, and, conversely, bicolour fish can darken overall; and second, juveniles, regardless of their colour pattern in the field, darken when captured and within a week assume the brown or bicolour phase and retain such colours permanently. The different colour phases of the Coney vary widely in their geographical distributions, perhaps as a result of different genes being dominant in different populations. The most conspicuous phase, the Golden Coney, for example, is uncommon in the Bahamas, is common in parts of the West Indies, and in a few areas, such as around the islands offshore of Puerto Rico, may constitute more than half the population of Coneys. In all areas, the distribution of Coneys on the reef is to a large extent a function of water conditions. They seem to prefer clear water and so are more common around small oceanic islands and offshore reefs.

Epinephelus cruentatus (= *Petrometopon cruentatum*) is another small species, common on shallow reefs both in the islands and off the coast of Florida. Normally copper-brown and peppered with solid black spots on both the body and fins, like the Coney, the Graysby has a variety of base colours; those of the Graysby, however, are limited to white, grey, or some shade of brown. With such variation, the species is best characterized by a row of three (sometimes four) large, black spots located in a horizontal line on its back, immediately below its dorsal fin. On very dark-coloured fish, these spots are often white.

The Red Hind, *Epinephelus guttatus*, and the smaller Rock Hind, *Epinephelus adscensionis*, are slightly larger as adults than either of the previous two species, and like the Graysby, are spotted. The spots of the Red Hind are red, or reddish brown, on an olive or pale grey background; they are often highlighted by a darker red or brown centre. The spots on the Rock Hind can be either entirely red or red with a black highlight, on a brown or olive background. Members of the two species can be told apart most readily by the presence of a colour feature unique to each – black margins, edged with a thin white line, on the caudal, anal, and dorsal fins of the Red Hind, and several large, dark blotches high on the back of the rock hind.

The groupers in the genus *Mycteroperca* are less common on the shallow reef than are those in the genus *Epinephelus* and all reach a length of at least several feet. Heavy bodied, most are good eating and commercially important food fish. Juveniles of the various species differ markedly in colour pattern, but are often some combination of black, white, or yellow. Juvenile Yellowfin Groupers, *Mycteroperca venomosa*, for example, are sharply bicolour, black above and white below; juvenile Tiger Groupers, *Mycteroperca tigris*, are golden yellow with a black horizontal stripe down the centre of each side (the finer vertical stripes from which the species derives its common name do not develop until the fish matures); and juvenile Comb Groupers, *Mycteroperca rubra*, are black with irregularly shaped white blotches, underlaid by faint horizontal bands.

Along with the two major species of Caribbean groupers there is one other common and very distinctive species. *Paranthias furcifer*, the Creole Fish (not to be confused with the Creole Wrasse, *Clepticus parrai*), is an open-water predator which feeds mainly on planktonic animals. As specializations for its open-water lifestyle, it has developed a long, slender body, a relatively small mouth, and a lunate caudal fin. Its colour is a uniform purple-red. A distant relative of *Epinephelus, Paranthias* is typically found in areas with clean water and rapid changes in depth, usually swimming singly or in small groups a few feet off the bottom near the edge of deep water. *Paranthias* is common in the Caribbean proper, but is uncommon off the coast of Florida and has been reported in the Bahamas only from the southernmost islands in the chain.

Aside from the highly specialized Creole Fish, all groupers are generalized predators that will eat anything they can catch and fit in their cavernous jaws. Fishes and crustaceans are the major food items, though a wide variety of other benthic animals are eaten on occasion. Like all reef predators, groupers are opportunistic feeders, skulking around the reef during the day and taking prey any time the opportunity presents itself; they concentrate their hunting efforts during the half-light periods of dawn and dusk, however. A grouper's eyes function most effectively in dim light, when most reef fish are beginning to have difficulty seeing, which provides the predators a temporary advantage over the often much faster prey they pursue.

The groupers' dietary preference, of course, markedly influences their performance in an aquarium. Although hardy and, with the exceptions noted above, colourfast, groupers should be kept only with fish much larger than themselves. When in doubt, be conservative and err on the safe side. In the confines of an aquarium, with few places for prey to hide and many opportunities for the predator to strike, small groupers commonly eat fishes larger than themselves, and attack others larger still. The best policy for these otherwise personable and attractive fish would seem to be to keep them with fish which, if the latter were much larger, could conceivably eat a grouper. Needless to say, two small groupers in a single tank usually turn into one slightly larger grouper.

Because of this voracious appetite, small groupers grow rapidly and can outgrow a small tank in a month or two. Also because of it, groupers must be fed often; small ones will starve to death in only a few days if not fed large amounts several times daily. In general, the smaller the grouper, the more often it must be fed in order to survive.

Soapfish

The soapfish, family Grammistidae, are closely related to the groupers and have been classified by some ichthyologists as a sub-family of the Serranidae. They are characterized by large mouths, projecting lower jaws, and pointed snouts, rounded fins, and laterally compressed bodies. Many also secrete a characteristic mucous from pores in the skin which, when rubbed, froths like soap (thus the common name of the group); this mucous is thought to be distasteful and may deter predators from attacking a soapfish.

There are two genera of Caribbean soapfish: *Pseudogramma*, which is monospecific, and *Rypticus*. The former is a small and very shy fish, rarely seen on the reef despite its generally attractive colours. Reaching a maximum length of only an inch or two, *Pseudogramma bermudensis*, the Four-eye Basslet, has a red-brown body with brighter red anal, dorsal, and caudal fins, and a large white-ringed black spot on each gill cover (these spots, along with the large eyes, provide the fish with its common name). *Pseudogramma* is a predator which forages deep in the hollows of mounds of finger-shaped coral and other substrates that are full of small crevices and hollows. They are also common in the mounds of rubble built by the Sand Tilefish, *Malacanthus plumieri*, where they can be collected by anaesthetizing the entire mound and picking carefully through the rubble.

In contrast to the tiny and rarely seen *Pseudogramma*, *Rypticus* are large fish commonly seen slinking along under coral heads. The largest and most common species of the several in the Caribbean is known simply as *the* Soapfish, *Rypticus saponaceus*. A dark grey-black fish overlaid with irregularly shaped light grey blotches, it is most often seen lying on its side underneath a coral head or rocky outcrop and partially buried in the sand. From this position, it can rapidly dash out to catch passing prey – small fish and crustaceans.

Small soapfish are seen less often than the adults, which they resemble (very small juveniles are often uniformly dark with a single white stripe running down the centre of the forehead). This scarcity is unfortunate as these small fish do very well in aquaria and are engaging pets. I kept one for several years in a 40-gallon community tank (naturally with fish too large for it to eat) and finally released it only when it outgrew the tank. Nicknamed 'Sneak', the fish slithered from crevice to crevice in the tank, peering out at passers-by and rarely venturing into open water, even when being fed. Rather, it cautiously snuck up on even drifting flake food and brine shrimp, rushing out at its food to engulf it and then dashing back into its coral lair.

Tripletails

There is only one species in the family Lobotidae in the western Atlantic – *Lobotes surinamicus*, the

Tripletail. A brown-and-black, irregularly blotched species, in shape and finnage the Tripletail most closely resembles a soapfish, to which it is distantly related. Its common name is derived from its long and lobate dorsal and anal fins, which, combined with the caudal fin, give the impression the fish has 'three tails'.

Adult tripletails are rarely seen, but juveniles are commonly found drifting near the surface in mid-ocean in patches of the brown alga, *Sargassum*, which because of their colouration, irregular shape (even the fin edges are ragged), and passive head-down drifting, they strongly resemble. By mimicking such detritus, a Tripletail can drift close to its prey – small fish and crustaceans – and engulf them in a single rapid motion. In this regard, Tripletails parallel closely the freshwater species *Monocirrhus polyacanthus*, popularly known as the Leaffish, not only in shape and colour, but also in behaviour. Though found in very different habitats, the two species have converged on a common deceptive lifestyle to capture their prey.

Tripletails do well in captivity, where they are prone to spend most of their time drifting about the surface of the tank. They like to have a floating piece of wood or sargassum present, near which they will lie quietly for hours. They feed readily on live food, will take floating chunks of freeze-dried foods, and, if hungry enough, will even eat flake food. It is important that such food be at or near the surface as this species, being a passive hunter, will not leave the surface to eat. Because it is so passive, it will starve to death quickly if kept with bolder species which eat all of the available food before the Tripletail can reach it.

Grunts

The family Pomadasyidae is one of the most ubiquitous groups in the Caribbean. These small (most do not exceed a foot in length) snapper-like predators are common not only on and around reefs, but also around jetties and piers near shore, in estuaries, and around mangroves. Different species are found in different areas, but all are similar in basic morphology and behaviour.

A grunt is a laterally compressed fish with large, well-developed eyes, a spiny dorsal fin, a long and slender body, and usually a forked tail. Each has a terminal mouth composed of large, well-developed jaws and a long straight forehead, giving each a slightly prognathus look. They are closely related to the snappers, family Lutjanidae, from which they differ mainly on the basis of internal characteristics. Many grunts have complex, multi-hued colour patterns, most often involving fine horizontal stripes of alternating colours – blue and yellow, blue and white, black and white, and so on.

Only the juveniles are commonly kept in aquaria and these can, for all practical purposes, be divided into two groups – the *Haemulon* species, on the one hand, and *Anisotremus virginicus*, on the other. Juvenile *Haemulon*, regardless of species, are typically pale with a black lateral stripe running along the centre of each side of the body. The stripe ends as a black spot at the base of the caudal fin. Such juveniles are found in small schools near rocks, pilings, and other sheltered areas during the day, as are the adults, and both spread out over the surrounding area at night to feed. The Porkfish, *Anisotremus virginicus*, on the other hand, is coloured very differently as a juvenile and is generally found either singly or in very small groups. The fish is cream coloured with a yellow head and fins, a pair of black horizontal stripes on the body, a black spot at the base of the caudal fin, and red highlights on the edges of the unpaired fins. In healthy condition, they are strikingly attractive with brilliant contrasts of deep white, yellow, black, and red.

Grunts, including the Porkfish, are common near shore and can be easily collected in fair numbers. All do well in aquaria where, like the juveniles of most fish they will eat constantly if given the opportunity. In the field, most subsist on a combination of planktonic and benthic invertebrates, though young Porkfish have been observed picking ectoparasites off larger fish. In aquaria, all grow rapidly on virtually any food you care to give them and will outgrow a small tank within a few months.

The name 'grunt' is derived from the sounds these fish produce when removed from the water. The noise is made by the fish as it rubs its two plates of pharyngeal (throat) teeth back and forth over one another and, in the field, probably has a social function.

Snappers

Everything said about juvenile grunts is basically also true for young snappers in the genus *Lutjanus* as well. This, the only common inshore genus of large-bodied snappers, contains roughly half a dozen species, some of which attain a maximum size of almost 4 feet and are commercially important as food fish. Juveniles of all do well in aquaria. While several generally similar species can regularly be found in shallow water, the species most commonly kept is the Schoolmaster Snapper, *Lutjanus apodus*. Juveniles have a black diagonal bar running down the forehead, a series of brown bands on a yellowish body, and fins tinged with orange (often lost in aquaria). They are common around pilings, rocks, mangrove roots, and practically any other obstruction in shallow and sometimes dirty water. Unfortunately, their attractive colours fade in captivity and all tend to a uniform grey.

Juveniles of another, very different species of snapper are occasionally found in shallow water. Juvenile Yellowtail Snappers, *Oxyurus chrysurus*, are faintly lavender with a broad, yellow horizontal stripe running from a point on the snout down each side of the fish to broaden posteriorly until finally covering the entire caudal fin. A slender and longer species than the other inshore snappers, they are adapted to a pelagic existence and, as juveniles, feed on plankton several feet above the bottom around inshore reefs. Despite their attractive colours, these fish are recommended only for experienced aquarists since, in captivity, they are shy, tend to pale, and may not feed well.

In contrast, the juveniles of the deep-water snappers in the genus *Apsilus* are superb aquarium fish. Adults of these species are deep-bodied, large red fish found along the vertical wall of the deep reef at depths in excess of 250 feet. Juveniles are seen on rare occasions at shallower depths, 120 feet or so, as scattered individuals, and are hard to catch. But they are strikingly beautiful and well worth the effort. Such juveniles, nicknamed the Sky Snapper, are torpedo-shaped and laterally compressed, like the Yellowtail Snapper, but, unlike it, are iridescent blue with a pair of black lines that edge the top and bottom of the caudal fin. In captivity, these striking fish retain their colours well, are hardy, peaceful, and feed readily on practically anything.

Lizardfish

Lizardfish, genus *Synodus* and family Synodontidae, have a lizard-like head, a long cylindrical body, a large mouth with many fine and sharp teeth, and along with the normal complement of fins, a small adipose fin located between the dorsal and the caudal fins. Heavily scaled, they sit on sand bottoms and algae-covered rocks and dash upwards into the water column to seize passing small fish. They feed primarily on the small silvery fish commonly seen schooling around the shallow reef, and apparently move in and off shore during the day following schools of these fish. Lizardfish are, to put it mildly, voracious predators.

Small ones, though hard to find and still harder to catch, do well in captivity. Though mainly shades of grey and brown, they are unusual fish and certainly add a dimension to a tank, especially when sitting in a patch of sand partially buried. They adapt poorly to prepared food and do best when provided a combination of live brine shrimp and small fish.

Scorpionfish

Like the lizardfish, scorpionfish, family Scorpaenidae, are ambush predators, fabulously camouflaged to escape the wary eyes of approaching small fish and crustaceans, the principal prey items. While the lizardfish are adapted to match sand and rubble bottoms, scorpionfish duplicate algae-covered rocks and are intricately covered with hundreds of short fleshy flaps, mimicking the close-cropped algae growing on a lumpy rock. In form, the scorpionfish does indeed look like a rock, round and massive bodied with a broad grinning mouth and large camouflaged eyes. Its gill covers are ornamented with short spines and the dorsal fin has several massive spines, each associated with a poison gland, for which the group is given its common name. Though painful, wounds caused by stepping on these passive fish are rarely serious if well cleaned and treated to prevent subsequent infection.

There are two shallow water genera of scorpionfish – *Scorpaena* with 13 species and *Scorpaenodes* with one. The two genera can be separated on the basis of the number of dorsal fin spines; *Scorpaena* has 12, *Scorpaenodes* 13. All species are similar in shape, general colouration, and behaviour. All are various shades of red, brown, green, and grey. When young, several species, such as the common *Scorpaena plumieri*, have a white band across the rear half of the body. Young fish also tend to be less papilose and are rosier in colour than the adults.

Small scorpionfish are seen typically in caves and other such crevices on the reef. They move only infrequently and can be overlooked easily, even in areas where they are very common. Most often, they are collected accidentally when anaesthetics are being used to capture some more obvious fish hiding in a cave already occupied by the scorpionfish.

In captivity, such small individuals are hardy and bother no one too large to eat. They vary widely from individual to individual in terms of temperament and adaptability to prepared foods, but in general make excellent, very personable pets. Some reject anything but live shrimp, crabs, and fishes, while others will shift rapidly to pieces of shrimp and crab meat. Smaller ones will sometimes take frozen brine shrimp. In any case, the food must drift close to the fish, for, accustomed to ambushing prey, it will not move more than a few inches to seize prey. With time, however, they will often anticipate being fed and will patiently swim to the surface to await dinner. Larger ones can often be trained to eat from your hand.

Sharks

At one time or another, most marine aquarists fantasize about keeping a tiny shark in their aquarium. Unfortunately, such will have to remain pretty much a fantasy since most sharks are much too large to keep in any but large commercial aquaria and much too delicate, despite their fearsome reputations, to survive long without highly specialized treatment and equipment. The juveniles of one Caribbean species, however, while not a sleek, mid-water 'killer', are both small and rugged enough to do well in the home aquarium.

Nurse Sharks, *Ginglymostoma cirratum*, are roughly one to two feet long at birth and are a bottom-dwelling species, long and slender with rounded fins and a blunt, rounded head. On the underside of the head, on the upper jaw, there are several short barbels, each of which contains olfactory organs through which the shark smells and locates the benthic invertebrates that constitute the bulk of its diet. Adults range in colour from golden red to grey, while juveniles are generally greyish brown with many scattered, small black spots.

Nurse Sharks are lethargic and generally slow moving, spending most daylight hours sitting in small caves, empty pipes, and similar tubes on the bottom. Unlike most sharks, they have well-developed muscles which pump water over their gills and so are able to lie without moving for long periods of time. Because of this, they are are not particularly crowded in a 50 to 70 gallon aquarium and adapt well to captivity, feeding readily on pieces of fish and shrimp. Food should be offered on the end of a piece of wire, or with forceps (*never* by hand!), close to the shark, so that it can smell and so locate it. Nurse Sharks are messy eaters, and scattered debris and rejected food should be removed from the tank regularly to prevent fouling.

Relevant Literature

Anderson, W. D. 1967. 'Field guide to the Snappers (Lutjanidae) of the Western Atlantic', *Fish. Wildl. Circ.* (252): 14 pp

Anderson, W. D., Gehringer, J. W., & Berry, F. 1967. 'Family Synodontidae' in *Fishes of the Western North Atlantic* ed. Cohen, D. M., **1**(5): 30–102 (Sears Found. for Marine Res., Yale Univ., New Haven, Conn.)

Cressey, R. F. & Lachner, E. A. 1970. 'The parasitic copepod diet and life history of Diskfishes (Echeneidae)', *Copeia* 1970 (2): 310–318

Courtenay, W. R. Jr 1967. 'Atlantic fishes of the genus *Rypticus* (Grammistidae)', *Proc. Acad. Nat. Sci. Phila.* **119**(6): 241–293

Cummings, W. C., Brahy, B. D., & Spires, J. Y. 1966. 'Sound production, schooling, and feeding habits of the Margate, *Haemulon album* Cuvier, off North Bimini, Bahamas', *Bull. Mar. Sci.* **16**(3): 626–640

Eschmeyer, W. N. 1965. 'Western Atlantic Scorpionfishes of the genus *Scorpaena*, including four new species', *Bull. Mar. Sci.* **15**(1): 84–164

Kendall, A. W. Jr 1976. 'Pre-dorsal and associated bones in Serranid and Grammistid fishes', *Bull. Mar. Sci.* **26**(4): 585–592

Klimley, A. P. 1978. 'Nurses at home and school', *Mar. Aquar.* **8**(6): 5–13

Piastro, L. 1973. 'Behavioral ecology of the Lizardfish, *Synodus intermedius* (Synodontidae)', unpublished Master's thesis, University of Puerto Rico, Mayaguez, Puerto Rico

Randall, J. E., Aida, K., Hibaya, T., Mitsuura, N., Kamiya, H., & Hashimoto, Y. 1971. 'Grammistin, the skin toxin of Soapfishes, and its significance in the classification of the Grammistidae', *Publ. Seto Mar. Biol. Lab.* **19**: 157–190

Saksena, W. P., Richards, W. J. 1975. 'Description of the eggs and larvae of laboratory-reared White Grunt, *Haemulon plumieri* (Lacepede) (Pisces, Pomadasyidae)', *Bull. Mar. Sci.* **25**(4): 523–536

Smith, C. L. 1964. 'Hermaphroditism in Bahama groupers', *Nat. Hist.* **73**: 42–47

Smith, C. L. 1971. 'A revision of the American groupers: *Epinephelus* and allied genera', *Bull. Mus. Nat. Hist.* **146**(2): 67–242

Smith, C. L. 1972. 'A spawning aggregation of Nassau grouper, *Epinephelus striatus* (Bloch)', *Trans. Amer. Fish. Soc.* **101**: 256–261

Stark, W. A. & Schroeder, R. E. 1970. 'Investigations on the Gray Snapper *Lutjanus griseus*', *Stud. Trop. Oceanog.* **10**: 224 pp

Chapter 22

Miscellaneous Fish III
Odd Fellows

The remaining fish to be covered are a heterogeneous group, not fitting well either ecologically or systematically with any major group in particular. Their only common features are that they are common on or around Caribbean reefs, they are usually colourful, and often interesting.

Tilefish

The Sand Tilefish, *Malacanthus plumieri*, is the only shallow-water representative of the family Branchiostegidae in the Caribbean. Other western Atlantic members of the family include the Tilefish, *Lopholatilus chaemeleonticeps*, a heavy-bodied fish occasionally caught by fishermen, and the elongate and robust, green-and-yellow fish in the deep-water dwelling genus, *Caulolatilus*.

Malacanthus is elongate and very slender, with a long, undivided dorsal fin, a long anal fin, and a lunate caudal fin. The scales are small and the head is bluntly pointed. Its overall colour is golden blue with a conspicuously gold head and a bright gold-and-black patch on the upper lobe of the caudal fin; juveniles are more pale with a single gold stripe running down the centre of each side. *Malacanthus'*most diagnostic feature, however, is the burrow it constructs. Living on sand-and-rubble plains at practically any depth, Sand Tilefish construct a double-ended tunnel under a mound of rubble, rocks, and dead coral which they have laboriously scoured from the surrounding area. The fish are typically seen hovering a few feet above such a mound, their fins rippling in a long sinusoidal motion. When approached, each fish dives head-first into its burrow, reappearing only after danger has passed.

Little is known about the ecology and behaviour of the Tilefish. They are known to feed on ophiuroids, crustaceans, fish, and a variety of benthic animals. They clearly prefer sand areas, for obvious reasons, and they are found often in large numbers on such plains where the gravel is relatively coarse and adequate amounts of rubble for burrow construction are present. They are apparently territorial, individuals commonly being seen to chase others that approach their burrows too closely. Such territoriality is probably wise since, like the Jawfish which also construct rock-lined burrows, Tilefish are thieves, stealing rocks from one another's mounds whenever possible.

The reproductive behaviour of the Sand Tilefish is largely unknown. One frequently finds two living in the same burrow, or two whose burrows are close together, suggesting that these fish may represent mated pairs. Such pairs produce pelagic eggs, which hatch into tiny larvae, characterized by patches of spines on their heads, called 'dikellorhynchus'. Small Tilefish, roughly 3 inches long, are commonly found in shallow water from early summer through late fall. These small fish do not construct burrows under mounds, but rather dig unornamented burrows under rocks and debris. Mounds are not constructed by the fish until it reaches a length of approximately 7 inches.

In the aquarium, small Tilefish make amusing and interesting additions to a community tank. They are quite bold and rapidly select a rock or coral head under which to construct a burrow. They acclimate readily to prepared and frozen foods and are generally peaceful, so long as there are no other fish present which are small enough to constitute dinner.

Hawkfish

The Redspotted Hawkfish, *Amblycirrhitus pinos*, is the only member of the largely Indo-Pacific family Cirrhitidae found in the tropical western Atlantic. Hawkfish in general are characterized by a chunky body, a tapering snout with a terminal mouth, a spiny dorsal fin, and a large pectoral fin, the lower rays of which are thickened and partially free of the transparent web of skin that normally covers this fin. Similarly thickened pectoral fin rays are typical of another group of bottom-dwelling reef fish, the scorpionfish, family Scorpaenidae, suggesting that the hawkfish may represent the evolutionary link between these specialized ambush predators and the more generalized serranoid fish.

Amblycirrhitus is a delicately beautiful fish not often taken by amateur collectors, primarily because of its preference for cavernous coral heads with lots of hiding places. Its basic body colour is dark green with four pairs of parallel, thin white vertical stripes running down from the dorsal fin to merge with the pale venter. The head, the upper part of the back, and the dorsal fin are all peppered with brilliant red spots, while another larger, black spot sits on the top edge of the caudal peduncle. Just behind this black spot is a white band which goes completely around the caudal peduncle. A shy species which reaches a maximum length of only about 3 inches, the Hawkfish is seen most often sitting between blades of coral or under a rock overhang, where, despite its bright colours, it blends into its background. Quite often the fish is only seen as it scurries about its chosen coral head, always very close to its surface and always moving as though in a hurry.

Hawkfish feed primarily on small zooplankton that drift by their coral heads. The species is apparently territorial, such that one rarely finds two on the same head. Chases between them are commonly observed. Otherwise, its social and reproductive behaviour are totally unknown.

In aquaria, hawkfish make excellent pets as they scoot about the available cover, rapidly settling in and setting up a new territory. They are colourfast, active, and hardy fish that readily acclimate to the normal variety of aquarium foods. They do tend, however, to become bullyish and, like many other territorial species, will harass new introductions into their territories.

Goatfish

Goatfish, family Mullidae, are tapering, cylindrical fish characterized by a pair of long barbels hanging from the lower jaw. They live in close association with sand and mud bottoms and use their muscular barbels, each of which bears numerous sensory cells, to feel in the bottom for the benthic invertebrates that constitute their diet. When not in use, these barbels fit into a pair of grooves along the underside of the jaw, a device apparently to protect their sensitive sense organs.

Two species of goatfish are found around shallow Caribbean reefs, each of which has a distinctive colour pattern and behaviour. The Yellow Goatfish, *Mulloidichthys martinicus*, is a light bronze fish, pale below, with a broad yellow stripe running horizontally down the centre of each side of its body. Its fins are also yellow. The Yellow Goatfish is rarely seen as a solitary individual; typically, the fish roams and feeds in schools ranging in size from four to several dozen fish. The Spotted Goatfish, *Pseudupeneus maculatus*, in contrast, is usually a loner and aggregates only at dusk, shortly before settling down as a group for the night. Its colour pattern can vary from bright scarlet red to golden bronze and, on occasion, has a series of large brown spots along each side of its body. A fish can change its colour pattern rapidly and such patterns may have some social significance.

In this regard, little is known about the social behaviour of goatfish. Recently, mass spawning of the Spotted Goatfish was observed, such spawnings being similar to those previously described for the wrasses and the parrotfish. The pelagic eggs produced develop into elongate and slender larvae. Immediately prior to settling to the bottom, these, in turn, develop into distinctive post-larvae – heavy-bodied, silvery fish about $1\frac{1}{2}$ inches in total length with dark blue backs. Ultimately, these develop a red cast, then barbels, and finally settle on to the bottom.

Though temptingly attractive small fish on the reef, newly settled goatfish should be avoided by aquarists. They are constant eaters, so much so that even with several feedings daily they rapidly starve to death. The single specimen I kept was eating four times a day near the end, each time eating until its stomach looked like it was about to burst. Still it starved to death.

Remoras

Though not really reef fish, except when they happen to attach to a large snapper or parrotfish (both of which seem to be preferred hosts), the remoras, or sharksuckers, family Echeneidae, are included here because they make interesting and hardy aquarium inhabitants. One, *Echeneis naucrates*, does especially well.

Remoras need little description, being familiar to practically everyone who has even a slight interest in marine fish. It suffices to say that they are long and slender fish each with a specialized sucking disc (a highly modified first dorsal fin) on the top of the head, which is used to attach to sharks, swordfish, and other large fish. The Sharksucker, *Echeneis naucrates*, is a white fish, with a broad, deep black lateral stripe. It is the species most commonly seen near the reef, usually as small individuals.

In captivity, remoras spend most of their time slowly swimming about in the water near the top of the aquarium, on occasion sticking to the glass sides if no large fish are present. They feed readily on thawed brine shrimp and appear to thrive on it, growing rapidly. They will, however, also thrive on small fish and these, if placed in the tank with a remora, will quickly disappear.

Flounders

A number of small flounders are common on the sand flats surrounding the reef, the most readily identifiable of which is the Peacock Flounder, *Bothus lunatus*. A left-eyed species, the Peacock Flounder is mottled brown with numerous irregularly shaped rings of electric blue scattered across the body.

The juveniles of this flounder, and those of most other species, do well in community aquaria and are amusing oddities to keep. Most of the smaller individuals are scavengers and will take pieces of brine shrimp and flake food that wind up either sitting on the bottom or drifting close to it. All do best if there is at least a small patch of sand in the aquarium, in which the fish can partially bury themselves and with which they can match their colours.

Spadefish

The Spadefish, *Chaetodipterus faber*, is the only Caribbean representative of the family Platacidae, a group of schooling fish found around the world in the tropics and in a few temperate regions. *Chaetodipterus* is a large (maximum length approximately 3 feet), laterally compressed species that is round in profile, and that closely resembles an angelfish, to which it is related. The two fish can be readily told apart, however, from colour pattern or dorsal fin structure. Angelfish all have an even, continuous dorsal fin, while the Spadefish has a small, but conspicuous first dorsal fin, a short space, and then a prominent second dorsal. The second dorsal fin and the anal fin both end in long and tapering points which, coupled with a lunate caudal fin, give the fish a sleek appearance.

Colourwise, Spadefish are grey and silver with four prominent black bands across the body, the first immediately behind the gill covers and the last uniting the rear ends of the dorsal and anal fins, just ahead of the caudal peduncle. Such banding is darkest and most prominent on small fish, and can be so faded on large ones that they may lack it altogether.

Little is known about the field biology of the Caribbean Spadefish. They are usually found in large schools, eat practically anything, and live in a wide variety of habitats, ranging from the deep reef to pilings and mangrove roots close to shore. They are common around docks and bridges, where they feed on barnacles, molluscs, and other encrusting organisms. On docks at night, one can often hear the clicking and snapping noises made by Spadefish as they browse on the pilings below.

Juvenile Spadefish are often found close to shore, frequently right in the splash zone of the beach. Tall, thin, black fish, they drift motionless in such shallow areas among floating leaves, sea grasses, and scattered debris, which they strongly resemble. Though never proven, it has been suggested that by mimicking such debris in general, and floating leaves in particular, the fish hide from the ever-present sea birds.

Apparent spawning behaviour has recently been described for the spadefish. The observer reports seeing on two occasions large numbers of Spadefish milling about the surface. The fish separated into pairs and then proceeded to a 'jaw-fighting' in which members of a pair locked jaws and apparently pushed one another. After several such apparent tests of strength, the pair began to spiral to the surface, the male presumably behind the female. At the surface, the two fish swam in parallel, with their dorsal fins showing above the surface. Presumably eggs were released during this parallel swim. Nothing is known about the eggs or larvae of the species.

Small Spadefish are very hardy and adapt quickly to an aquarium. Not surprisingly, they eat anything. Large ones are equally adaptable and are a favourite schooling species for public display aquaria.

Relevant Literature

Chapman, R. W. 1978. 'Observations of spawning behavior in Atlantic spadefish, *Chaetodipterus faber*', *Copeia* 1978 (2): 336

Colin, P. L. & Clavijo, I. 1979. 'Mass spawning of the Spotted Goatfish, *Pseudupeneus maculatus* (Bloch) (Pisces, Mullidae)', *Bull. Mar. Sci.* **28**(4): 780–782

Randall, J. E. 1963. 'Review of the Hawkfishes (family Cirrhitidae)', *Proc. U.S. Nat. Mus.* **114**(3472): 389–451

Wicklund, R. J. 1972. 'Observations on the mating behaviour of the Peacock Flounder', *Hydro-lab J.* **1**(1): 47–48

Index

Drum), *108*, 115, 116
Eupomacentrus G., 55, 62−3
   E.diencaeus (Dusky Damselfish), 58
   E.dorsopunicans (Dusky Damselfish), *49*, 58
   E.fuscus (Dusky Damselfish), 58
   E.leucosticus (Beau Gregory), *48, 54*, 59, 64
   E.mellis (Honey Gregory), *49, 54*, 59
   E.otophorus (Dusky Damselfish), 58−9
   E.partitus (Bicolour Damselfish), *48*, 55, 58, 61−2, 64
   E.pictus, 58
   E.planifrons (Threespot Damselfish), *49, 54*, 59−60, 61
   E.rocasensis (Rocas Gregory), *54*, 59
   E.variabilis (Cocoa Damselfish), *49, 54*, 59, 61

Filefish (Balistidae), *109, 124−7*
Flameback Cherubfish *(Centropyge aurantonotus)*, 39, 43
Flamefish *(Apogon maculatus), 112, 131*
Flammeo marianus (Longspine Squirrelfish), *112*, 133
Flashlight Fish *(Kryptophanaron alfredi), 113*, 134−5
flounders, 162
Four-eye Basslet *(Pseudogramma bermudensis)*, 155
Four-eyed Butterflyfish *(Chaetodon capistratus)*, 47, 48, 52
French Angelfish *(Pomacanthus paru)*, 38−9, *40*, *41*, 42, 43
Frillfin Blenny *(Labrisomus filamentosus)*, 102
Fringed Filefish *(Monacanthus ciliatus)*, 125

Garden Eel *(Nystactichthys halis)*, 138, 139, 140
Ginglymostoma cirratum (Nurse Shark), 158
Ginsburgellus novemlineatus (Ninelined Goby), 73
Glass-eye Snapper *(Priacanthus cruentatus), 112*, 134
Glassy Sweeper *(Pempheris schomburgki), 113*, 134
Gnatholepsis thompsoni (Goldspot Goby), 74
goatfish (Mullidae), *149*, 161
gobies (Gobiidae), *57*, 72−84
Gobionellus G., 74−5
   G.sepaepaellens (Dash Goby), 75
   G.stigmalophius (Spotfin Goby), 74−5
Gobiosoma G., 77, 78−84
   G.atronasum, 80, 81, 82
   G.chancei (Shortstripe Goby), 77, 79
   G.evelynae (Sharknose Goby), 77, 79, *84*
   G.genie (Cleaning Goby), 77, 79
   G.horsti, 77, 79−80
   G.illecebrosum, 77, 78

   G.louisae, 77, 79, 80, *84*
   G.macrodon (Tiger Goby), 72−3
   G.multifasciatum (Greenband Goby), 72−3
   G.oceanops (Neon Goby), 77, 78, 81, *84*
   G.prochilos (Limpiador), 77, 79, *84*
   G.randalli (Yellownose Goby), 77, 78−9, *84*
   G.tenox (Slaty Goby), 77, 79, *84*
   G.xanthiprora, 77, 79, 80
Golden Coney, *145*, 153, 154
Golden Hamlet *(Hypoplectus gummigutta)*, 23, *25*
Goldenspotted Snake Eel *(Myrichthys oculatus)*, 138
Goldentail Moray *(Muraena miliaris), 113*, 137
Goldline Blenny *(Malacoctenus aurolineatus)*, 102
Goldspot Goby *(Gnatholepsis thompsoni)*, 74
Gorgonasia sillneri, 139
Gramma G., 31−3, 34, 35
   G.linki (Dusky Gramma), *32*, 33, 34
   G.loreto (Royal Gramma), 32
   G.melacara (Blackcap Basslet), 32, 34
Grammidae (basslets), 31−6
Grammistidae (soapfish), 28, *145*, 155
Graysby *(Epinephelus cruentatus)*, 153, 154
Green Moray *(Gymnothorax funebris)*, 137
Green Razorfish *(Hemipteronotus splendens)*, 85, 88
Greenband Goby *(Gobiosoma multifasciatum)*, 72−3
Grey Angelfish *(Pomacanthus arctuatus)*, 38−9, *40, 41*, 42
Grey Chromis *(Chromis multilineata)*, *56*, 67, 68, 69, 70
grey reef fish *see* Grey Chromis
groupers *(Epinephelus)*, *145*, 153−5
grunts (Pomadasyidae), *148*, 156
Gymnothorax G., *113*, 137
   G.funebris (Green Moray), 137
   G.moringua (Spotted Moray), *113*, 137

Haemulon sciurus (Bluestriped Grunt), *148*, 156
Hairy Blenny *(Labrisomus nuchipinnis)*, 102
Halichoeres G., *85*, 86−7, 89, 90, 91
   H.bivittatus (Slippery Dick), *56*, 86
H.caudalis, 87
   H.cyanocephalus (Yellowback Wrasse), 87
   H.garnoti (Yellowhead or 'T' Wrasse), *85*, 87, 88−9
   H.maculipinna (Clown Wrasse), *85*, 86−7, 89, 90
   H.pictus (Painted Wrasse), 87
   H.poeyi (Black-ear Wrasse), 87
   H.radiatu (Puddingwife), 87
hamlets, 21−7, 82
Harlequin Bass *(Serranus tigrinus)*, 16, *17*
Heliases G., 67−8, 69, 70